NATURE'S OPEN SECRET

NATURE'S OPEN SECRET

Introductions to Goethe's Scientific Writings

RUDOLF STEINER

Translated by John Barnes and Mado Spiegler

With an Essay on Participatory Science
by John Barnes

& Anthroposophic Press

© Copyright, Anthroposophic Press, 2000

Published in the United States by Anthroposophic Press
www.anthropress.org

Library of Congress Cataloging-in-Publication Data

Steiner, Rudolf, 1861-1925.
 Nature's open secret : Rudolf Steiner's introductions to Goethe's
scientific works / translated from the German by John Barnes with
Mado Spiegler ; with an essay "Participatory science as the basis for
a healing culture" by John Barnes.
   p. cm. – (Classics in anthroposophy)
 Includes bibliographical references.
 ISBN 0-88010-393-0 (hardcover)
   1. Goethe, Johann Wolfgang von, 1749-1832 – Knowledge – Science.
2. Science in literature. 3. Anthroposophy. I. Goethe, Johann Wolfgang
von, 1749-1832. Goethe's naturwissenschaftliche Schriften. II. Barnes,
John, 1943- III. Title. IV. Series.

PT2206 .S85 2000
831'.6 – dc21

00-038987

10 9 8 7 6 5 4 3 2 1

Printed in the United States of America

Contents

16. Goethe As Thinker and Researcher   166

17. Goethe versus Atomism   192

18. Goethe's Worldview in His *Verses in Prose*   209

Essay: Participatory Science as the Basis   219
for a Healing Culture

Bibliography and Further Reading   303

Editor's Introduction

One thing that distinguishes Rudolf Steiner from other explorers of the human psyche is the success of his pioneering work in practical fields such as education, medicine, and agriculture. Steiner was at home in the realm of science and practical life as well as in the world of the human spirit. For him, spiritual experience had become concrete and practical; practical, physical experience had revealed its spiritual dimension.

The unity of these realms was not initially given to Steiner, however. It was, rather, the result of an arduous search involving rigorous self-development. Steiner's penetrating study of Goethe's science played a pivotal role in this process. His introductions to Goethe's scientific works, which comprise the main content of this volume, can be seen as the foundation of his later work: They establish the epistemological basis for a science that reveals the essential, spiritual nature of the sense-perceptible world.

In his autobiography, Steiner describes his own development and the path that led him to his crucial encounter with Goethe's science. He describes how, as a child, he distinguished between things and beings that are "seen" and those that are "not seen," the latter category comprising his rich inner experience of spiritual realities. Even later, when he entered the Technical University in Vienna,

> Spirit and nature manifested before my soul and in full contrast. I experienced a world of spiritual beings, and to me it was a matter of direct perception that the I — which is itself spirit — lives in a realm of spirits. But I could not reconcile physical nature with my experience of the spiritual world. (p. 41)[1]

---

1. Unless otherwise noted, page numbers refer to *Autobiography: Chapters in the Course of My Life, 1861–1907*.

His study of the idealist philosopher Fichte confirmed his conviction that thinking, the spiritual activity of the I, is the starting point of all knowledge.

> To me, the experience of thought was a direct experience of reality, unassailable by doubt, since it is a thoroughly experienced reality. It seemed to me that the sensory world could not be experienced as thoroughly. It is present, but one does not grasp it as one grasps thought. Something essential and unknown can be hidden in it — or behind it. (p. 48)

However, the young Rudolf Steiner was determined to develop his cognitive powers to the point where they could penetrate to the hidden reality concealed within nature. Overcoming the dualism of his experience appeared to him to be a precondition for establishing a meaningful worldview. Already in high school he had come to the conviction that "one could come to terms with the spiritual world through the soul as long as thinking assumes a form capable of grasping the true nature of physical phenomena" (p. 32).

As Steiner immersed himself in the study of physics and physiology, he was met everywhere by the assumption that the qualities perceived by the senses are only subjective sensations triggered by objective material processes. This "caused my thinking inconceivable difficulties. It drove all spirit from the objective external world" (p. 52).

A breakthrough came when he had sufficiently penetrated the field of optics: "It seemed to me that the ideas I gained about optics built a bridge between what spiritual insight reveals and the results of scientific research" (p. 69).

Steiner's experiments led him to the conclusion that light itself belongs to the realities that are "not seen." The emptiness of outer space, for example, though flooded with sunlight, appears to us as utter darkness. Light, however, is a powerful reality that illuminates the physical world and brings warmth, life, joy, and color to our Earth. Yet, like the power of human love or human thinking, it remains beyond the realm of the sense perceptible. It is an invisible reality manifesting in the visible world.

Light is, of course, accompanied by electromagnetic phenomena just as our thinking is accompanied by electrical impulses in the brain, or as any organic growth is accompanied by subtle electromagnetic forces. Declaring that light, life, or thought are nothing but electromagnetic activity, however, would be equivalent to arguing that happiness itself does not exist and that a joyous smile is nothing but a contraction of certain facial muscles. It would be a rejection of the most self-evident realities, a denial of the very heart of our experience. Electromagnetic phenomena, like color, are *manifestations* of light.

At this time, Steiner encountered in Goethe's color theory a view akin to his own, one that did not simply explain colors in terms of an angle of refraction or a particular wavelength but, by immersing itself in the world of the colors themselves, came to understand them as lawful expressions of the interplay of light and darkness.

Having come to a certain clarity regarding the nature of light, Steiner now turned to the study of anatomy and physiology. He writes, "This led me in my own way to Goethe's theory of metamorphosis. I became increasingly aware how the picture of the physical world, tangible to the senses, related to what I saw spiritually" (p. 70).

At the age of twenty-one, Steiner was asked to edit and introduce Goethe's scientific works for Kürschner's edition of German National Literature.

> For me this task meant that I had to come to terms with both natural science and Goethe's worldview. As it would be presented to the public, I also had to reach a certain conclusion about what I had attained at that point as my own worldview. (p. 78)

Throughout the next fourteen years of his life, Steiner engaged in this work — at first intensively as editor, then more intermittently as a researcher at the Goethe and Schiller archives in Weimar.

It was at this time that Steiner gained his first insights into what he was later to develop in detail as his view of the threefold nature of the human being. Over the next thirty years he pursued this research into the complex interrelationships of the human body, soul, and spirit, research that provided the basis for the practical renewal of education and medicine that Steiner initiated during the last phase of his life.

Both Steiner and Goethe are often somewhat mistakenly referred to today as proponents of German idealist philosophy. In a lecture on April 22, 1915,[2] Steiner characterized German idealist philosophy through an analogy, setting it off from contemporary empirical sci-

---

2. "The World View of German Idealism," not translated.

ence on the one hand and Goethe's scientific approach (which was
also his own) on the other. He described the German idealists as
forming their ideal philosophical view of the world *within* a house,
i.e., in pure thought — without going outside to actually observe the
world they are picturing. The English empiricists, on the other hand,
look out of the window as it were, but do not enter the outer world
with their inner experience. They form a detached view of the outer
world at the same time that they remain within their experience of
the inner, moral, or divine world. Isaac Newton, for example, known
for his mathematical optics and his discovery of the universal law
of gravitation, was in many ways typical of contemporary scientists.
"But throughout his life he saw the limits of the capacity of human
reason to encompass experience, which explained, too, his unflagging
interest in the Bible and in Prophecy."[3] Goethe, however, goes further.
He opens the door and carries his inner experience out into the world.
He participates in nature with his full being, enters into it, and becomes one with it. Goethe's worldview is not thought out as was the
philosophical worldview of the idealists. It is experienced directly.
Nor is there a dichotomy of inner "subjective" and outer "objective" experience as there is with Newton and with most contemporary
scientists.[4]

Whereas the detachment of the empiricists lends itself to the
analysis and technical manipulation of inorganic nature, Goethe's
participatory approach is particularly suited to research in the organic realm. Steiner saw Goethe's dynamic idea of metamorphosis as
a decisive breakthrough to a deeper understanding of living nature.
He saw Goethe's central achievement in "his discovery of how one
thinks about the organic in order to understand it" (p. 79).

Steiner described how this transformed cognitive capacity leads
to a comprehensive worldview rising from organic life to ever more
immediate manifestations of spiritual reality:

Ascending in our observations from plant nature to the various
animal forms, organic, creative forces can be seen as progres-
sively more similar to the spirit. In the organic form of the
human being, spiritual formative forces are active that bring

---

3. D. Boorstin, *The Discoverers*, p. 407.
4. Steiner explores Goethe's relationship to idealistic philosophy in chapter 6, "Goethe's
Way of Knowing."

the animal form to its highest metamorphosis. These forces are active in the manifestation and growth of the human organism, and are finally expressed as human spirit after they have shaped a vessel in a natural foundation in which they can live free of nature.... In this light, one sees that a Goethean observation of nature — tracing the development from the inorganic to the organic — is a science of nature that leads to a science of spirit. (pp. 80–81)

Through his study of Goethe's science, Steiner laid the foundations for a scientific worldview that opens itself to the rich qualities of the sense-perceptible world and comes to see them as expressions of creative spiritual principles. Though this study certainly benefitted from the inner clarity of the German idealist philosophers, the enduring success of the practical applications of Steiner's participatory science in education, medicine, and agriculture demonstrates its capacity for profound and very concrete insight into organic and human nature.

Steiner wrote his introductions to Goethe's scientific works with the immediacy of youthful enthusiasm. Reading them, we can almost witness the birth of the seminal ideas that led to his more elaborated philosophical works, and ultimately to his later lectures on the practical renewal of culture.

These introductions follow in a new translation that attempts, once again, to capture the meaning of the original in good, readable English.

An essay exploring the profound implications of participatory science for our time comprises the last section of this volume.

JOHN BARNES

Chapter 1

Introduction

On August 18, 1787, Goethe wrote to Knebel from Italy:[1]

> After what I have seen of plants and fishes around Naples and in Sicily, I would be greatly tempted, if I were ten years younger, to make a journey to India — *not for the purpose of discovering anything new, but to observe in my own way what has already been discovered.*

These words provide the viewpoint from which to consider Goethe's scientific works. For him it was never a question of discovering new facts but of opening up *a new perspective* and viewing nature in a particular way. It is true that Goethe made a number of great discoveries, such as the intermaxillary bone and the vertebral theory of the skull in osteology, the inner identity of plant organs with the leaf in botany, and so on. But the animating soul that imbued all these particular achievements was the magnificent view of nature upon which they are based. In Goethe's study of organisms one great discovery overshadows all else — *the discovery of the nature of the organism itself.* Goethe expounded the principle of how an organism manifests as it does, the causes leading to the outer expressions of life. Indeed, he illuminated everything related to the principles involved in such matters.[2]

---

1. Karl Ludwig von Knebel (1744–1834), German poet and translator, was associated with Goethe and Schiller in their literary circle in Weimar. — ED.

2. Those who from the outset declare such a goal to be unattainable will never understand Goethe's views of nature. But those who study his views in an unbiased way and leave this question open will certainly reach an affirmative answer. Some may well be led to doubt this assertion by certain remarks of Goethe himself, such as, "*Without presumptuously wishing to discover the primal driving forces of nature,* we have focused on the manifestation of those forces through which the plant gradually transforms one and the

From the very beginning, this was the goal of Goethe's efforts in the organic sciences. As he pursued this goal, his discoveries occurred as of themselves; he had to make them in order not to be hindered in his further striving. Natural science before Goethe was unaware of the essential nature of living phenomena. It simply investigated organisms with regard to the composition of their parts and external characteristics, just as one investigates inorganic phenomena. Consequently, that older science often interpreted details incorrectly and presented them in a false light. Investigation of the particulars themselves cannot, of course, reveal any such error. Interpretive judgments can only be made after we have first understood the organism, because the particulars, considered separately, do not contain the principle that explains them. They can be explained only through the nature of the whole, because it is the *whole* that gives them being and significance.[3]

It was not until after Goethe had discovered the nature of the whole that he realized those interpretations were erroneous. They could not be reconciled with his theory of living beings; they contradicted it. Before he could go any further he had to eliminate such preconceptions. This was the case with the intermaxillary bone.[4] Facts that are valuable and interesting only if one has a theory like the vertebral nature of the skull were unknown to previous natural science. All these hindrances had to be cleared away through individual discoveries. In Goethe's case, therefore, these discoveries were never ends in themselves, but were always necessary to corroborate a great thought — to confirm his *central* discovery.

We cannot deny that Goethe's contemporaries eventually made the same observations and that perhaps all of them would be known today even without Goethe's endeavors. But it would be even more difficult to deny that, until today, no one else has independently formulated in such an outstanding way his great discovery embracing all

---

same organ." Such statements by Goethe, however, are never intended to deny the possibility in principle of coming to know the essential nature of things. He was simply being careful not to make premature judgments about the physical-mechanical conditions upon which the organism depends, for he knew very well that it takes time to resolve such questions. — R. STEINER.

3. Intrinsic in Goethe's scientific method is that its explanations move from the whole to the parts, from the central principle to the outer particulars. — ED.

4. Goethe knew that the intermaxillary bone must also be present in the human being only because he had recognized the fundamental formative principle, the "type," that gives rise to the human form and the forms of the higher animals. — ED.

of organic nature; indeed, even a somewhat satisfactory assessment of his discovery is still lacking.[5]

Whether Goethe was the first to discover a fact or only rediscovered it seems irrelevant when viewed in this fundamental way; for the fact only gains real significance because of the way he fits it into his view of nature. Thus far, this has been overlooked. The particulars have been overemphasized, and this has caused undue provocation and polemics. Goethe's conviction of nature's consistency has in fact often been pointed out, but without realizing that this is only a very insignificant characteristic of his views. In organic science, for example, the primary goal is to reveal the basis of this consistency. If we call it the *type,* then we must identify what the essential nature of the type is according to Goethe.

What is significant in the metamorphosis of plants, for example, is not the discovery of the single fact that leaf, calyx, corolla, and so on, are identical organs; rather, it is the magnificent thought structure of a living whole consisting of mutually interpenetrating, formative principles. This dynamic thought structure, which arises from that discovery, determines out of itself the details and individual stages of plant development. The greatness of this idea — which Goethe then sought to extend to the animal world as well — dawns on us only when we try to bring it to life in our own mind and attempt to rethink it. That is when we become aware of how this thought is the very nature of the plant itself, translated into the form of an *idea,* and living in our mind just as it lives in the object. We observe also that we bring an organism to life for ourselves — right down into its smallest parts — when we picture it not as a dead, finished object, but as evolving and becoming and never at rest within itself.

As we endeavor in what follows to present in detail all that has been indicated here, we will also come to see the true relationship between the Goethean view of nature and that of our own time, especially modern evolutionary theory.

---

5. We do not mean to say that Goethe has never been understood at all in this regard. On the contrary, we refer repeatedly in this text to people who seem to us to carry further and elaborate Goethean ideas. Among these are names such as Voigt, Nees von Esenbeck, d'Alton (senior and junior), Schelver, C. G. Carus, Martius, and others. But these people based their systems on the views laid down in Goethe's writings, and one cannot say of them that they would have arrived at their concepts *without* Goethe. On the other hand, contemporaries of Goethe — for example, Josephi in Göttingen in the case of the intermaxillary bone, and Oken in the case of the vertebral theory — arrived at their discoveries independently. — R. STEINER.

The Origin of Goethe's Concept of Metamorphosis

When tracing the historical development of Goethe's thinking on organic morphology, one will certainly wonder what to ascribe to the poet's youth — that is, to the time before he arrived in Weimar. Goethe himself did not think very highly of his knowledge of the sciences during that period: "I had no concept of what external nature actually is, and not the least knowledge of her so-called three kingdoms." On the basis of this statement, it is generally thought that Goethe's scientific reflections began only after his arrival in Weimar [in 1775, when he was 26]. Nevertheless, it seems necessary to go back further if we do not wish to leave unexplained the whole spirit of his views. The powerful impetus that guided his studies in the direction described below already manifested itself in his earliest youth.

When Goethe entered the University of Leipzig, all scientific endeavors there were still dominated by a spirit characteristic of most of the eighteenth century, which split science as a whole into two extremes that no one felt the need to unite. On the one hand there was the philosophy of Christian Wolff,[1] entirely immersed in a realm of abstractions; on the other stood the various branches of science that lost themselves in external descriptions of endless details, making no attempt to find higher principles in the world of their investigations. Wolff's philosophy could not find its way out of the realm of abstract concepts into the world of immediate reality, of individual existence. The most obvious things were treated with utmost thoroughness. One

---

1. Freiherr Christian von Wolff (1679–1754), German philosopher and mathematician. — ED.

learned that a "thing" is something that contains no contradictions, that there are finite and infinite substances, and so on. But if these generalities were applied to the things themselves in an attempt to understand their life and working, investigators were soon at a complete loss; they could not apply these concepts to the world that we live in and seek to understand. The actual things around us, however, were described in a manner largely void of any principle, purely according to appearances and external traits. A science of principles that lacked all living content, all loving absorption in immediate reality, was juxtaposed with a science devoid of principles and ideal meaning. These confronted one another without mediation; each remained fruitless for the other. Goethe's healthy nature found both equally repulsive in their one-sidedness; and by struggling against them he developed views that later led him to a productive understanding of nature in which idea and experience, in full interpenetration, mutually enliven one another and become one whole.

Goethe therefore first developed the concept that those extremes were least able to grasp: *the concept of life.* A living being, observed in its outer appearance, presents itself as a sum of particulars that appear to us as its members or organs. Describing these members — their shapes, relative positions, sizes, and so on — can become the object of extensive research of the kind conducted by the second school of science mentioned above. But any mechanical assemblage of inorganic bodies can also be described in this way. It was altogether forgotten that, in considering an organism, the main thing to keep in mind is that its outer appearance is governed by an inner principle, that the whole is working in every organ. The outer appearance, the spatial juxtaposition of its members, can also be examined after its life has been destroyed, for it continues to exist for a time. But the dead organism before us is, in reality, no longer an organism. The principle that permeated all the particulars has vanished. *Early on, Goethe confronted the approach that destroys life in order to investigate it, with the possibility of and need for a higher view.* This can already be seen in a letter dated July 14, 1770, during his Strasbourg period, in which he wrote of a butterfly:

> The poor creature trembles in the net, rubs off its most beautiful colors; and if one captures it unharmed, it ends up stuck upon a pin, stiff and lifeless. The corpse is not the whole creature,

something else belongs to it — an important thing, and in this case, as indeed in all others, the main thing: *its life....*

These words from *Faust* arise from the same view:

> Who would study and describe the living starts
> By driving the spirit out of its parts:
> In the palm of his hand he holds all the sections,
> Lacks nothing, except the spirit's connections.
>
> (*Faust,* lines 1936–1939)

Since it was not in his nature to remain satisfied with the negation of a way of looking at things, Goethe increasingly sought to develop his own view; and we can recognize the seeds of his later works in indications of his thinking available to us from 1769 to 1775. Here we find him developing the idea of a being whose every part animates the others, in whom one principle permeates every particular. In *Faust* he says:

> How all within the whole are weaving,
> Each in the other working, living....
>
> (lines 447–448)

and in *Satyros* [Act 4]:

> The primal thing from no-thing sprang,
> The power of light through darkness rang,
> In beings' depths igniting fire:
> Creation's joy, born of desire;
> The elements poured into the world,
> Rapaciously one into the other whirled,
> *All-permeating, all permeated.*

Goethe conceived of this being as subject to continuous changes in time; yet, throughout all the stages of these changes, it is always only *one and the same* being that manifests itself, that asserts itself as enduring and stable amid change. In *Satyros* there is more about this primordial thing:

> And up and down and in full swing
> Came the all and one eternal thing,
> *Ever changing, ever enduring.*

Compare this with what Goethe wrote in 1807 as an introduction to his study of metamorphosis:

> If, however, we observe all forms, especially organic ones, we find that nothing is permanent, nothing is at rest or complete, but rather that everything is in continuous fluctuating movement.

In contrast to this flow, Goethe now posits the idea or "something held fast in experience only for a moment"[2] as the *constant*. It will be recognized clearly enough from the *Satyros* passage that the foundation for Goethe's morphological ideas had already been laid before he came to Weimar.

It must be noted, however, that this idea of a living being is not applied to an individual organism — the entire universe is conceived of as such a living being. This concept originates, of course, in Goethe's alchemical studies with Fräulein von Klettenberg and in his reading of Theophrastus Paracelsus after returning from Leipzig [1768–1769]. At that time the attempt was made, through some kind of experiment, to reveal the principle that permeates the whole universe, to bring it to manifestation through some substance. However, this way of looking at the world, bordering on the *mystical*, constitutes only a passing episode in Goethe's development and soon gives way to a healthier and more objective manner of thinking. Nevertheless, a view of the entire universe as a great organism — as indicated in the passages from *Faust* and *Satyros* — remains integral to Goethe's thinking until around 1780, as we shall see later in connection with his essay "Nature." Once again in *Faust* we find the earth spirit described as the life principle that permeates the universal organism:

> In tides of life, in action's storm
> To and fro I wave,
> Weave eternally!
> Birth and grave,
> An eternal sea,
> A changeful strife,
> A glowing life.
>
> (lines 501–507)

---

2. In this formulation we see Goethe's participatory thinking apprehending the idea *in* experience. — ED.

While Goethe was thus developing certain views, he came upon a book in Strasbourg that sought to establish a worldview directly opposed to his own — Holbach's[3] *Système de la Nature*. Until then, Goethe had only had to criticize the tendency to describe what was alive *as though* it were a mechanical conglomeration of particulars; in Holbach he now encountered a philosopher who actually *regarded* the living organism as a mechanism. What formerly had arisen merely out of an inability to recognize the roots of life led in Holbach to a life-denying dogma. In his autobiography, *Poetry and Truth*, Goethe writes of this:

> Matter was supposed to have existed from eternity, to have been in motion from eternity, and now, without further ado, it was to bring forth, with this motion, right and left and in all directions, the endless phenomena of existence. We would indeed have been satisfied with all this if the author had in fact built up the world before our own eyes out of his agitated matter. But he might have known as little about nature as we do; for hardly has he rammed in a few general concepts when he immediately leaves them in order to transform what appears higher than nature or as a higher nature in nature into a material, heavy element — in motion, to be sure, yet without direction or form — and he believes that he has thus achieved a great deal.

Goethe could find nothing in all of this but "matter in motion," and it was in opposition to this that his own concepts of nature took on ever clearer form. We find these presented as a coherent whole in his essay "Nature," written around the year 1780. This essay takes on special significance because it brings together all of Goethe's thoughts about nature, which until then we find only in scattered indications. Here we meet the idea of a being undergoing continuous change but nevertheless remaining the same:

> Everything is new, and yet always the old.... She [nature] is forever transforming herself, and there is within her no moment of standing still, [yet] her laws are unchangeable.

---

3. Baron Paul-Henri-Dietrich d'Holbach (1723–1789), French atheist and materialist who wrote extensively for the *Encyclopédie*. — ED.

We shall see later that Goethe sought the one archetypal plant in the endless multitude of plant forms, a thought already indicated here:

> Each of her [nature's] works has its own being, each of her manifestations has the most isolated concept, and yet all constitute One.

Indeed, even his later position with respect to exceptions — namely, not to regard them simply as defective formations, but to explain them as manifestations of natural laws — is already very clearly expressed: "Even the most unnatural is nature [and] her exceptions are rare."[4]

We have seen that even before Weimar Goethe had already developed a definite concept of an organism. For while "Nature" was written long after his arrival there, it nevertheless largely contains his earlier views. He had not yet, however, applied this concept to a specific order of natural phenomena, to individual creatures. To do this he needed access to the actual world of living nature in its immediate reality. Goethe could not be stimulated by a reflection of nature that had passed through the human mind. Conversations about botany with Privy Councillor Ludwig in Leipzig and dinner conversations with his medical friends in Strasbourg had no deeper effect. In his scientific studies, the young Goethe appears to us very much like *Faust*, who, deprived of the fresh, direct beholding of nature, expresses his longing for it:

> Ah, could I but on mountain height
> Wander in thy [the moon's] lovely light,
> Hover with spirits round caves and trees,
> Weave in your twilight through the leas....
>
> (lines 392–395)

This longing seems to have been fulfilled when, upon his arrival in Weimar, Goethe was permitted "to exchange chamber and city air for the atmosphere of country, forest, and garden."[5]

The direct incentive for the poet's study of plants was, we find, his involvement with the planting of the garden given him by the Duke

---

4. In section 15, paragraph 103, of his *Metamorphosis of Plants*, Goethe describes a proliferous rose in which the abnormal growth of a sprouting stem out of the center of a blossom reveals the hidden potential of the blossom's central organs to become a whole plant. — ED.

5. From the essay "History of My Botanical Studies." — ED.

Karl August. Goethe accepted the garden on April 21, 1776, and his diary (edited by Keil) informs us frequently from then on of his work in this garden, which had become one of his favorite occupations. An additional field for this kind of endeavor was afforded him by the Thuringian forest where he had the opportunity to acquaint himself with the phenomena of lower organisms. He was especially interested in the mosses and lichens. On October 31, 1777, he asked Frau von Stein[6] for mosses of all kinds, with roots and damp if possible, so that they would continue to propagate. It must be considered highly significant that, already at this time, Goethe occupied himself with the world of these lower organisms, and later nevertheless derived the laws of plant organization from the higher plants. When we consider these circumstances we will not ascribe this fact to Goethe's underestimation of the importance of less-developed organisms, as many commentators have done, but to his fully conscious intention.

From this point on, the poet never left the world of plants. He most probably took up the writings of Linné[7] at a very early date. We first hear of his acquaintance with them in letters to Frau von Stein from 1782.

Linné tried to bring a systematic overview into the knowledge of plants. He strove to find a definite sequential order in which every organism would occupy a specific place so that it could be easily located at any time — indeed, so that there would be a means of orientation within the infinite multitude of particulars. To this end, plants had to be examined to determine their degree of interrelatedness and then grouped accordingly. Since the main point was to identify and easily classify any plant within the system, special attention had to be given to the characteristics that distinguish one plant from another. To make confusion impossible, one sought primarily for these distinguishing traits. Thus, Linné and his students regarded external traits — size, number, position of individual organs — as characteristic.

The plants were indeed ordered sequentially, but in the same way that one might also have arranged a group of inorganic objects: according to traits taken, not from the inner nature of the plant, but from their outer appearance. The way they are ordered appears su-

---

6. Charlotte von Stein (1742–1827), German writer, lady-in-waiting at the court of the Duchess of Weimar, corresponded extensively with Goethe. — ED.

7. Carl von Linné, or Linnaeus (1707–1778), Swedish botanist and professor at Uppsala University. He traveled extensively and wrote many important works in his field. — ED.

perficial, without any necessary inner connection. Because Goethe had a significant concept of living organisms, this way of looking at them could not satisfy him. For it did not include any research into the essential nature of the plant. Goethe had to ask himself: What is it that makes a particular being of nature into a plant? Moreover, he had to acknowledge that whatever it is, it must occur in all plants in the same way. And yet there was an endless differentiation of individual entities that demanded explanation. How is it that this oneness reveals itself in such manifold forms? These must have been the questions that Goethe raised as he read Linné's writings, for he himself says: "What he, Linné, tried to force apart could, according to the innermost urge of my own being, only strive toward unity" ("History of My Botanical Studies").

Goethe's encounter with Rousseau's botanical endeavors came at about the same time as his first acquaintance with Linné. On June 16, 1782, he wrote to Karl August:

> Among Rousseau's works there are the loveliest letters about botany in which he expounds this science to a lady in the most intelligible and charming way. It is truly a model of how one should teach, and a supplement to Emile. I therefore now take occasion to recommend to my beautiful lady friends the beautiful kingdom of the flowers.

Rousseau's botanical studies were bound to make a deep impression on Goethe. The emphasis upon a nomenclature that arises out of and corresponds to the nature of the plants, the originality of observation, the contemplation of the plant for its own sake apart from any utilitarian considerations — all these aspects of Rousseau's work strongly appealed to Goethe. The two also had in common that they had not come to the study of plants for any specific scientific purposes but rather out of general human motives. The same interest drew them to the same subject.

Goethe's next thorough observations of the plant kingdom occurred in 1784. Wilhelm Freiherr von Gleichen, called Russwurm, had just published two works dealing with research that interested Goethe intensely: "The Latest from the Plant Kingdom" and "Selected Microscopic Discoveries in Connection with Plants, Flowers and Blossoms, Insects, and other Noteworthy Things." Both writings dealt with fertilization processes in plants. Pollen, stamens, and pis-

tils were carefully examined, and the processes occurring within them
were portrayed in beautifully executed plates. Goethe now repeated
these investigations. On January 12, 1785, he wrote to F. H. Jacobi:
"My microscope is set up so that, come spring, I can repeat and verify the experiments of von Gleichen, (called Russwurm)." During that
same spring he also studied the nature of the seed, as we see in a letter
to Knebel of April 2, 1785: "I have thought through the subject of
the seed as far as my experience permits." In all these investigations,
Goethe was not concerned with detail; the goal of his endeavors was
to explore the essential nature of the plant. On April 8, 1785, he
reported to Merck that he had "made nice discoveries and combinations in botany." The expression "combinations" also shows that his
intention was to construct a thought-picture of processes in the plant
world. His study of botany was rapidly approaching a definite goal.

In this connection we must of course bear in mind that in 1784
Goethe had already discovered the intermaxillary bone, which we
shall later discuss in detail, and had thereby come a significant step
closer to the secret of nature's way of forming organisms. We must
also bear in mind that the first part of Herder's *Reflections on the
Philosophy of the History of Humanity* was completed in 1784 and
that Goethe and Herder conversed frequently at that time on subjects
pertaining to nature. Thus Frau von Stein reports to Knebel on May 1,
1784:

> Herder's new work makes it seem probable that we were first
> plants and animals.... Goethe is pondering these things very
> thoughtfully now, and everything that has gone through his
> mind becomes extremely interesting.

This indicates the nature of Goethe's interest in what were the
greatest scientific questions of that time. His reflections on the nature of the plant and his combinations in the spring of 1785 seem
therefore quite comprehensible. In mid-April of that year he went to
Belvedere for the express purpose of solving his doubts and questions,
and on May 15, he shared with Frau von Stein:

> I cannot tell you how readable the book of nature is becom-
> ing for me; my long efforts at deciphering, letter by letter, have
> helped me; now all of a sudden it is having its effect, and my
> quiet joy is inexpressible.

11-21-00
16-42 02631

1 • 17·50
1 • 11·95
29·4
·2·3
·3L

Shortly before this he had even wished to write a brief botanical treatise for Knebel to win him over for this science.[8] Botany attracted him so strongly that the journey he began on June 20, 1785, to Karlsbad, where he was to spend the summer, became a botanical expedition. Knebel accompanied him. Near Jena they met a seventeen-year-old youth, Dietrich, whose specimen box showed that he had just returned from a botanical excursion. We learn more about this interesting journey from Goethe's "History of My Botanical Studies" and from reports of Cohn in Breslau, based on a manuscript of Dietrich's. In Karlsbad, botanical conversations frequently provided pleasant entertainment. Upon returning home, Goethe devoted himself with great energy to his study of botany; with the aid of Linné's *Philosophica Botanica* he made observations of mushrooms, mosses, lichens, and algae, as we see from his letters to Frau von Stein. Only after he had thought and observed a great deal did Linné become more useful to him; through Linné he found information on many details that helped him forward in his combinations. On November 9, 1785, he reported to Frau von Stein:

> I am continuing to read Linné; I have to, for I have no other book with me; it is the best way to read a book conscientiously, which I must practice more often since I do not easily read a book to the end. This one was not made for reading but for recapitulation, and it has done me the most valuable service because I have thought about most of its points myself.

In the course of these studies it became ever clearer to him *that what appears in the endless multiplicity of individual plants is, after all, only one basic form; this basic form itself was becoming more and more perceptible to him.* He realized, furthermore, *that within this basic form lies a capacity for endless modification, whereby diversity is created out of unity.* On July 9, 1786, he wrote to Frau von Stein: *"It is a becoming aware of the form with which nature is always only playing, as it were, and in playing, bringing forth its manifold life."*[9]

What he now needed to do was to take this enduring, constant element, this archetypal form with which nature plays, as it were, and develop it in detail into a graspable picture. In order to do this he

---

8. "I would have gladly sent you a lesson in botany if it were only already written," from a letter to Knebel of April 2, 1785. — R. STEINER.

9. This is a beautiful example of Goethe's creative, participatory view of nature. — ED.

needed an opportunity to separate the truly constant and enduring element in the plant form from the changing and mutable. The scope of Goethe's research was as yet too narrow for observations of this kind. He would have to observe the same species of plant under different conditions and influences, for only then would the changeable element really become visible. It is less noticeable in plants of different kinds. All this was granted to Goethe through his fortunate journey to Italy, which he had undertaken from Karlsbad on September 3.

The flora of the Alps already afforded him many observations. Here he found not only new plants he had never seen before, but also some he already knew, *but changed.*

> Whereas in the lower regions the stalks and stems were stronger and thicker, the buds closer together and the leaves broad, higher in the mountains the stalks and stems became more delicate, the buds moved further apart so that there was more space between the nodes, and the leaves assumed a more lanceolate shape. I noticed this in willows and gentians and assured myself that they were not of different species. At the Walchensee [Bavaria], as well, I noticed that the rushes were longer and more slender than in the lowlands. (*Italian Journey,* Sept. 8, 1786)

Similar observations occurred repeatedly. In Venice, by the sea, he discovered various plants that presented him with qualities that only the old salt of the sandy soil, and, still more, the salty air, could give them. There he found a plant that appeared to him like "our innocent coltsfoot, but armed with sharp weapons and with leaves like leather, as were also the seedpods and stems; everything was thick and fat" (ibid., Oct. 8, 1786).

Goethe was encountering the inconstancy, the continually changing nature of all the external characteristics of the plant, of everything belonging to its outer appearance. From this he concluded that the essential nature of the plant does *not* lie in these characteristics but must be sought at a deeper level.

Darwin proceeded from similar observations when he asserted his doubts about the constancy of the outer forms of genera and species. The conclusions the two thinkers reached are entirely different, however. Whereas Darwin believed that the nature of the organism is, in fact, limited to those external characteristics, and thus concluded from their variability that there is nothing constant in the life of plants, Goethe went deeper and concluded that if the outer characteristics are not constant, then what is constant must be sought in something else underlying those changeable externalities. To develop a concept of this "something else" became Goethe's goal, while Darwin's efforts went toward exploring and explaining in detail the causes of the organism's variability. Both approaches are necessary and complement one another. It is altogether a mistake to believe that Goethe's greatness in organic science is that he was a mere forerunner of Darwin. Goethe's approach is far broader. It embraces two aspects: first, the *type* — that is, the lawfulness that manifests in the organism, the being of the animal in the animal, the life that unfolds out of itself, which has the power and capacity to develop itself in diverse outer forms (species, genera) through the possibilities lying within it; second, the interaction of organisms with inorganic nature and with each other (adaptation and the struggle for existence). Darwin developed only the latter aspect of organic science. Therefore one cannot say that Darwin's theory is the elaboration of Goethe's basic ideas — it is actually only the development of one aspect of those ideas. It looks only at those facts that cause the world of living organisms to evolve in a certain way, but not at the "something" that comes under the determining influence of those facts. This one aspect, pursued exclusively, can never lead to a complete theory of organisms. Such a theory must be pursued essentially in the spirit of Goethe; this one aspect must be complemented and deepened through the other aspect of his theory.

A simple comparison will make the matter clearer. Take a piece of lead, heat it until it becomes liquid, and pour it into cold water. The lead undergoes two successive stages; it passes through two states, the first caused by the higher temperature, the second by the lower. How the two stages take form depends not only on the nature of heat and cold but also, quite essentially, on the nature of the lead itself. A different substance, subjected to the same influences, would manifest very different changes. Organisms, likewise, are subject to the influence of their surroundings; as they are affected by this influence, they also take on different states, and they do so very much in accordance with their nature, with that essential being that makes them organisms. And it is this essential being that we find in Goethe's ideas. Only when equipped with an understanding of this, their essential nature, can we comprehend why organisms respond to specific influences in one particular way and not another. Only then will we be able to form correct views of the variability in the manifest forms of organisms and of the related laws governing their adaptation and struggle for existence.[10]

The idea of the archetypal plant assumed an increasingly clear and definite shape in Goethe's mind. In the botanical garden in Padua where he moved amid a vegetation strange to him, "the thought became more and more alive that one could, perhaps, develop all plant forms out of one" (*Italian Journey,* Sept. 27, 1786). On November 17, he wrote to Knebel:

> Thus, after all, my little bit of botany is granting me great pleasure, especially in these lands where a happier, less interrupted vegetation is at home. I have already made rather pleasing observations that tend toward the general and that you will also find agreeable.

On February 19, 1787, he wrote in Rome that he was on his way "to discovering new and beautiful relationships — how nature, such an enormity, a baffling profusion, develops the manifold out of the simple." On March 25 he requested that Herder be informed that he would soon be ready with the archetypal plant. On April 17, in Palermo, he wrote of the archetypal plant:

> Surely there must be such a thing! How else would I recognize that this or that formation is a plant if they were not all formed according to the same model? (*Italian Journey*)

He had in mind the complex of formative principles that organizes the plant, that makes it what it is — the principle through which a particular object in nature evokes in us the thought: "This is a plant" — that is, the archetypal plant. As such, it is something ideal that can only be grasped in thought; but it takes on shape, it takes on a specific form, size, color, number of organs, and so on. This outer phenomenon is nothing fixed but can undergo endless variations, all of which are in keeping with that complex of formative principles and follow from it with necessity. When we have grasped these formative principles — this archetypal picture of the plant — then we have taken hold

---

10. It should be clear that this view casts no doubt on the modern theory of evolution and that it does not attempt to restrict its claims. On the contrary, it establishes a firm basis for such claims. — R. STEINER.

of, as idea, the very foundations upon which nature bases every single individual plant, from which she derives it and through which she allows it to come into being. Indeed, in accordance with this lawfulness one can even invent plant forms that follow with necessity from the essential nature of the plant and that could exist if the necessary conditions arose.

Thus Goethe seeks to reproduce in thought what nature accomplishes in the formation of her works. On May 17, 1787, he wrote to Herder:

> Moreover, I must confide to you that I have come very close to the secret of the generation and organization of plants and that it is the simplest thing one can imagine.... The archetypal plant will be the most extraordinary creature in the world, for which nature herself will envy me. With this model and the key to it one will then be able to invent plants ad infinitum that must be consistent. In other words, even if they do not exist, they could exist and are not merely painterly or poetic whims but possess an inner truth and necessity. It will be possible to apply the same law to all living things. (Ibid.)

At this point a further difference between Goethe's view and Darwin's becomes apparent, especially when we consider how the latter is usually represented.[11] This view assumes that outer influences work like mechanical causes upon the nature of an organism and modify it accordingly. For Goethe, individual modifications are various expressions of the archetypal organism, which has within it the capacity to take on manifold forms and, in any given case, takes on the form most suited to the conditions in its environment. These external conditions are only the outer inducement for the inner formative forces to manifest in a particular way. These forces alone are the constitutive principle, the creative element, in the plant. Therefore, on September 6, 1787, Goethe also called them the ἕν καὶ πᾶν ("one and all") of the plant world.

Now, when we consider this archetypal plant itself, we can say:

---

11. We are not referring here so much to the theory of evolution put forward by scientists who base their conclusions on empirical fact but rather to the theoretical foundations, the principles, that underlie Darwinism — especially as represented by the Jena school led by Haeckel. In this first rate mind, the Darwinian theory in all its one-sidedness has probably reached its most consistent expression. — R. Steiner.

Anything that is alive is a self-contained whole that brings forth its various states out of itself. Both in the spatial juxtaposition of its members and in the succession of its stages over time, every living entity manifests interrelationships that do not appear to be determined by the sense perceptible characteristics of its members, nor by some kind of mechanical causality through which earlier stages determine later ones. These interrelationships are governed, rather, by a higher principle that stands above the members and stages. It is inherent in the nature of the whole that a specific stage arises as the first, another as the last; and the sequence of the intermediary stages is also determined within the idea of the whole; what comes before is dependent on what comes later, and vice versa. In short, in a living organism there is *development* of one thing out of another, transition from one stage into another — there is no finished, completed existence of any one particular, but rather continuous *becoming*.

In the plant this determination of each single member by the whole arises insofar as all its organs are built according to the same basic form. On May 17, 1787, Goethe conveyed this thought to Herder:

> I have come to realize that the organ of the plant we ordinarily call the leaf conceals the true Proteus,[12] who can conceal and reveal himself in all formations. Backward and forward, the plant is only leaf, linked so inseparably to the future seed that one should not think one without the other.

Whereas in the animal the higher principle governing every particular comes to meet us concretely as that which moves its organs, uses them according to its needs, and so on, the plant still lacks such a palpable life principle. Its life principle manifests only in the less distinctive fact that all its organs are built according to the same formative type — indeed, that the whole plant is potentially present in each of its parts and can, under favorable conditions, be brought forth from them. This became especially clear to Goethe in Rome when Councillor Reiffenstein, on a walk with him, broke off a twig here and there and asserted that if they were stuck in the ground they would grow and develop into a whole plant. A plant is thus a being that, over successive periods of time, develops specific organs that are all built according to one and the same idea, both in relation to one

---

12. *Proteus* was the Grecian god able to assume any shape or form. — ED.

another and in the relationship of each to the whole. Every plant is a harmonious whole composed of plants.[13] When Goethe came to see this clearly, it only remained for him to make the individual observations that would enable him to describe in detail the various developmental stages of the unfolding plant.

The necessary groundwork for this had already been done. As we have seen, Goethe had already made a study of seeds in the spring of 1785. On May 17, 1787, he reported to Herder from Italy that he had found very clearly and without doubt the point where the germ is concealed. This took care of the first stage of plant life. But the unity in the formation of all the leaves also soon revealed itself. In numerous examples, but in fresh fennel above all, Goethe found a strong differentiation of upper and lower leaves that nevertheless always remain the same organ. On March 25 [1787] he asked that Herder be informed that his study of cotyledons was so sublimated that it would be difficult to take it further. Only a small step remained to recognize that petals, stamens, and pistil are also metamorphosed leaves. The research of the English botanist Hill was at that time becoming more generally known; it dealt with the transformation of specific organs of the blossom into others, and paved the way for Goethe in this respect.

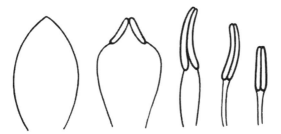

Fig. 1. Transition from petal to stamen.
(White Water Lily). (from Grohmann, 1989).

As the organizing forces of the plant's being come into actual existence, they assume a sequence of spatial formations. What was now

---

13. Just how these particulars relate to the whole will be discussed at various points in these introductions. Borrowing a concept for a whole composed of living part-entities from contemporary zoology, we could take the example of an insect colony. This is a kind of community of living beings, an individual consisting of independent individuals, an individual of a higher sort. — R. STEINER.

called for was a living concept to connect these forms backward and forward.

By examining Goethe's study of metamorphosis as formulated [in *The Metamorphosis of Plants*] in 1790, we find that for Goethe this concept was one of alternating expansion and contraction. In the seed the formation of the plant is most strongly contracted, or concentrated. With the leaves the first unfolding and expansion of the formative forces takes place. What is compressed into one point in the seed now reaches outward into space in the leaves. In the flower bud the forces draw together once more around an axial point in the calyx; the corolla is the result of the next expansion; stamens and pistil come about through the next contraction; and the fruit arises through the third and last expansion, whereupon the entire force of the plant's life (its entelechial principle) once again conceals itself in its most intensely contracted state in the seed. Whereas we can now follow nearly all the details of Goethe's thoughts on metamorphosis up to their final formulation in his essay of 1790, it will not be so easy to do the same with his concept of expansion and contraction. Still, we will not go wrong in assuming that this thought (which is, incidentally, deeply rooted in Goethe's spirit) was also already woven into his concept of plant formation in Italy. Since it involves a greater or lesser spatial unfolding, as determined by the shaping forces, and since this presents itself directly to the eye, the concept of expansion and contraction will certainly arise most easily when we draw the plant in accordance with its natural formation. In Rome Goethe found a bushlike carnation plant in which he could perceive metamorphosis with particular clarity:

> Seeing no way to preserve this marvelous form, I attempted an exact drawing of it, whereby I deepened my insight into the fundamental concept of metamorphosis.

He may have made such drawings often, and this may have led to the concept in question.

In September 1787, during his second stay in Rome, Goethe expounded the matter to his friend Moritz; he found how alive and vivid it became through such a presentation. Whatever had been discussed was always written down. From this passage [in his *Italian Journey*] and some other remarks of Goethe's, it seems likely that the first — at least aphoristic — formulation of his study of metamorphosis also occurred already in Italy. He continued: "Only in this way — through my presentations to Moritz — could I get some of my thoughts down on paper." There is now no doubt that the work in its present form was written at the end of 1789 and the beginning of 1790; however, it remains difficult to determine how much of this manuscript was a mere editing and how much was added at that time. The announcement of a book for the next Easter Book Fair, which might have contained some of the same thoughts, induced Goethe in the autumn of 1789 to take up his ideas and to arrange for their publication. On November 20 he wrote to the Duke that he had been spurred on to write down his botanical ideas. As early as December 18 he sent the manuscript to the botanist Batsch in Jena to read; on the twentieth he went there himself to discuss it with Batsch; on the twenty-second he informed Knebel that Batsch had received it favorably. He returned home, worked the manuscript through once more, and then again sent it to Batsch, who returned it on January 19, 1790. What vicissitudes the manuscript as well as the printed edition then went through have been described at length by Goethe himself. The great significance of his concept of metamorphosis, as well as its specific nature, will be treated later in chapter 4, "The Nature and Significance of Goethe's Writings on Organic Morphology."

Chapter 3

The Origin of Goethe's Thinking on Animal Morphology

Lavater's *Essays on Physiognomy* was published in 1775–1778.[1] Goethe took a lively interest in this work, not only as director of its publication but also as a contributing author. Of particular interest to us now, however, is that in these contributions we find the seeds of his later zoological works.

Physiognomy sought to determine the inner nature, or spirit, of people through their external form. Form was considered not for its own sake but as an expression of the soul. Goethe's sculptural spirit — as though created to grasp things in their outer, formal relationships — was not to be limited to this approach. While engaged in these studies that approached the outer form only as a way to know the inner being, Goethe came to realize the independent significance of form in its own right. This can be seen in his 1776 studies of animal skulls, which we find inserted into part two of the second volume of *Essays on Physiognomy.* He was stimulated to begin these studies that year by reading Aristotle on physiognomy. He also attempted to examine the difference between human beings and animals. Goethe found this difference in the way the structure of the human form as a whole gives rise to the preeminence of the head, in the highly developed human brain, toward which all parts of the body point as their center: "How the whole human figure stands there as the supporting column of the dome in which the heavens are to be reflected." In the structure of the

---

1. *Physiognomische Fragmente zur Beförderung der Menschenkenntnis und Menschen-liebe* (Physiognomic Fragments to Advance Human Knowledge and Human Love). Johann Kaspar Lavater (1741–1801), Swiss mystic, poet, philosopher, dramatist, and clergyman. — ED.

animal he found the opposite. "The head only appended to the spinal column! The brain, the end of the spinal cord, has no greater compass than necessary for expressing the animal spirits and for directing a creature that lives through its senses in the immediate present."

With these indications Goethe went beyond the consideration of individual interrelationships between the outer and inner nature of the human being to a grasp of a comprehensive whole and to the contemplation of the form as such. He came to view the *whole* of the human form as the basis for the higher expressions of human life. And in the particular character of that whole he recognized the precondition that places the human being at the pinnacle of creation. In forming this concept, we must keep in mind that Goethe sought to relate the animal shapes to the fully developed human form. But in the animals the organs that serve primarily the animal functions predominate, as it were, and become the point toward which their entire organization is directed and which it serves, whereas the human organism develops those organs in particular that serve spiritual functions.

Even at this early stage we find that what Goethe envisioned as the animal organism is no longer any particular one as we find it in sensory reality; it is, rather, an ideal organism that develops more toward a lower aspect of its nature in the animals and toward a higher aspect in the human being. Here lies the seed of what Goethe later called the *type,* by which he did not intend "any particular animal" but the idea of the animal. Yes, and more — we find here intimations of a law that he formulated later and that has significant implications: namely, that "diversity of form springs from a preponderance of one part over the others." Indeed, the contrast between the animals and the human being is already seen here as arising through the development of an ideal form in two diverging directions, whereby different systems of organs gain a preponderance and give the entire creature its particular character.

In the same year (1776), we also find that Goethe became clear about a way of approaching the forms of animal organisms. He realized that the bones are the foundations of the form, a thought he later upheld in his anatomical studies, in which he always proceeded from osteology. In that year he wrote the pertinent sentence, "The mobile parts form according to them [the bones] — or better, with them — and play their own role only to the extent that the solid parts allow." And another indication in Lavater's *Physiognomy:*

It may already have been noticed that I consider *the skeletal system to be the basic sketch of the human being,* the skull to be the foundation of the skeletal system and all fleshy parts to be scarcely more than the coloration of this drawing.

This was probably inspired by Goethe, who often discussed these things with Lavater. Such views are indeed identical with Goethe's. But Goethe now makes a further observation that we must consider:

This comment (that by studying the bones, and especially the skull, one can see most clearly how the skeleton is the foundation of the form) will encounter considerable opposition when applied to the dissimilarity of human skulls, though it is indisputable here (in animals).

What is Goethe doing here but looking for the simpler animal in the composite human being as he later put it (in 1795)![2] This leads us to conclude that Goethe established the fundamental concepts upon which he based his later thoughts on animal morphology through his preoccupation with Lavater's *Physiognomy* in 1776. This was also the year that Goethe began to study anatomy in detail. On January 22, 1776, he wrote to Lavater, "The Duke had six skulls sent to me; [I] have made glorious observations, which are available to you if you haven't already made them without me."

Goethe's connections with the University of Jena further stimulated his study of anatomy. Our first indications of this are from 1781. In a diary edited by Keil, on October 15, 1781, Goethe noted that he went to Jena with "old Einsiedel" and busied himself with anatomy. At Jena there was a scholar named Loder who advanced Goethe's studies tremendously. It was he who also led Goethe further into the field of anatomy, as he wrote to Frau von Stein on October 29,[3] and

---

2. In the section "The Purpose Set Forth" of his essay "On Morphology," Goethe sheds light on this statement: "The more imperfect a creature is, the more [its] parts appear identical or similar to each other and the more they resemble the whole. The more perfected the creature is, the more dissimilar its parts become. In the first case, the whole is more or less identical to its parts; in the second case, the whole is dissimilar to its parts. The more similar the parts, the less they will be subordinated to each other. Subordination of the parts betokens a more perfected creature."

Compare also to the statement by Herder quoted on p. 28. — ED.

3. "A troublesome labor of love that I have undertaken leads me further in my pursuit. Loder is explaining to me all the bones and muscles, and I shall understand a great deal in a few days." — R. STEINER.

to Karl August on November 4.[4] In the second letter he spoke of his intention

> to explain the sketches to the young people [of the Art Academy] and to lead them to a knowledge of the human body.... I am doing this both for my sake and for theirs; the method I have chosen will familiarize them completely with the fundamentals of the body over the course of this winter.

Goethe's diary entries show that he actually gave these lectures, ending them on January 16, 1782. At the same time there must have been a good deal of discussion with Loder about the structure of the human body. On January 6, Goethe's diary notes, "Demonstration of the heart by Loder." We have seen that as early as 1776 Goethe harbored farsighted thoughts on the structure of animal organisms.

Thus, there can be no doubt at all that his intensive preoccupation with anatomy at this later time raised itself beyond details to higher perspectives. He wrote to Lavater and Merck on November 14, 1781, that he was treating "the bones as a text to which all life and everything human can be appended." When we read a text, pictures and ideas form in our mind that seem to be evoked or created by the text. Goethe treated the bones as such a text; that is, while he observed them, thoughts arose within him concerning all of life and everything human. In the course of these contemplations, certain ideas on the formation of the organism must have made an impression on him. Goethe's ode of 1782 "The Divine" can help us understand to some degree his thinking at the time on the relationship of the human being to the rest of nature. The first verse reads:

> Let us be noble,
> Helpful and good!
> For this alone
> Distinguishes us
> From all the beings
> That we know.

Having characterized the spiritual attributes of the human being in the first two lines of this verse, Goethe asserts that these *alone* distin-

---

4. "He [Loder] has demonstrated to me osteology and myology in eight days, which we have devoted almost entirely to this — to the extent that my attentiveness held out." — R. STEINER.

guish us from all the other beings in the world. This "alone" shows us very clearly that Goethe considered the physical constitution of the human being to conform entirely with the rest of nature. The thought we drew attention to earlier was growing more and more alive within him: that one basic form governs both human and animal shapes, but that in the human it attains such perfection that it becomes the vehicle for free spiritual beings. With regard to our sense-perceptible characteristics, as human beings we must also, as the ode says,

> Complete the circles
> Of our existence...
> According to eternal laws
> Of mighty, iron necessity.

But in our case, these laws develop in a way that allows us to do the "impossible":

> We distinguish,
> Choose and judge,
> And to the moment
> Give permanent form.

We must also bear in mind that, while Goethe's views were becoming more and more definite, he was in lively communication with Herder, who in 1783 was beginning to formulate his *Reflections on the Philosophy of the History of Humanity.* This work might almost be said to have arisen from those two men's discussions, and many of its ideas may well be traced to Goethe. The thoughts expressed there are often entirely Goethean but phrased in Herder's style, so that we can draw from them a reliable conclusion about Goethe's thoughts at the time.

In the first part of his work, Herder develops the following view of the natural world: We must presuppose a principal form that moves through all beings and realizes itself in various ways,

> from the stone to the crystal, from the crystal to the metals, from these to the creation of plants, from plants to animals, from these to the human being — we saw the *organizational form ascend,* and with it the forces and drives of this creature grow more versatile and finally unite in the form of the human being, to the extent that it can encompass them.

This thought is perfectly clear: an ideal, typical form that, as such, has no sensory reality, realizes itself in an endless multiplicity of spatially separated and qualitatively differentiated beings all the way up to the human being. On the lower levels of organization it always realizes itself in a particular direction, and develops toward it in a very pronounced way. As this typical form rises toward the human being, it gathers all the formative principles developed in a one-sided way in the lower organisms (which it distributed among various beings) into *one* form. This creates the possibility of such high perfection in the human being. Here, nature has bestowed upon one being what she dispersed among many classes and orders of animals. This thought had an uncommonly fruitful effect on subsequent German philosophy. To further clarify this concept, let us quote here its later formulation by Oken:

> The animal kingdom is only *one* animal; in other words, it represents animality in such a way that each of its organs exists as a whole in itself. An individual animal comes into existence when an individual organ separates from the general animal body while nevertheless accomplishing the essential animal functions. The animal kingdom is merely the dismembered highest animal — the human being. There is only one human kind, one human race, one human species, for the simple reason that the human being is the entire animal kingdom. (*Lehrbuch der Naturphilosophie*, Jena, 1831)

Thus there are, for example, animals in whom the organs of touch are developed, whose whole organization, in fact, is oriented toward touching, in which it finds its goal; there are others in which the organs for eating are especially developed; and so on. In other words, within each species of animal, one organ system becomes prominent in a one-sided way; the whole animal is entirely immersed in it, and all else recedes into the background.

In the formation of the human being, however, all organs and organ systems develop *in such a way* that each leaves the others enough room to develop freely; each withdraws enough to allow all the others to likewise come into their own. Thus a harmonious interaction of the individual organs and systems arises, creating a harmony that makes the human the most perfect of beings, uniting the perfections of all the other creatures. These thoughts comprised the substance of Goethe's conversations with Herder, who expressed them in this way:

> The human race [can be seen] as *the great confluence of lower organic forces* that gather to achieve humanity.... Thus we can assume that *the human being is a central creature among animals; that is, the finished form in which the characteristics of all the various species are assembled in their finest essence.*[5]

The following passage from Goethe's letter to Knebel (December 8, 1783) indicates the extent of Goethe's participation in Herder's *Reflections on the Philosophy of the History of Humanity:*

> Herder is writing a philosophy of history — new from the ground up, as you can imagine. The day before yesterday we read the first chapters together; they are delightful.... World history and natural history are simply raging along with us now.[6]

Herder's observation (that the upright posture inherent in the human organism and everything connected with it is the fundamental precondition for human thinking)[7] is directly reminiscent of Goethe's above mentioned indications of 1776 concerning the generic difference between the human being and the animals (in Lavater's *Essays on Physiognomy*).[8] Herder's expositions are only one formulation of this thought. All of this justifies our assumption, however, that Goethe and Herder essentially agreed at the time (1783) on the place of the human being in nature.

Now, one of the consequences of such a basic view is that each organ, or part, of an animal will be found also in the human being, but restrained within the limits imposed by the harmony of the whole. A particular bone, for example, must in fact develop in a certain way in a particular animal species in which it will predominate, but it must also be at least indicated in all other animals, and it must not be absent in human beings. Whereas in the animal it assumes the form that corresponds to its own lawfulness, in the human being it must acquiesce to the whole and adapt its formative laws to those of the

---

5. Herder, *Reflections on the Philosophy of the History of Humanity*, book 5, part I, or book 2, part I. — R. STEINER.
   6. Compare letter of Frau von Stein to Knebel on p. 12. — ED.
   7. Ibid., book 3, VI, and book 4, I. — R. STEINER.
   8. *Essays on Physiognomy*, vol. 2, section 2. See also p. 22 of the present volume. — ED.

organism as a whole. If nature's web is not to tear, however, it cannot be absent entirely, since this would disturb the consistent elaboration of the type.

These were Goethe's views when he suddenly became aware of an opinion that completely contradicted this great thought. The scholars of that time were concerned primarily with finding the traits that distinguish one animal species from another. It was believed that the difference between animals and human beings was that animals have a little bone — the *intermaxillary* — located between the two symmetrical halves of their upper jaw and holding the upper incisors. This bone was thought to be absent in human beings.

In 1782, Merck was beginning to take a lively interest in osteology and turned to some of the most prominent scholars of that time for help.[9] On October 8, 1782, the distinguished anatomist Sömmerring responded with information regarding the difference between animals and human beings:[10]

> I wish you would look into Blumenbach on the subject of the *ossis intermaxillaris*.[11] All other things being equal, it is the only bone found in all animals from the ape up, including the orangutan, but is *never found in the human being;* with the exception of this bone, there is nothing that prevents you from transferring everything found in the human being to the animals. I am therefore providing you with the head of a doe in order to convince you that this *os intermaxillare* — as Blumenbach calls it, or *os incisivum* [according to Camper] — is present even in animals with no incisors in their upper jaw.

Although Blumenbach found rudimentary traces of the *ossis intermaxillaris* in the skulls of unborn or young children — indeed, in one such skull even two entirely separate little kernels of bone as actual

---

9. Johann Heinrich Merck (1741–1791), a German writer and critic who helped to promote the *Sturm und Drang* movement. Merck, a friend of Goethe, funded the publication of his tragic play *Götz von Berlichingen* (1773), the success of which established the Shakespearean form of drama in Germany. — ED.

10. Samuel Thomas von Sömmerring (1755–1830), anatomist and professor in Kassel, established the number and names of the cranial nerves as well as other neuroanatomical discoveries. — ED.

11. Johann Friedrich Blumenbach (1752–1840), German zoologist and anthropologist and professor of medicine at Göttingen. He was among the first to study humankind as a species and was considered the founder of modern anthropology. He pioneered craniology and was the first to classify human races as Caucasian, Mongolian, Ethiopian, American, and Malayan. — ED.

intermaxillary bones — he nevertheless refused to admit its existence. He said, "There is still a world of difference between this and the true *osse intermaxillari*." Camper, the most famous anatomist of the time, shared this opinion.[12] He referred, for example, to the intermaxillary bone as having "never been found in the human being."[13] Merck had the greatest admiration for Camper and occupied himself with his writings.

Merck, as well as Blumenbach and Sömmerring, were in communication with Goethe. Goethe's correspondence with Merck shows that he took the liveliest interest in his osteological research and exchanged ideas with him on the subject. On October 27, 1782, he asked Merck to write something for him about Camper's *"incognitum"* [unknown animal] and to send him Camper's letters. Furthermore, we should note a visit by Blumenbach to Weimar in April, 1783. In September of the same year Goethe went to Göttingen in order to visit Blumenbach and all the professors. On September 28, he wrote to Frau von Stein, "I have decided to visit all the professors, and you can imagine how much running that will mean if I am to make the rounds in a few days."

He then went to Kassel, where he met with Forster and Sömmerring. From there he wrote to Frau von Stein on October 2:

> I am seeing very beautiful and good things and being rewarded for my quiet industriousness. Most fortunate of all is the fact that I can say now that I am on the right track and that from now on nothing will be lost on me.

It was probably during this interchange that Goethe first learned of the prevailing view regarding the intermaxillary. In his view of matters, this immediately seemed to be an error; it would destroy the typical, fundamental form according to which all organisms must be fashioned. Goethe could not doubt that this member, found in various stages of development in all higher animals, must also take part in the structuring of the human form and recedes here only because the alimentary organs as a whole recede before those that serve spiritual

---

12. Pieter Camper (1722–1789), Dutch anatomist and professor in Franeker and Amsterdam, was known for his work in human comparative anatomy and in surgery and obstetrics. He tried to determine the degree of human intelligence by measuring the facial angle. — ED.

13. In "Natuurkundige verhandelingen over den Orang Outang" (Amsterdam, 1782). — ED.

functions. Because of his whole inner orientation, Goethe could not help thinking that there must be an intermaxillary bone in the human being as well. It would only be a question of proving it empirically by investigating its form in human beings and the extent of its adaptation to the human organism as a whole. In the spring of 1784 — together with Loder, with whom he compared human and animal skulls in Jena — Goethe succeeded in finding that proof. On March 27, he announced his discovery to both Frau von Stein[14] and Herder.[15]

We should not overestimate this single discovery in weighing it against the great thoughts upon which it was based. Its value for Goethe lay simply in clearing away a preconception that seemed to obstruct a consistent pursuit of his ideas right into the smallest detail of an organism. Neither did Goethe view this as an isolated discovery but always saw it in relation to his larger view of nature. Thus, this is how we should understand Goethe when he wrote to Herder in his letter, "It should greatly please you, because it is like the keystone to the human being; it is not missing — it is there as well! But how?" And he immediately reminded his friend of other perspectives: "I have also thought of it in relation to your whole picture; how beautiful it will be there!"

To Goethe it was meaningless to argue that animals have an intermaxillary bone but that human beings do not. If the forces that form the organism insert an intermaxillary between the two upper jaw-bones in animals, then these same forces must also be active in human beings — in a location that corresponds to where that bone is found in animals, in essentially the same way but with a different outer expression. Goethe never thought of the organism as a dead, fixed assembly, but one that constantly arises from inner formative forces. Consequently, he had to ask, What are those forces doing in the human upper jaw? He could not ask whether or not the intermaxillary is present, but rather only seek to determine its characteristics and form. This had to be done empirically.

As various of his statements show, the thought of writing a more comprehensive work on nature now began to stir in Goethe with

---

14. "It is a rare pleasure, I have made an anatomical discovery that is significant and beautiful." — R. STEINER.

15. "I have found — neither gold nor silver, but something that gives me unspeakable joy — the human *ossis intermaxillaris!*" — R. STEINER.

increasing vitality. Thus, when sending Knebel his treatise on his discovery in November 1784, Goethe wrote to him:

> I have refrained from calling attention *at this time* to the conclusion, which Herder has already alluded to in his *Reflections* — that *the difference between the human being and the animals cannot be found in any particular.*

The most important thing here is that Goethe says he has refrained from calling attention to this fundamental thought "at this time." He thus intended to do so later within a larger context. Furthermore, this statement shows that the fundamental thoughts most interesting to us — Goethe's great ideas about the animal type — were alive in his mind long before that discovery. Here Goethe admits that they were suggested in Herder's *Reflections,* and the passages in which this occurs were written before the discovery of the intermaxillary bone. *The discovery of the intermaxillary is therefore only a result of these far-reaching views.*

To those who did not hold such views, the discovery must have remained incomprehensible. They had been deprived of the single feature in natural history that could distinguish the human being from the animals. They had hardly an inkling of Goethe's prevailing view — that elements distributed among the animals unite harmoniously in the *single* human form, thus establishing — despite the identity of all particulars — a differentiation of the whole that gives humankind its high rank in nature's hierarchy. Their way of observing was not through ideas but by external comparison, for which the intermaxillary in fact did not exist in the human being. They had little understanding for what Goethe demanded — that is, seeing with *the eyes of the spirit.*

This was also the reason for the difference in judgment between them and Goethe. Whereas Blumenbach — who also saw the matter very clearly — concluded that "there is a world of difference between it and the true *osse intermaxillari,*" Goethe judged the matter by asking, How can such an external difference, no matter how great, be explained when there is a *necessary inner* identity?

Goethe now clearly wanted to elaborate this thought in a consistent way, and he occupied himself with it a great deal during the following years. On May 1, 1784, Frau von Stein wrote to Knebel:

Herder's new work makes it seem likely that we were originally plants and animals.... Goethe is now pondering these things very thoughtfully, and everything that goes through his mind becomes extremely interesting.[16].

Goethe longed to present his views on nature in a major work. And the intensity of that desire can be seen vividly in the strength with which, with each new discovery, he emphatically told his friends about the possibility of expanding his ideas to embrace all of nature. In 1786, he wrote to Frau von Stein of his wish to expand "to all the kingdoms of nature, to her whole kingdom" his ideas on how nature produces her manifold life by playing, as it were, with one primary form. And in Italy, when the concept of metamorphosis in the plant world stood before his spirit with sculptural clarity, right down into every detail, he wrote in Naples on May 17, 1787, "It will be possible to apply the same law to all living things." The first essay in his *Morphological Notebooks* (1817) contains the words, "Thus, what in my youthful enthusiasm I often dreamt of as a completed work now presents itself as a draft, as a fragmentary collection."

We must regret that such a work never flowed from Goethe's pen. Judging by all that we do have, such a production would have far surpassed anything of its kind achieved in recent times. It would have become the standard body of principles, from which every scientific endeavor would have had to proceed, and against which we could weigh its spiritual substance. The most profound philosophical spirit (which only a superficial mind fails to see in Goethe) would have united there with loving immersion in what is given through sensory experience; far from a one-sided obsession with systems claiming to encompass all beings in one general scheme, his work would have done justice to every single individual. Here we would have had the work of a mind that never favors one area of human endeavor at the expense of all the others, but for which — even while devoted to a single subject — the whole of human existence is always present in the background. In this way each individual activity takes its rightful place in relation to the whole. When the mind objectively immerses itself in the contemplated objects, it enters them fully. Thus, Goethe's theories do not appear as though abstracted from objects, but

---

16. This statement was quoted in another context on p. 12. See also Goethe's comment to Knebel on p. 28. — Ed.

rather as though they were being formed by the objects themselves in a mind that forgets itself in contemplation. This strictest objectivity would make Goethe's work the most perfect of scientific works, an ideal toward which every scientist would have to strive. For philosophers it would be an archetypal model for discovering the laws of objective, world contemplation. We can assume that epistemology — now arising everywhere as a philosophical foundation of science — will not become fruitful until it makes Goethe's way of observing and thinking its point of reference.

In the *Annals* of 1790, Goethe himself gave the reason why this work never came about: "The task was so great that it could not be resolved in a single, distracted lifetime." From this point of view, the available fragments of Goethe's scientific work assume tremendous significance. Indeed, we will never value and understand them properly until we see how they arose from that greater whole.

In 1784, however, the treatise on the intermaxillary bone was to be formulated merely as a preliminary exercise, so to speak. To begin with, it was not intended to be published; as Goethe wrote to Sömmerring (March 6, 1785), "Since my little treatise has no claim whatever to publicity and should be regarded as merely a first draft, I would be pleased to hear whatever you might wish to share with me on this subject."

The project was nevertheless accomplished with great care and with all the necessary individual studies. Some young people were immediately enlisted to help make drawings (under Goethe's guidance) according to Camper's method. On April 23, 1784, Goethe therefore asked Merck for information on this method and had Sömmerring send him drawings in Camper's style. Merck, Sömmerring, and other acquaintances were asked for all kinds of skeletons and bones. On April 23 Goethe wrote to Merck that he would be very pleased to have the following skeletons: a "*myrmecophagus* [South American anteater], *bradypus* [sloth], lions, and tigers, or similar skeletons." On May 14 he asked Sömmerring for the skull of his elephant skeleton and that of a hippopotamus and, on September 16, for the skulls of the following animals: "wildcat, lion, young bear, incognitum, anteater, camel, dromedary, and sea lion." Particular items of information were also requested from his friends: from Merck a description of the palate of his rhinoceros, particularly an explanation of "how the horn of the rhinoceros is actually seated on the nasal bone."

Goethe was utterly absorbed in these studies. Waitz drew the elephant skull from many sides according to Camper's method, and when Goethe discovered that most of the sutures in this skull were not yet grown together, he compared it with a large skull in his own possession and with other skulls. While studying this skull he made an important observation. It had been assumed previously that in all animals only the incisors were embedded in the intermaxillary, whereas the canine teeth belonged to the upper jawbone; the only exception was thought to be the elephant, in which the canines were supposedly contained in the intermaxillary. That this is not the case was now also demonstrated to Goethe by this skull, which he wrote of in a letter to Herder. Goethe's osteological studies accompanied him that summer on a journey to Eisenach and Braunschweig. While in Braunschweig, he intended to "look into the mouth of an unborn elephant and carry on a hearty conversation with Zimmermann." He wrote further about this fetus to Merck:

> I wish we had in our own cabinet the fetus that they have in Braunschweig; it would be quickly dissected, skeletonized, and prepared. I do not know what such a monstrosity in alcohol is good for if it is not dismembered and its inner structure explained.

These studies led to a treatise[17] included in volume one of Goethe's scientific works in Kürschner's National Literature.[18] Loder was very helpful to Goethe in composing this treatise, and Latin terminology was introduced with his assistance. He also prepared a Latin translation. In November 1784, Goethe sent the treatise to Knebel, and on December 19 to Merck, though shortly before (December 2) he had doubted that much would come of it before the year's end. The work was accompanied by the necessary drawings, and for Camper's sake, by the Latin translation. Merck was to send the work to Sömmerring, who received it in January 1785. From there it went to Camper.

If we now look at how Goethe's treatise was received, we are faced with a rather unpleasant picture. Initially, no one had the capacity to

---

17. "An Intermaxillary Bone Is Present in the Upper Jaw of Man As Well As in Animals." An English translation of this treatise is included in *Goethe, Scientific Studies,* Suhrkamp edition, p. 111. — ED.

18. The volume mentioned here was introduced by the essays of Rudolf Steiner that comprise chapters 1 through 4 of this book. — ED.

understand it, with the exception of Loder (with whom Goethe had worked) and Herder. Merck took pleasure in the treatise but was not convinced that its assertions were true. Sömmerring wrote to inform Merck of its arrival:

> Blumenbach already had the main idea. He [Goethe] begins one paragraph saying, "There can therefore be no doubt, since the rest of them [the sutures] grow together." The only problem is that they never existed. I have before me now the jawbones of embryos ranging from three months to maturity, and not one of them contains a suture that can be seen toward the front. And to explain it through the pressure of the bones against one another? Indeed, as though nature worked like a carpenter with hammer and wedges!

On February 13, 1785, Goethe wrote to Merck, "I received a very thoughtless letter from Sömmerring. He actually wants to talk me out of it. Oh!" And Sömmerring wrote to Merck on May 11, 1785, "I see from Goethe's letter of yesterday that he is not ready to abandon his idea concerning the *ossis intermaxillaris.*"

And now Camper: On September 16, 1785, he reported to Merck that the accompanying illustrations were certainly not drawn according to his method. He even found them quite faulty. He praised the outer appearance of the beautiful manuscript but criticized the Latin translation and even suggested that the author brush up on his Latin. Three days later he wrote that he had made a number of observations on the intermaxillary but must continue to maintain that there is no such bone in the human being. He conceded that all of Goethe's observations were correct except those pertaining to the human being. And again on March 21, 1786, he wrote that, based on numerous observations, he had concluded that *the intermaxillary does not exist in the human being.* Camper's letters show clearly that he was very willing to go into the matter but that he was not at all capable of understanding Goethe.

Loder immediately saw Goethe's discovery in the right light. He gave it a prominent place in his *Anatomical Handbook* of 1788, and after that addressed it in all his writings as a fully accepted fact of science that could not be doubted.

Herder wrote to Knebel that "Goethe has presented us with his treatise on the bone, which is very simple and beautiful; *this man travels the true path of nature,* and fortune comes to meet him." Herder was indeed capable of seeing the matter, as Goethe did, with his "spiritual eye." Without this capacity there was no way of coming to terms with it. This can best be seen from the following, written by Wilhelm Josephi, instructor at the University of Göttingen, in his *Anatomy of Mammals* (1787):

> The *ossa intermaxillaria* are considered one of the main characteristics that distinguish apes from human beings; yet according to my observations, human beings also have such *ossa intermaxillaria*, at least during the first months of life. But they usually grow together with the true upper jawbones, especially on the outside, at a very early stage, indeed while still in the mother's womb, so that often no noticeable trace of them remains.

Goethe's discovery is, in fact, fully confirmed here, although not as a consequence of the consistent elaboration of the type, but as an expression of what is directly visible to the eyes. If one relies only on the eyes, then of course it depends only on chance whether one happens to find specimens in which one actually *sees* the matter with precision. But, when one grasps the matter as Goethe did — through the idea — then these particular specimens only confirm the idea and *openly* reveal what nature otherwise conceals. But the idea itself can be traced in any specimen; each reveals a particular instance of the idea. Indeed, when we possess the idea, then we can find through it just those examples in which it is most distinctly revealed. Without the idea, however, we are at the mercy of chance. It can in fact be seen that after Goethe had given the impetus through his great thought, the scientific community was gradually convinced of the truth of his discovery through the observation of numerous cases.[19]

It seems that Merck continued to waver. On February 13, 1785, Goethe sent him a human upper jawbone that had been split apart, along with one from a manatee, and gave him clues as to how to understand them. It appears from Goethe's letter of April 8 that Merck had been more or less won over. But he soon changed his mind again, for on November 11, 1786, he wrote to Sömmerring: "I hear

---

19. Goethe wrote: "An idea about objects of experience is, in a manner of speaking, an organ that I use in order to grasp them, in order to make them my own." See p. 270 of the accompanying essay. — ED.

that Vicq d'Azyr has actually included *Goethe's so-called discovery* in his book."[20]

Sömmerring gradually abandoned his opposition. In his work *On the Structure of the Human Body* he stated:

> Goethe's ingenious attempt in 1785 to demonstrate through comparative osteology that the intermaxillary bone of the upper jaw is found in the human being as well as other animals — with its very accurate illustrations — deserves to be publicly known.

It was more difficult to win over Blumenbach. In his *Handbook of Comparative Anatomy* (1805), he maintained his conviction that human beings do not have an intermaxillary bone. In his essay "Principles of Zoological Philosophy" (1830–1832), Goethe was nevertheless able to speak of Blumenbach's conversion. After personal communication, he came over to Goethe's side. On December 15, 1825, he even provided Goethe with a beautiful example that confirmed his discovery. A Hessian athlete sought help from Blumenbach's colleague Langenbeck for an "*os intermaxillare* quite animal-like in prominence." We shall speak further of later advocates of Goethe's ideas. Let us only add here that, by using diluted nitric acid, M. J. Weber successfully separated the intermaxillary bone even after it had fused with the upper jawbone.

Goethe continued his study of bones after finishing this treatise. His simultaneous discoveries in botany intensified his interest in nature. He was constantly borrowing relevant objects from his friends. On December 7, 1785, Sömmerring became angry "that Goethe had not returned his heads." From Goethe's letter to Sömmerring (June 8, 1786), we learn that he still had those skulls.

Goethe's great ideas also went with him to Italy. While the thought of the archetypal plant took shape in his mind, he also developed concepts about the human form. In Rome, on January 20, 1787, Goethe wrote:

> In anatomy I am fairly well prepared, and have acquired a certain knowledge of the human body, though not without effort.

---

20. Dr. Felix Vicq d'Azyr (1748–1794), French neuroanatomist whose treatises helped lay the foundation for neuroanatomy. He was one of the first to section the brain horizontally and created a classic anatomic folio of the brain. He identified many of the cerebral convolutions, as well as the deep gray nuclei of the cerebrum and basal ganglia. The mamillo thalamic trait was also described by him and bears his name. — ED.

Here, by endlessly contemplating statues, one's attention is continually drawn to the human body, but in a more elevated way. Our medical-surgical anatomy is concerned only with knowing the parts, and to this end a miserable muscle will do. In Rome, however, the parts mean nothing if they are not also part of a noble, beautiful form.

In the great hospital of San Spirito, a very beautiful musculature model has been set up for artists in a way that fills one with admiration for its beauty. It could pass as a flayed demigod, a Marsyas.

The custom here, following the ancients, is to study the skeleton not as an artificially arranged mass of bones but with the ligaments attached, giving it life and movement.

Goethe was primarily seeking to acquaint himself with the laws according to which nature shapes organic, especially human, forms — the tendency she follows in forming them. Just as Goethe searched amid the multiplicity of innumerable plant forms for the archetypal plant, with which one can endlessly invent plants that are necessarily consistent — that accord perfectly with nature's tendency and would exist if corresponding conditions arose — he was likewise intent on studying animals and the human being "to discover ideal characters" that accord fully with the laws of nature. Soon after his return from Italy, Goethe became "diligent in *anatomicis*," and in 1789 he wrote to Herder, "I have a newly discovered *harmoniam naturae* to present." His new discovery may have been part of his vertebral theory of the skull. The completion of this discovery, however, came in 1790. Before then he knew that all the bones that make up the back of the head represent three modified spinal vertebrae.

Goethe conceived of the matter this way: The brain represents a mass of spinal cord material raised to the highest level of perfection. Whereas the nerves serving primarily the lower organic functions end in, and branch out from, the spinal cord, the nerves serving the higher (mental) functions — primarily the sensory nerves — end and begin in the brain. What appears in the brain is simply the fully developed form of what is indicated but latent in the spinal cord. The brain is a fully developed spinal cord, the spinal cord an unelaborated brain. Now the vertebrae of the spinal column are shaped in complete conformity with the various parts of the spinal cord and form the protective structures necessary to enclose them. If the brain is in fact a spinal cord raised to its highest potential, it would seem probable that the bones enclosing it are also simply vertebrae that are more highly developed. Thus, the entire head appears to be preformed in the bodily organs existing at a lower level. The forces active on a subordinate level are also at work here, but they are developed to their highest potential.

Again, Goethe was concerned only with determining how this matter actually manifests in external reality. He said that he recognized this relationship very early on in relation to the occipital bone at the back of the cranium and the posterior and anterior sphenoid bones. But on his journey to northern Italy, when he found a sheep's skull that had burst open among the dunes of the Lido, he recognized that the palatine bone, the upper jaw, and the intermaxillary are also modified vertebrae. The sheep's skull had fallen apart in such a fortunate way that the various pieces could be recognized clearly as individual vertebrae. On April 30, 1790, Goethe showed this beautiful discovery to Frau von Kalb, and said,

> Tell Herder that I have come a whole formula closer to the animal form and its various transformations — and that through the strangest accident.

The significance of this discovery is very far-reaching. It showed that all members of an organic whole are identical in idea, and that "inwardly unformed" organic masses develop in different ways as they open up toward the outside. In other words, one and the same thing manifests at a lower level as spinal nerve and, on a higher level, reaches out as a sensory nerve into the organs of the senses, which take in, grasp, and comprehend the outer world. Thus everything living was revealed in its capacity to form itself from the inside out as form-creating force; only now could it be comprehended as a *truly living* entity.

Goethe's essential ideas about the formation of animals had now also reached a conclusion. It was time to work them through, though he had planned to do this earlier, as shown in his correspondence with F. H. Jacobi. When Goethe followed the Duke into the Silesian encampment (Breslau, July 1790), he was busy studying animal morphology, and it was there that he began to write out his thoughts on the subject. On August 31, he wrote to Friedrich von Stein, "Amid all this commotion, I have begun to write my discourse on animal morphology."

In a larger sense, the idea of the animal type is contained in the poem "Metamorphosis of Animals," first published in 1820 in Goethe's second "Morphological Notebook." Between 1790 and 1795, Goethe primarily pursued his scientific research into color. At the beginning of 1795, he was in Jena along with the von Humboldt brothers, Max Jacobi, and Schiller. Goethe presented his ideas on comparative anatomy to these friends, who found his presentations so significant that they urged him to write them down. Goethe's letter to the elder Jacobi shows that he immediately complied with that suggestion by dictating to Max Jacobi his outline of comparative osteology. The introductory chapters were elaborated in 1796. These discourses contain Goethe's basic views on animal morphology just as his views on plant morphology may be found in his "Attempt to Explain the Metamorphosis of the Plant."[21] Through his friendship with Schiller (begun in 1794), his views took a turn in that he now began to observe his own methods of research, thereby *becoming conscious* of his way of observing things.[22]

Having followed these historical developments, we will now consider the nature and significance of Goethe's views on the formation of organisms.

---

21. This was the original title of Goethe's treatise *The Metamorphosis of Plants.* — ED.
22. Steiner's formulation is "wobei ihm seine Anschauungsweise *gegenständlich* wurde." The original meaning of *gegenständlich* is "standing over and against," that is, becoming able to clearly observe something because one has gained the necessary distance from it. Through his acquaintance with Schiller, Goethe became able to observe his own way of thinking; in this sense it became *gegenständlich* to him. — ED.

Chapter 4

The Nature and Significance of Goethe's Writings on Organic Morphology

Goethe's morphological works are so important because they establish the theoretical foundations and methodology for studying organic nature: *a scientific accomplishment of the highest order.* To properly appreciate this fact, we must, above all, consider the tremendous difference between inorganic and organic phenomena. The collision of two billiard balls, for example, is an inorganic phenomenon. If one ball is at rest and another strikes it from a certain direction with a certain velocity, the one at rest will begin to move in a certain direction with a certain velocity. We can *comprehend* such phenomena only by transforming what is given directly to the senses into concepts. We are able to do this to the extent that nothing sense perceptible remains that we have not penetrated conceptually. We watch one ball approach and strike the other and see the other move on. We have *comprehended* this phenomenon when — from the mass, direction, and velocity of the first ball, and from the mass of the second — we are able to predict the velocity and direction of the second: in other words, when we see that, under given conditions, this phenomenon occurs *with necessity.* This, however, means only that what presents itself to our senses must appear as a *necessary consequence* of what we postulate as idea. If this is the case, then we can say that concept and phenomenon coincide. *There is nothing in the concept that is not also in the phenomenon, and nothing in the phenomenon that is not also in the concept.*

Let us consider more closely the conditions that lead necessarily to an occurrence in inorganic nature. Here we encounter the significant fact that conditions determining sense-perceptible occurrences in inorganic nature also belong to the sensory world. In our example, mass, velocity, and direction come into consideration — conditions that in fact belong to the *sensory* realm. No other conditions determine the phenomenon; only factors directly perceptible to the senses determine *one another.* A conceptual understanding of such occurrences thus simply deduces tangible reality from tangible reality. Spatial and temporal factors — mass, weight, or sense-perceptible forces such as light or warmth — all invoke phenomena belonging to the same category. A body is heated and thereby increases in volume; both the cause and the effect, the heating as well as the expansion, belong to the sensory world.

Thus, we do not have to go beyond the sensory world to grasp such occurrences. We simply deduce one phenomenon from another *within* that world. Therefore, when we wish to explain such a phenomenon and understand it conceptually, we need to include only those elements that can be *perceived* by the senses; everything we wish to understand can be perceived. Therein lies the coincidence of percept (appearance) and concept. Nothing in such events remains obscure to us, because we know the conditions that led to them. Thus, we have developed the essential nature of the inorganic world and, in doing so, have shown the extent to which we can explain it *through itself,* without going beyond it. There has never been any question about this since human beings first began to think about the nature of such things. They did not, of course, always follow the above course of reasoning that leads to the coincidence of concept and percept, but they never hesitated to explain phenomena through their own essential nature as indicated.[1]

This was not true, however, with regard to phenomena in the *organic* realm *until Goethe.* The sense-perceptible aspects of the organism — its form, size, color, temperature, and so on — do not seem

---

1. Some philosophers maintain that, although we can trace the phenomena of the sense-world back to their original elements (forces), yet we can no more explain these than we can the essential nature of life. As to this it must be remarked that those elements are *simple* — that is, they cannot themselves be composed of even simpler elements. But the impossibility of deriving them, explaining them, in their simplicity, is not due to a limitation of our cognitive capacity but to the fact that they rest upon themselves; they are present to us in all their immediacy; they are complete in themselves and cannot be derived from anything else. — R. STEINER.

to be determined by the same kind of factors. One cannot say, for example, that the size, form, position, and so on, of a plant's roots determine the sense-perceptible characteristics of the leaf or blossom. A body in which this were the case would not be an organism, but a machine. Rather, it must be granted that the sense-perceptible characteristics of a living being do not appear as a result of other sense-perceptible conditions as in inorganic nature.[2] Indeed, all sensory qualities arise in an organism as the result of something *no longer perceptible to the senses*. They appear as the result of a higher unity hovering over the sense-perceptible processes. It is not the form of the root that determines that of the stem, and not the form of the stem that determines that of the leaves, and so on. All of these forms are determined instead by something that exists above them and whose form is inaccessible to the senses. The perceptible elements exist for one another, but not as a result of one another. They are not mutually determined by one another but by something else. Here what we perceive with our senses cannot be reduced to other sensorial factors; we must include in our concept of events elements that do not belong to the world of the senses; *we must go beyond the sensory world*. What we *perceive* is no longer enough; to comprehend the phenomena, we must conceptually grasp the *unifying principle*. Consequently, however, a distance arises between percept and concept, and they no longer seem to coincide; the concept hovers over what is observed and it becomes difficult to see how they are connected.[3]

---

2. Herein lies the difference between organisms and machines. What is essential in the machine is only the interaction of its parts. The unifying principle that governs that interaction does not exist in the object itself but outside it as a plan in the head of its builder. Only the most extreme shortsightedness can deny that the difference between an organism and a mechanism is precisely the fact that in a machine the determining principle governing the interrelationship of its parts is external (and abstract), whereas in an organism it assumes a real existence in the object itself. Thus, the sense-perceptible conditions of an organism do not appear merely to follow one from another, but are governed by an inner principle that is imperceptible to the senses. In this sense this principle is no more perceptible to the senses than the plan in the builder's head, which is also present only to the mind. Essentially, it is such a plan, except that it has entered the organism's inner being and affects it directly, not through a third party, the builder. — R. STEINER.

3. This apparent distance between the concept and percept of an organism is true of *intellectual* thinking that is geared to an inanimate world governed by material cause and effect. Focusing on the raw, bodily nature of an organism, such thinking cannot see any connection to an inner principle that informs the whole. To such an intellectual consciousness, therefore, this inner principle, or concept, appears to hover above the sense-perceptible organism. It is different for *intuitive* thinking, in which external particulars appear as immediate expressions of an inner principle. How intuitive thinking comprehends organic nature is explained in the following pages. — ED.

Whereas concept and sensory reality were one in inorganic nature, they seem to diverge here and belong, in fact, to two different worlds. What is perceived and presents itself directly to the senses no longer seems to bear its own explanation, or essence, within itself. The object does not seem to be self-explanatory because its concept is taken from something other than itself. Because the object is present to the senses but does not seem to be governed by the laws of the sensory world, it is as though we were confronted by an insoluble contradiction in nature. It is as though there were a gulf between inorganic phenomena, which are self-explanatory, and organic beings, where natural laws are intruded upon, and *legitimate laws seem suddenly to be broken.* This chasm was in fact generally taken for granted in science *until Goethe,* who succeeded in solving this mystery. Until then, it was assumed that only inorganic nature could be explained through itself; the human capacity for knowledge was believed to end at the level of organic nature.

We can comprehend the magnitude of Goethe's achievement when we consider the fact that *Kant,* the great reformer of recent philosophy, not only shared that old erroneous concept fully, but even sought for a scientific *reason* why the human mind would never be able to explain organic entities. He did, in fact, acknowledge the possibility of an intuitive intellect (*intellectus archetypus*) capable of grasping the connection between concept and sensory reality both in organic beings and in the inorganic realm. But he denied humankind the possibility of such an intellect. According to Kant, the human intellect can conceive of the unity, or concept, of a thing only as arising from the interaction of its parts, as an analytical generalization arrived at through abstract reasoning, but not in such a way that each part appears as the result of a definite, concrete (or synthetic) unity — that is, as the result of an intuitive concept. Consequently, he considered it impossible for the human intellect to explain organic nature, the activity of which must be viewed as emanating from the whole into the parts. Kant said,

> Thus, our intellect has this peculiarity with regard to our power of judgment: namely that, in cognition by it, the particulars are not determined by the universal and cannot, therefore, be derived from it alone. (*Critique of Judgment,* paragraph 77)

According to this, when studying organic entities, we would have to give up the possibility of knowing the necessary relationship between the idea of the whole (which can only be thought) and what appears to our senses in space and time. According to Kant, we would have to be content with knowing that such a relationship exists; but we could not satisfy the demand of our logical thinking to know *how* the general thought, or idea, steps out of itself and manifests as sensory reality. We would have to assume, instead, that concept and sensory reality confront each other without mediation, having been brought about by an influence external to both, such as when a person assembles some composite object — say, a machine — according to an idea. Thus any possibility of explaining the organic world was denied — in fact, its impossibility seemed to be proven.

This was the situation when Goethe began to devote himself to the organic sciences. He came to these studies, however, after having prepared himself most appropriately by repeatedly reading Spinoza's philosophy. Goethe first took up Spinoza in the spring of 1774. In *Poetry and Truth* he wrote about his initial encounter with this philosopher: "After searching the world in vain for a way to educate my extraordinary being, I finally came upon this man's *Ethics.*"

During the summer of that same year, Goethe met with Fritz Jacobi, who was studying Spinoza at the time (as shown by his letters of 1785 about Spinoza's teachings). Jacobi was just the person to lead Goethe more deeply into the nature of that philosopher. They discussed Spinoza a great deal at that point, since for Goethe "everything was still having its first effects and countereffects, fermenting and churning."

Some time later he discovered in his father's library a book by an author who viciously attacked Spinoza and, indeed, distorted him to the point of complete caricature. Goethe's response was to again seriously study this profound thinker. In Spinoza's writings, he found the key to the deepest scientific questions he was capable of asking at the time. In 1784, the poet read Spinoza with Frau von Stein, and on November 4 he wrote to her, "I am bringing along Spinoza in Latin, in which everything is much clearer." The philosopher had a tremendous effect on Goethe, who was always quite outspoken in acknowledging this fact. In 1816, he wrote to Zelter, "Except for Shakespeare and *Spinoza*, I do not know of any departed soul who has affected me as much [as Linné]." He therefore regarded Shakespeare and *Spinoza* as the two who had the greatest influence on him.

We see most clearly how this influence manifested in his morphological studies when we consider what he had to say about Lavater in his *Italian Journey*. Lavater maintained the prevalent view that a living organism can only arise through an influence not inherent in its own nature — through the violation of universal, natural laws. Goethe wrote:

> Recently I found these silly words in a pitifully apostolic and monkish declamation by the prophet of Zurich: *Everything that has life lives through something outside itself.* At least it sounded something like that. Now this is just what such a missionary to the heathen might write; and no genius tugs at his sleeve as he does so. (*Italian Journey*, Oct. 5, 1787)

This was entirely in the spirit of Spinoza. Spinoza distinguishes three kinds of knowledge. The first occurs as we hear or read certain words; we remember the things referred to and form mental images of them like those we generally use to picture things to ourselves. In the second kind of knowledge, we create general concepts from our adequately formed mental pictures of the characteristics of things. In the third kind of knowledge, we advance from an adequate image of the actual nature of certain attributes of God to an adequate knowledge of the essential nature of things. Now Spinoza calls this kind of knowledge *scientia intuitiva,* or "knowledge in *beholding.*" It was this highest kind of knowledge that Goethe strove toward.

Let us be clear about what Spinoza meant when he said that things should be known in such a way that, in their essential nature, we recognize certain attributes of God. Spinoza's God is the idea-content of the world — the driving, all-supporting, all-sustaining principle. Now we can imagine this by postulating that principle as a being that is independent and exists for itself, isolated from the finite world and maintaining itself apart from finite beings while governing and animating them. On the other hand, we can conceive of this being as having entered the finite world, no longer abiding above and alongside temporal things but existing only *within* them. This view in no way denies that primordial principle but fully acknowledges it. However, it views this principle as having been *poured out into* the world.

The first view sees the finite world as a revelation of the infinite, but this infinitude remains within its own being and relinquishes none of itself. It never goes beyond itself but remains as it was before its revelation. The second view also sees the finite world as a manifestation of the infinite. It assumes, however, that this infinite being, by manifesting, has gone entirely beyond itself, that it has laid its own being and life into its creation and now exists *only in that creation.* Now, since knowledge is clearly a perception of the essence of things, and since this essence exists only to the degree that it participates as a finite being in the primal principle of all things, thus knowing means perceiving the infinite in things.[4]

Before Goethe it was indeed assumed, as we have described above, that inorganic nature could be explained through itself — that it contains its own explanation and its own nature within itself — but that this was not the case with organic nature. Here, the essential nature, or being, that manifests in the object, could not be found within the object itself. Consequently, it was assumed to exist outside the object. In other words, organic nature was explained according to the first view, and inorganic nature according to the second.

As we have seen, Spinoza proved the necessity of a unified knowledge. He was too much the philosopher, however, to demonstrate this theoretical insight in the various specialized branches of organic science. This task remained for Goethe, whose unwavering adherence to Spinoza's views is demonstrated not only by the statements quoted, but by many others as well. In *Poetry and Truth* he wrote, "Nature works according to eternal, immutable laws, so divine that the Godhead itself can alter nothing in them" (part 4, book 16). Referring to a book by Jacobi published in 1811 (*Of Divine Things and Their Revelation*), Goethe remarked:

> How could I welcome the book of such a dearly loved friend after finding that it developed the thesis that nature conceals God? With my pure, profound, inborn and practiced way of contemplating things, *which had taught me above all to see God in nature and nature in God,* so that this way of thinking formed the foundation of my whole existence — must not such a strange, one-sidedly limited assertion forever estrange me spiritually from this noblest of men, whose heart I have revered and loved?[5]

Goethe knew full well that the step he was taking had far-reaching significance for science; he realized that, by breaking down the

---

4. That is, certain attributes of God within them. — R. STEINER.
5. *Tag- und Jahreshefte* (1811). — R. STEINER.

boundary between inorganic and organic nature and thus advancing Spinoza's thinking, he was significantly changing the direction of science. That recognition is expressed in his essay "Judgment through Intuitive Perception." Goethe expressed his opposition after noting Kant's attempt in *Critique of Judgment* to prove the inability of the human intellect to explain an organism:

> It is true that the author seems to refer here to a divine intellect. However, if in fact we seek, in the moral sphere — through faith in God, virtue, and immortality — to raise ourselves up into a higher realm and to approach the primal being, then may we not also, in the intellectual sphere — through the contemplation of an ever creating nature — make ourselves worthy of spiritual participation in her productions? Since I had, after all, ceaselessly pressed on, at first unconsciously and out of an inner urge, toward the archetypal, the typical, since I had even succeeded in demonstrating how it unfolds in accordance with the laws of nature, there was nothing to stop me now from boldly embarking on the *adventure of reason*, as the sage of Königsberg himself called it.

This is the essential thing: an occurrence in inorganic nature — that is, something that takes place only in the sensory world — is caused and determined by a process that likewise occurs only in the sensory world. Imagine that the causal process consists of elements m, d, and v (mass, direction, and velocity of a moving billiard ball), and the resulting process of elements m', d', and v'. Whenever m, d, and v are given, m', d', and v' will be determined by them. If I wish to understand this occurrence, I must formulate the entire event, consisting of cause and effect, with one concept that includes both. But this kind of concept cannot exist within the occurrence itself and determine it. It encompasses both processes in a common expression; but it does not cause or determine. Only the objects of the sensory world determine one another. The elements m, d, and v are also perceptible to the outer senses. The concept, in this case, simply serves to summarize the external event; it *expresses* something that is not real as an idea, or concept, but is real to the senses. This "something" it expresses is an object of sensory perception. Knowledge of inorganic nature is based on the possibility of comprehending the external world through the senses and expressing its interactions through concepts. Kant re-

garded the possibility of knowing things in *this* way as the only kind
of knowledge accessible to the human being. He called this kind of
thinking discursive. *What* we wish to know is an external perception;
the concept, or combining unity, is merely a means.

If, however, we wish to comprehend organic nature, then, according to Kant, we cannot apprehend the ideal, conceptual aspect as
something that borrows its meaning by expressing or indicating something else; rather, we would have to apprehend the *ideal element as
such*. It would have to contain its own meaning, stemming from itself,
not from the spatial-temporal world of the senses. The unity that our
mind merely abstracts in the case of the inorganic would have to build
upon itself, forming itself *out of itself*; it would have to be fashioned
according to its own being, not according to the influences of other
objects. According to Kant, the comprehension of such a self-forming
and self-manifesting entity is denied to the human being.

What is needed to attain such comprehension? We need a kind of
thinking that can give a thought a substance not derived from outer
sensory perception, a thinking that comprehends not only what is
perceived externally by the senses, but also apprehends pure ideas
apart from the sensory world. A concept that is not abstracted from
the sensory world but whose content develops out of itself and only
out of itself can be called an *intuitive concept,* and the comprehension of such a concept may be called "intuitive knowledge." What
follows from this is clear: *A living organism can be comprehended
only through an intuitive concept.* Goethe actually demonstrated that
it is in fact possible for us to know in this way.

The inorganic world is governed by the interaction of the individual
elements comprising an event, by the reciprocal way they determine
one another. This is not true of the organic world, where one member
of an organism does not determine another, but where the whole (or
idea) determines each particular out of itself in accordance with its
own being. In referring to this self-determining entity, we can follow
Goethe's terminology and call it an *entelechy.* An entelechy, therefore, is a force that calls itself into being. The resulting manifestations
have sensory existence, but they are determined by this entelechial
principle. This creates an apparent contradiction: the organism is self-
determining and creates its characteristics out of itself according to a
postulated principle, and yet it has sense-perceptible reality. An organism thus attains sense-perceptible reality in a way that is completely

different from the other objects of the sensory world. Consequently, it seems to arise unnaturally.

It is also entirely understandable that, externally, an organism is exposed to the effects of the sensory world, as is any other body. A tile falling from the roof can strike a living creature as well as an inorganic object. An organism is related to the outer world through its intake of nourishment and so on; it is affected by the physical circumstances of the outer world. This can, of course, occur only to the degree that the organism is an object of the spatial-temporal world of the senses. This object of the outer world — the entelechial principle that has manifested outwardly — is the external appearance of the organism. Consequently, it seems neither to fully accord with itself nor to adhere strictly to its own nature. But since the organism is subject not only to its own formative laws but to conditions of the outer world as well, since it is not only as it should be according to its own self-determining entelechial principle, but also what it has become through the influence of other factors upon which it depends, it never seems to fully accord with itself nor to adhere strictly to its own nature.

This is where human reason enters and, *within the realm of ideas*, develops an organism that corresponds only to its own principle, setting aside the influences from the outer world. Every incidental influence that has nothing to do with the organic *as such* thus falls away completely. This idea, which corresponds purely to the organic aspect of the organism, is the archetypal organism; it is Goethe's *type*.

Thus, the eminent validity of the idea of the type becomes apparent. It is not merely an *intellectual concept* but the truly organic aspect of every organism, without which it would not be an organism. Because it manifests in *every* organism it is more real than any actual, particular organism. It also expresses the essence of an organism more *fully* and *purely* than *any individual organism in particular.* The way we arrive at the idea of the type is fundamentally different from the way we arrive at a concept of an inorganic process, which is abstracted from external reality and is not active within it. The idea of the organism, on the other hand, works actively within the organism as its entelechy — it is the essence of the entelechy itself in a form apprehended by our reason. The idea is not a summary of experience; it *produces* experience. Goethe expresses this as follows: "A concept is the *sum* of experience, an idea is its *result;* to understand

a concept requires intellect, to comprehend an idea requires reason."
This explains the kind of reality that must be attributed to Goethe's
archetypal organism (the archetypal plant or animal). This Goethean
method is clearly the only way we can apprehend the essential nature
of the organic world.[6]

Within the inorganic realm we must realize the essential circumstance that the phenomenon in its multiplicity is not the same as
the lawfulness that explains it, but merely points to this lawfulness
as to something external to it. The relationship between what we
perceive — the material element in our knowledge given through the
outer senses — and the *concept* — or formal means of recognizing the
necessity of what we perceive — is their objective need of each other.
But this relationship is such that the concept does not live in the particulars of an experienced event but in the interrelationship of those
particulars. This interrelationship, which combines the multiplicity
into a unified whole, is based on the *particulars* of the given, but as
a *whole* (or unity) it does not actually manifest concretely. Only the
particulars of that relationship manifest in outer existence — in the
object. The unity or concept, *as such*, manifests only in our intellect,
whose task is to combine the multiplicity of the phenomena; the concept is related to this multiplicity as its *sum*. Here we are dealing with a
duality: the manifold phenomena we *perceive* and the unity we *think*.

In organic nature the diverse particulars of an organism do not have
such an external relationship to one another. The unity manifests in
what is perceived; it comes into existence together with the diversity
and is identical with it. The relationship between the individual members of a phenomenal whole (an organism) has become a reality and
manifests concretely, no longer only in our intellect but in the object
as well, where it produces multiplicity out of itself. The concept does
not merely play the role of a summarizing element with its object *out-*

---

6. Here Steiner introduces a new concept of scientific method. The distinction he makes
here between *concept* and *idea* has important consequences, particularly for the methodology of organic science. The dynamic, living idea of the *type* leads research along a very
different path and to a very different result than do the analytical methods of inorganic
science. Grasping the idea of the *type* requires a different quality of thinking (here called
reason or, in the following, *judgment through intuitive perception*) which is essential to
Goethe's method of organic science. It is only this kind of active, participatory thinking
that can apprehend the type in its various metamorphoses. Thus exact, participatory thinking becomes the method of organic science. This method is discussed in the section on
Goethe in the concluding essay of this volume and in Henri Bortoft, *The Wholeness of
Nature: Goethe's Way toward a Science of Conscious Participation in Nature.* — ED.

side itself; it has *united* with its object completely. The object of our perception is no longer different from the concept through which we think it; we perceive that concept itself as idea.[7]

Therefore Goethe calls the capacity through which we grasp organic nature *judgment through intuitive perception.* That which explains — the formal element in our knowledge, the concept — and that which is explained — the material element, or percept — are identical. The idea, through which we comprehend the organic, is therefore essentially different from the concept, through which we explain the inorganic; it does not merely combine a given multiplicity, like a summary, but brings forth its own content out of itself. It is the *result* of the given (of experience); it is concrete appearance.[8] This is why in inorganic science we speak of *laws* (natural laws) and use them to explain the facts, whereas in organic science we use *types.* A *law* is not the same as the perceived multiplicity it governs but stands above it. In the type, however, the ideal and the real have united; the multiplicity can only be explained as arising from a point within the whole, with which it is identical.

The significant aspect of Goethe's research is its insight into this relationship between inorganic and organic science. It is wrong therefore to say (as it often is today) that Goethe's science anticipated a kind of monism whose goal is a unified view of nature that encompasses the organic and the inorganic by reducing the organic to the same principles (mechanical and physical categories and laws) used to determine inorganic nature. We have seen how Goethe conceived of a monistic view. His method of explaining the organic was fundamentally different from his approach to the inorganic realm. Whenever principles of a higher nature were involved, he wanted to see mechanistic explanations strictly rejected.[9] He criticized Kieser and Link for wanting to trace organic phenomena back to inorganic causes.

7. We see the concept, or idea, as it manifests *in* the organism itself. — ED.

8. Thus, for example, the concept of a clock does not express itself directly through its parts but can be comprehended only through an intellectual understanding of their interactions and purpose. Here the unity, or purpose, does not manifest directly through the parts. In an organism this is different. The formation of every organ of an animal, for example, and every aspect of its behavior, are direct expressions of its essential nature, or idea. This idea can be perceived directly and enlivened and deepened through experience; in this sense, it is the *result* of experience. — ED.

9. "We see significant things assembled in parts. Consider the works of architecture. We see how many things arise, in a regular or irregular fashion, through agglomeration; therefore atomistic concepts are very convenient and we do not shy away from applying them in cases involving organic life. For it is just when one pushes aside problems that can

This mistaken view of Goethe arose because of the position he took toward Kant concerning the possibility of comprehending organic nature. When Kant asserts that our intellect cannot explain living organisms, he does not mean that they are determined by mechanical laws and that he is unable to grasp them as stemming from physical or mechanical categories. According to Kant, the reason for this inability lies precisely in the fact that our intellect can explain only what is physical-mechanical, and that the essential being of an organism is *not* of that nature. If it were so, the intellect could easily comprehend it through the categories at its command. Goethe, of course, was not trying to contradict Kant by expounding a mechanical view of the organic world; his point was that we certainly do not lack the ability to grasp the higher form of generative activity that is the essence of organic nature.

When we consider what was just said, we quickly encounter an important difference between inorganic and organic nature. Since in inorganic nature, *any* process can cause another, and that in turn another, and so on, the series of occurrences never seems to complete itself. Everything is open to continued interaction without any one particular group of objects being able to close itself off from the influence of others. Chains of inorganic events do not begin or end; there is only an incidental relationship between one event and the next. If a stone falls to the earth, its effect depends coincidentally on the kind of object it strikes. In an organism this is very different. Here the unity is the primary factor. The self-sustaining entelechy comprises a number of sense-perceptible developmental forms, one of which must be first and another last, and among which one follows another only in a specific way. The ideal unity produces a series of sense-perceptible organs over time and in a certain spatial relationship. It closes itself off in a very definite way from the rest of nature and produces its various states out of itself. These can therefore be grasped only by following the formation of successive states proceeding from an ideal unity. In other words, *an organism can be comprehended only in its becoming, in its development.* An inorganic body is finished and fixed — it is inwardly immobile and can be moved only from outside. An organism is never at rest, it is constantly reshaping itself from within outward, transforming and creating metamorphoses. Thus Goethe stated,

only be explained dynamically, that mechanical ways of explaining again become the order of the day" (*Verses in Prose*). — R. STEINER.

Reason finds its field of activity in what is becoming, the intellect in what is finished. Reason does not bother to ask: What for? The intellect does not ask: Where from? Reason delights in *ongoing development;* the intellect tries to hold everything fast so that it can put it to use.... Reason governs only the living; the world that has already come to be, the concern of geology, is dead. (*Verses in Prose*)

The organism presents itself to us in nature in two main forms: as plant and as animal, each in a different way. The plant distinguishes itself from the animal through its lack of any *real* inner life. In an animal, this inner life manifests as sensation, intentional movement, and so on. The plant has no such soul principle. It does not go beyond the development of its external *form.* As the entelechial principle unfolds its formative activity out of one point, so to speak, it manifests in the plant through the fact that each organ is shaped according to a common formative principle. The entelechy appears here as the force that forms the individual organs. The organs are all shaped according to one formative type, and they appear as modifications of *one* fundamental organ; they are repetitions of that organ at various developmental levels. What makes the plant a plant, a *particular formative force*, is active in every organ in the same way. In this sense each organ is *identical* with all the others and also with the plant as a whole. Goethe expressed it this way:

I have come to realize that the organ of the plant we ordinarily call the *leaf* conceals the true Proteus, who can conceal and reveal himself in all formations. Backward and forward, the plant is only leaf, linked so inseparably to the future seed that one should not think one without the other. (*Italian Journey,* May 17, 1787, included in Report of July, 1787)

Thus the plant appears to be made up of many individual plants, so to speak, like a complex individual made up of less complex individuals. The development of the plant progresses from stage to stage and forms its organs; each organ is identical to every other in its formative principle, though different in appearance. The plant's inner unity spreads itself into outer breadth; it expresses and loses itself in diverse forms, so that it does not (as it does in the animal) attain its own concrete existence and a certain independence, which then, as a center of life, encounters the multiplicity of its organs and uses them as mediators with the outer world.

We must now ask, What causes the external differentiation of plant organs, which are otherwise identical in terms of their inner principle? How can formative laws, guided by a *single* formative principle, produce a leaf in one instance and a sepal in another? Since plants exist entirely in the external realm, this differentiation must be based on outer, spatial factors. Goethe considered alternating expansion and contraction to be just such factors. When the plant's entelechial principle enters outer existence, working from a point outward, it manifests as a spatial entity. The formative forces are active in space and create organs of a specific spatial form. Now these forces either concentrate and draw inward to a single point during a stage of contraction, or they spread by unfolding, striving as it were to distance themselves from one another during a stage of expansion. Over the course of the plant's life, three expansions alternate with three contractions. This alternating expansion and contraction causes the essentially identical formative forces of the plant to differentiate.

Initially, the whole potential of the plant — *contracted* to a single point — is dormant in the seed (*a*). It then emerges, unfolds, and *expands* in the formation of the leaves (*c*). The formative forces increasingly repel one another; consequently, the lower leaves appear rudimentary and compact (*cc'*); farther up, they become more ribbed and indented. All that was crowded together begins to diverge (leaves *d* and *e*). All that was previously separated by successive intervals (*zz'*) appears — as the formation of the calyx (*f*) — drawn into a single point on the stalk (*w*). This is the second contraction. In the corolla of the blossom a new unfolding, or *expansion*, takes place. Compared with the sepals (*f*) of the calyx, the petals (*g*) are finer and more delicate, which could be caused only by diminishing contraction toward one point, that is, by a greater extension of the formative forces. The next contraction takes place within the reproductive organs, the stamens (*h*) and pistil (*i*). After that a new expansion begins with the formation of the fruit (*k*). In the seed (*a_1*) that emerges from the fruit, the whole being of the plant is again condensed to a single point.[10]

10. The fruit develops through the growth of the lower part of the pistil (the ovary, *l*); it represents a later stage of the pistil and can therefore only be drawn separately. The formation of the fruit is the final expansion of the plant. Its life now differentiates itself in an organ that closes itself off from its environment — the fruit and the seed. In the

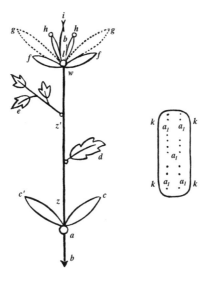

The entire plant represents the unfolding, or realization, of the potential of the bud or seed, which requires only the right outer influences to fully develop as a plant formation. The only difference between a bud and a seed is that the seed requires the earth as its ground, whereas the bud generally represents the formation of a plant upon a plant. The seed represents an individual plant of a higher nature, or a whole cycle of plant formations, so to speak. With each new bud, the plant begins a new phase of its life; it regenerates itself and concentrates its forces to renew them. Consequently, the formation of a bud interrupts the vegetative process. The life of the plant can withdraw into a bud when the conditions for manifest life are lacking, and sprout again when the right conditions reappear. This is why vegetative growth is interrupted during the winter. Goethe spoke of this:

> It is very interesting to observe how vegetation continues its vigorous growth when it is not interrupted by severe cold; here [in Italy] there are no buds, and one begins to understand what a bud actually is. (*Italian Journey*, Dec. 2, 1786)

---

fruit everything has become appearance; it is outward appearance only, and estranges itself from life to become a dead product. All the essential inner life impulses of the plant are concentrated in the seed, from which a new plant arises. The seed has become almost entirely idea; its outer appearance has been reduced to a minimum. — R. STEINER.

Thus, what in our climate lies hidden in the bud is there openly displayed. Indeed, true plant life lies hidden within it; it lacks only the conditions for its unfolding.

Goethe's concept of alternating expansion and contraction has encountered especially strong opposition. All of those attacks, however, stem from a misunderstanding — the belief that these concepts cannot be valid unless a physical cause can be found for them, and unless it is possible to demonstrate the means whereby the inner laws of the plant cause this expansion and contraction. This, however, places the cart before the horse. Nothing should be postulated as the cause of expansion and contraction — on the contrary, everything else follows from them; they themselves cause the progressive metamorphosis, stage by stage.

Such misunderstandings arise whenever we fail to apprehend a concept in its own intuitive form; we then insist that it must be the result of an external occurrence. We can think of expansion and contraction only as caused and not as causing. Goethe did not regard expansion and contraction as resulting from inorganic processes in the plant; rather, he saw them as the way in which the plant's inner entelechial principle shapes itself. Thus, he could not view them as a summation of sense-perceptible processes from which they could be deduced, but was obliged to see them as resulting from the inner unitary principle itself.

A plant's life is maintained by its metabolism. There is a fundamental difference between the metabolism of those organs closer to the roots, that take in nourishment from the earth, and those receiving nourishment that has passed through other organs. The organs closer to the earth seem to depend directly on their inorganic environment; the other organs, on the other hand, depend on the parts of the organism that precede them. Each succeeding organ thus receives nourishment especially prepared for it as it were by the preceding organs. Nature progresses from seed to fruit in successive stages, so that what follows manifests as the result of what came before. Goethe referred to this step-by-step progression as "progress on a spiritual ladder." Nothing more than what we have indicated lies in his words,

> because an upper node arises from the preceding one and receives the juices mediated by it, a node higher on the stem must receive its juices in a finer and more filtered state, and it must

benefit from the previous development of the leaves, refine its form, and direct a still finer sap to its leaves and buds.

We begin to understand all of these things when we see them in the light of Goethe's ideas. The ideas presented here are the elements that lie in the nature of the archetypal plant in a way that corresponds only to the archetype itself, and not as they manifest in any particular plant where they do not appear in their original form but adapted to outer conditions.

In animal life, of course, something else intervenes. The life of the animal does not lose itself in its outer features, but separates itself, severs itself from its corporeality and uses its bodily manifestation only as a tool. It no longer manifests merely as the capacity to shape the organism from within; rather it expresses itself within the organism as something beside the organism, acting as its governing force. The animal manifests as a self-contained world, or microcosm, in a much higher sense than does the plant. It has a center that is served by each of its organs.

> Thus every mouth is adept at grasping the fodder
> Fit to the body's need, whether weak and toothless its jaw,
> Or mighty with menacing teeth; in every case
> An organ perfectly suited provides for all other organs.
> Also each foot and leg, be it a long or a short one,
> Moves to serve with great skill the impulse and need of the
> creature.
>
> (from "The Metamorphosis of Animals")

Each organ of the plant contains the whole plant, but the life principle exists nowhere as a definite center; the identity of the organs lies in the fact that they are all formed according to the same laws. In the animal, each organ appears to proceed from this definite center; the center shapes all organs according to its own nature. Thus the shape of the animal provides the basis for its outer existence, but it is determined from within. The animal's way of life is therefore directed by those same inner formative principles. The inner life of the animal, on the other hand, is free and unrestricted within itself; within certain limits, it can adapt to outer influences, but it is determined by the inner nature of the type and not by outer, mechanistic influences. In other words, adaptation cannot go so far as to cause the organism to appear as a mere product of the outer world. Its formation is restricted within certain limits.

No god can extend these limits, since they are honored by nature; Perfection was never achieved except through such limitation.

(from "The Metamorphosis of Animals")

If every animal conformed only to the principles of the archetypal animal, all animals would be the same. But the animal organism is differentiated into several organ systems, each of which has the capacity for a certain degree of development. This forms the basis for differentiated evolution. Ideally they are all equally important, but one system may nevertheless predominate and draw the organism's whole store of formative forces to itself and away from the other organs. Such an animal will appear especially developed in the direction of that organ system, whereas another animal will develop in another way. This gives rise to the possibility for the differentiation of the archetypal organism when it enters the phenomenal realm as the various genera and species.

The actual (factual) causes of this differentiation have not been mentioned yet. This is where external factors come into play — *adaptation,* through which the organism shapes itself in terms of its outer environment, and the *struggle for existence,* which allows only those creatures to survive that adapt most successfully to the prevailing conditions. Adaptation and the struggle for existence, however, would have no effect at all upon the organism if its formative principle could not assume diverse forms while maintaining its inner unity. We should not imagine that this principle is influenced by external formative forces in the same way that one inorganic entity affects another. The outer conditions are indeed responsible for the fact that the type assumes a particular form; the form itself, however, is not derived from those outer conditions but from the inner principle. When explaining the form we must always consider outer conditions, but we should not think that the form itself results from *them.* Goethe would have rejected the idea that environmental influences lead to organic forms simply through causality, just as he rejected the teleological principle that explains the form of an organ in terms of an external purpose.

In the organ systems of an animal that are related more to its outer structure (the skeleton, for example) we see a law observed in plants appearing again — for example in the formation of the bones of the skull.[11] Goethe's talent for seeing the inner lawfulness within purely external forms is especially evident here.

This distinction between plants and animals, based on Goethe's views, might seem irrelevant, given the fact that recent science has found good reason to doubt that there is any fixed boundary between plants and animals; but even Goethe was aware that it is impossible to establish any such boundary.[12] This did not prevent Goethe from clearly defining the plant and the animal; this is related to his worldview as a whole. Goethe assumed that absolutely *nothing is constant or fixed in the phenomenal realm* where everything continually fluctuates and moves. The *essence* of a thing, however, which we grasp in concepts, cannot be derived from fluctuating forms but from certain *intermediate stages* in which it can be observed. The way Goethe views the world naturally establishes certain definitions, which, nevertheless, are not rigidly held when we experience particular transitional forms. In fact, this is exactly where Goethe sees the flexibility of natural life.

With the ideas described here, Goethe laid the theoretical foundation for organic science. He discovered the essential nature of the organism. It is easy to miss this fact if we assume that the type (the principle that forms itself out of itself, the entelechy) can be explained in terms of something else. But such an assumption is unjustified, because the type, when apprehended intuitively, is self-explanatory. Anyone who has understood this "forming itself according to itself" of the entelechial principle will see this as the solution to the mystery of life. Any other solution is impossible, because this is the essence of the matter. If Darwinism is compelled to postulate a primal organism, then we can say that Goethe discovered the essential nature of that primal organism.[13]

---

11. This is a reference to Goethe's vertebral theory of the skull (see pp. 39–40) — ED.

12. See Goethe's essay "On Morphology: The Purpose Set Forth" in *Goethe, Scientific Studies,* Suhrkamp edition, p. 65. — ED.

13. In modern science, the term *primal organism* usually refers to a primal cell (primal cytode), a simple entity at the lowest stage of organic evolution. This is a very specific, concrete, sense-perceptible entity. In a Goethean sense, the term *primal,* or *archetypal, organism* does not refer to this but to the essence (being), or formative entelechial principle, that makes the "primal cell" into an organism. This principle manifests in both the simplest and the most perfected organisms, but developed differently. It is the animality in the animal, and that which makes a living being into an organism. Darwin assumes it from the beginning; it is there, is introduced, and then he says that it reacts one way or another to environmental influences. For Darwin, it was an indefinite X; Goethe wanted to explain this indefinite X. — R. STEINER.

It was Goethe who broke with merely classifying genera and species and initiated a regeneration of organic science in keeping with the true nature of the organism. Whereas systematizers before Goethe required as many different concepts, or ideas, as there are externally differentiated species (between which they could find no mediation), Goethe declared all organisms to be the same in idea, differing only in appearance. And he explained why this is so. Thus a philosophical basis was created for a scientific system of organisms; all that remained was to elaborate it. In what sense all existing organisms are only revelations of an idea, and *how* they reveal it in particular cases would have to be demonstrated.

This great scientific accomplishment was widely acknowledged by the more deeply educated scientists. The younger [Edward Joseph] d'Alton wrote to Goethe on July 6, 1827:

> I would consider it the most gratifying reward if Your Excellency — to whom natural science is indebted not only for *a complete transformation through magnificent perspectives and new views* in botany, but also for many first-rate contributions to the field of osteology — were to see in the accompanying pages an endeavor deserving of praise.

Nees von Esenbeck wrote on June 24, 1820:

> In your essay "An Attempt to Explain the Metamorphosis of Plants," the plant spoke to us about itself for the first time and, in this beautiful humanization, captivated me also when I was still young.

And finally Voigt, on June 6, 1831:

> With lively interest and humble gratitude I have received your little book on metamorphosis, which most graciously includes me as an early participant in the history of this theory. It is strange that animal metamorphosis (not the old metamorphosis of insects, but the one that proceeds from the spinal column) has been treated more fairly than plant metamorphosis. Apart from plagiarism and misuse, such quiet recognition may spring from the belief that animal metamorphosis involves *less risk*.

(Steiner compares Goethe's and Darwin's views from a somewhat different point of view on pp. 14–15. — ED.)

For in the skeleton, the separate bones always remain the same, whereas in botany, metamorphosis threatens to revolutionize the whole terminology and, consequently, the *identification of species;* this frightens the weak because they do not know where such a thing might lead.

Here we find complete understanding for Goethe's ideas. There is an awareness that a new way of viewing the individual [organism] is needed, and that only such a new view should form the foundation for a new scientific system that investigates the particular. The *type,* which is self-generating, has the capacity to assume endlessly diverse forms as it manifests. Such forms are the objects of our sensory perception, the genera and species of organisms actually living in space and time. To the degree that our mind has understood that general idea — the type — it has also comprehended the entire world of organisms in its unity. When we then *see* the type as it has taken shape in each particular phenomenal form, those forms become intelligible; they appear as stages, as metamorphoses, in which the type realizes itself. Essentially, the task of the new systematic science based on Goethe's insights is to point out these various stages.

In both the animal and the plant kingdoms, an ascending evolutionary sequence prevails; organisms are differentiated by their degree of development. How is this possible? We can characterize the ideal form, or type, of organisms by the fact that it is made up of spatial and temporal elements. Consequently, it appeared to Goethe as a *sensory/ supersensory* form. It contains spatial-temporal forms that can be perceived as idea (intuitively). When it manifests in the phenomenal realm, the actual sense-perceptible form (now no longer intuitively perceived), may or may not correspond completely to the ideal form; the type may or may not attain its full development. Certain organisms are lower because their phenomenal forms do not correspond fully to the organic type. The more the outer appearance and the organic type coincide in a particular being, the more perfect it is. This is the objective reason for an ascending evolutionary sequence. It is the task of any systematic presentation to investigate this relationship within the form of each organism. When establishing the type, the primal or archetypal organisms, however, this cannot be taken into consideration; one must find a form that represents the most perfected expression of the type. Goethe's archetypal plant provides such a form.

Goethe has been criticized for ignoring the world of the *cryptogamia* in establishing his type.[14] We have already noted the fact that this must have been a fully conscious decision, because he had also studied such plants. This has objective reasons. *Cryptogamia* are, in fact, plants in which the archetypal plant manifests only in an extremely one-sided way. They represent the idea of the plant only in a one-sided sense-perceptible form and may be assessed according to the established idea; but the idea itself achieves its actual breakthrough only in the *phanerogamia*.[15]

The important matter here, however, is that Goethe never elaborated his basic thoughts; he did not go deeply enough into the realm of particulars. All his works thus remain fragmentary. A statement in his *Italian Journey* (September 27, 1786) shows that he also intended to clarify this realm, and that his ideas would make it possible "to truly determine genera and species, which until now, I think, has occurred only in a very arbitrary way." He did not follow through with this intention by presenting in any concerted way the connection between his general ideas and the world of particulars, the reality of specific forms. This he himself regarded as a deficiency in his fragments, to which he referred when writing to F. J. Soret (June 28, 1828) about de Candolle:

> I also see with increasing clarity how he regards the intentions with which I continue to live and which *are expressed clearly enough in my little essay about metamorphosis, but whose connection with empirical botany, as I have long known, does not emerge clearly enough.*

It seems also that this is why Goethe's views have been so misunderstood; they were misunderstood simply because *they were not understood at all.*

Goethe's ideas also provide a conceptual explanation for a discovery by Darwin and Haeckel: that the development of an individual [ontogeny] represents a repetition of its entire evolution [phylogeny]. After all, what Haeckel presents here must be considered no more than an unexplained fact — that is, the fact that each individual passes, in an abbreviated way, through all the developmental stages described by

---

14. *Cryptogamia* are plants that reproduce by spores, producing neither flowers nor seeds: mosses, algae, and ferns, for example. — ED.

15. *Phanerogamia* are flowering, seed-producing plants. — ED.

paleontology as individual organic forms. Haeckel and his followers attributed this to the law of heredity. But that law itself is only an *abbreviated expression* of this fact. The explanation is that the various paleontological forms, as well as any living individuals, are all manifestations of a single archetype, which, over successive periods of time, unfolds the formative forces that lie within it as potential. Each higher individual is, in fact, more perfected because favorable environmental influences allow it to develop freely according to its inner nature. If, on the other hand, various influences force an individual to remain at a lower stage, only some of its inner forces will manifest; and what thus manifests as a whole would comprise only a part of the more highly developed organism. In this way the developing higher organism appears to be composed of lower organisms, or, by the same token, the lower organisms appear in their development as parts of the higher. We can therefore discern in the development of a higher animal the development of all the lower ones (Haeckel's biogenetic law).

A physicist is unsatisfied with merely stating and describing the facts, and searches instead for the *laws* that govern them — for the ideas of the phenomena. Similarly, those who wish to penetrate the nature of living beings find it unsatisfying simply to cite facts of kinship, heredity, the struggle for existence, and so on; they will want to know the ideas that underlie those things. This is what Goethe was striving for. His thoughts regarding the type are to the organic scientist what Kepler's three laws are to the physicist. Without such laws, we would experience the world as a mere labyrinth of facts.

This has frequently been misunderstood. Some insist that Goethe's idea of metamorphosis is merely an *image* that arises abstractly in our intellect — that he did not realize that the concept of leaves transforming into the organs of the blossom is meaningful only if these organs (the stamens, for example) had once actually been leaves. But this turns Goethe's view on its head. It makes one sense-perceptible organ primary in principle, and derives the other organ from it in a literal way. Goethe never intended it that way. For him, the organ that arises first chronologically is not at all primary in terms of the idea, or principle. Stamens are not related to leaves because they were once actual leaves; no, it is because they are related in principle, through their inner nature, that they once appeared as leaves. The sense-perceptible transformation is the result of their ideal relationship, not the other way round.

It has now been established empirically that all the lateral organs of the plant are identical. But why are they considered identical? According to Schleiden, it is because they *all* develop on the stem as lateral protuberances and are pushed outward so that the lateral cell formation continues near the stem, and no new cells are formed at the tip that was first to emerge. This purely external relationship forms the basis of the idea of identity. Again, according to Goethe, the matter is different; the lateral organs are identical in their ideal, essential nature. Therefore, they also *manifest* outwardly as identical formations. According to him, the relatedness that appears to the senses is a result of an inner, ideal connection. Goethe's perspective differs from the materialistic view because of the way it frames its questions; they do not contradict but complement each other. Goethe's ideas provide the basis for the materialistic view.

Goethe's ideas are more than poetic prophecies of later discoveries; they are independent, theoretical discoveries whose value has only begun to be recognized, and from which science will continue to draw sustenance for a long time to come. The particular empirical facts that Goethe used may be superseded, even disproved to some degree by more exact and detailed research, but the ideas he established will always remain fundamental to organic science, because they are independent of those empirical facts. Just as every newly discovered planet must orbit its star according to Kepler's laws, every process in organic nature must accord with Goethe's ideas. Events in the starry heavens were known long before Kepler and Copernicus; but these men were the first to discover their laws. Organic nature was observed long before Goethe; but he discovered its laws. *Goethe is the Copernicus and Kepler of the organic world.*

The nature of Goethe's theory can also be explained in the following way. Besides ordinary empirical, purely fact-gathering mechanics, there is also a rational mechanics that derives a priori laws from the inner nature of fundamental mechanical principles. Empirical mechanics relates to its rational counterpart in the same way that the theories of Darwin, Haeckel, and so on, relate to Goethe's rational organic science. Initially, Goethe was not clear about this aspect of his theory, but later he expressed it very emphatically. Thus he wrote to H. W. F. Wackenroder, "Continue to acquaint me with everything that interests you; *somewhere it will connect with my observations*" (January 21, 1832). Which is to say that he had discovered the fundamental principles of organic science, from which it should be possible to deduce everything else.

Earlier, however, all this had been working unconsciously in Goethe's mind, and he approached the facts accordingly. It only became conscious to him through his first conversation about science with Schiller (which we will describe later). Schiller immediately recognized the ideal nature of Goethe's archetypal plant and claimed that external reality could never be fully consistent with it. This stimulated Goethe to think about the relationship between what he called the *type* and empirical reality. He now encountered one of the most significant problems in all of human research: What is the relationship between idea and external reality, between thinking and experience? It became increasingly clear to him that no individual empirical object corresponds fully to his type; there is nothing in nature that is identical to it. The concept of the type cannot, therefore, stem *from* the sensory world as such, even though it is acquired *through the encounter with* the sensory world. Consequently, it can only arise from the type itself. The idea of the archetypal being must, by virtue of an inner necessity, develop its content out of itself, which then appears in the phenomenal world in another form — as a percept.

It is interesting in this regard to see how Goethe upheld the *validity of experience* and strictly separated idea and object, even in his encounters with empirical scientists. In 1796 Sömmerring sent him a book in which he had attempted to discover the seat of the soul. In a letter to Sömmerring (August 28, 1796), Goethe found that he had woven too much metaphysics into his views. He said that an idea about *objects of experience* has no justification if it goes beyond them and is not based on the essential nature of the objects themselves. He maintained that, when dealing with objects of experience, the idea is an organ for apprehending the necessary interrelationships of phenomena that would otherwise be perceived blindly as random occurrences in space and time. Because the idea may not add anything new to the object, it follows that the object in its actual essence is of an ideal nature; in fact, all of empirical reality must have two sides — one through which it is of a particular, individual nature, and another through which it is of an ideal, universal nature.

Goethe's association with the philosophers of his time and their works allowed him a number of perspectives on this question. He was stimulated by Schelling's *On the World Soul* and his (first) "Outline for a System of Natural Science" (see Goethe's *Annals,* 1798–1799), and Henrik Steffens's *Fundamentals of Philosophical Natural Science.* He also discussed many questions with Hegel. All this finally led Goethe to again study the work of Kant, which he had done before at Schiller's urging. In 1817 (see his *Annals*) he assessed how years of studying Kant had influenced his ideas about nature and natural phenomena. These reflections led to the following essays in which Goethe addresses the most central questions of science:

> "Fortunate Encounter,"
> "Judgment through Intuitive Perception,"
> "Reconsideration and Resignation,"
> "The Formative Impulse,"
> "The Enterprise Justified,"
> "The Purpose Set Forth,"
> "The Content Prefaced,"
> "History of my Botanical Studies,"
> "The Origin of the Essay on the Metamorphosis of Plants."

These essays all express the thought mentioned — that every object has two sides: the immediate one of its appearance (phenomenal form), and the second containing its *essence* (being). Goethe thus came to the only satisfactory view of nature, and it laid the foundation for the one truly objective method. Any theory that views the idea as alien to the object itself — as merely subjective — cannot claim true objectivity if it uses ideas at all. Goethe, on the other hand, can claim to add nothing that does not already lie within the object.

Goethe also pursued the detailed, factual aspect of those branches of science to which his ideas related. In 1795 he attended Loder's lectures on the ligaments, and throughout that period he kept anatomy and physiology in view. This is all the more significant because he was writing his lectures on osteology at the time. In 1796 he experimented with growing plants in the dark and under colored glass. Later he also studied insect metamorphosis.

Goethe was also stimulated by philologist F. A. Wolf, who called Goethe's attention to Wolff (his namesake) who, already in 1759 in his *Theoria Generationis,* had expressed ideas similar to those of Goethe on the metamorphosis of plants. This led Goethe to study Wolff more closely during 1807. Later, however, he discovered that Wolff, despite his acuity, was not clear on the essential questions. He had not yet conceived of the type as an entity imperceptible to the senses, developing its content purely out of inner necessity. He still viewed the plant as an outer, mechanical complex of individual details.

This interaction with his many scientist friends and his happiness at being recognized and emulated by numerous kindred spirits, led Goethe in 1807 to consider publishing the fragments of scientific works he had withheld thus far. He gradually abandoned the idea of writing a larger scientific work. But he did not get around to publishing his individual essays that year. His interest in the theory of color again pushed morphology into the background for a while. The first booklet of his essays was not published for another ten years, and by 1824 two volumes had been published — the first in four booklets, and the second in two. In addition to the essays on his own views, we find discussions of significant literary publications on morphology as well as the treatises of other scholars whose presentations, nevertheless, always complement Goethe's interpretation of nature in some way.

Twice again, Goethe was challenged to take up natural science more intensively. Both instances involved significant scientific publications that were intimately connected with Goethe's own work. The first was stimulated by works on the spiral tendency in plants by botanist Karl Friedrich Philipp von Martius (1794–1868), the second by a scientific dispute in the French Academy of Sciences.

Martius saw the plant's form in its development as a combination of a spiral and a vertical tendency. The vertical tendency leads it to grow in line with the root and stem; the spiral tendency is revealed by the spreading leaves, blossom, and so on. Goethe saw in this thought only an elaboration that emphasizes the spatial (vertical and spiral) aspects of his own ideas, which had been established in 1790 with his essay on metamorphosis. We refer here to our comments on Goethe's "On the Spiral Tendency of Vegetation," which make it clear that Goethe did not, in this essay, present anything essentially new in relation to his earlier ideas. We emphasize this especially for those who say they see a regression in Goethe's essay, from his earlier clear views to the "deepest depths of mysticism."

At a very advanced age, Goethe finished two more essays (1830–1832) on the dispute between French scientists George Baron von Cuvier and Etienne Geoffroy Saint-Hilaire. These essays contain the principles of Goethe's view of nature, again assembled with striking conciseness.

Cuvier was an empiricist of the old school. He sought appropriate, individual concepts for each animal species. He believed that,
within the conceptual edifice of his system of organic nature, he had
to include as many types as there are various animal species displayed
in nature. But these types stood side by side without any mediation
whatsoever. He disregarded the fact that those who strive for knowledge are not satisfied with the particular as such confronting us in its
immediate, phenomenal form. But, because we approach an object
in the sensory world with the intention to know it, we should not
assume that we are unsatisfied with the particular because we lack
the capacity for knowledge. Rather, the object itself must contain the
reason for our dissatisfaction. The nature of the particular is by no
means exhausted in this its particularity; as we strive to understand
it, we are urged not toward something particular, but something general. This general idea is the real being — the essence — of all that
exists as particular; its particularity is only one side of its existence;
its other aspect is the general, or the type.[16]

This should be understood when referring to the particular as a
form of the general. Because the general idea is the true being, or
essence, of the particular, it is impossible to deduce or abstract it
from the particular. Because the general cannot borrow its essence
from anywhere else, it must provide its own. Thus the nature of the
general type is such that its essence and form are identical. Consequently, it can be comprehended only as a whole, independent of the
particular. Science has the task of showing how each particular, by
adhering to its own nature, relates to the general idea. In this way,
particular kinds of existence enter the cognitive realm where we recognize their mutual determination and interdependency. Things that
would otherwise be perceived only in a dissociated way — as isolated
entities in space and time — may now be seen in their *necessary, lawful* interrelatedness. Cuvier, however, flatly rejected this view, which
Geoffroy Saint-Hilaire maintained. This is, in fact, the aspect of their

---

16. Goethe states, "The fundamental characteristic of a living whole: to separate, to
unite, to merge into the universal, to abide in the particular, to self-transform, to specify
itself, and — because living things tend to manifest under a thousand conditions — to
come forward and to vanish, to solidify and melt, to rigidify and flow, to expand and
contract. Since all these effects occur simultaneously, any or all may occur at the same
moment. Growth and decay, creation and destruction, birth and death, joy and sorrow
are all interwoven in the same sense and in the same measure; therefore, even the most
particular thing that occurs always appears as a picture and parable for the most universal"
(*Verses in Prose*). — ED.

dispute that Goethe was interested in. This question has often been distorted by recent views that show the facts in a very different light than is the case when one approaches them without bias. Geoffroy Saint-Hilaire's arguments were based not only on his own research but on the work of a number of like-minded German scientists, among whom he mentions Goethe. Goethe was extraordinarily interested in this matter, and was deeply pleased to find a comrade in Geoffroy Saint-Hilaire. On August 2, 1830, he said to Eckermann:

> Geoffroy Saint-Hilaire is now definitely on our side, and with him all his important students and followers in France. For me this is an event of incredible value, and I rightly rejoice over the final victory of a cause to which I have devoted my life, and which in a very special sense is also my own.

It is indeed a remarkable phenomenon that, in Germany, the positive response to Goethe's research was mainly among philosophers, but less among scientists, whereas in France the positive response came from scientists. Augustin Pyrame de Candolle gave utmost attention to Goethe's theory of metamorphosis, and his approach to botany was close to Goethe's own. Goethe's "Metamorphosis" essay [1790 edition] had already been translated into French by Gingins-Lassaraz. Under such circumstances, Goethe was right to hope that a French translation of his botanical writings (if done with his collaboration) would not fall on barren ground. In 1831, with Goethe's constant assistance, that translation was produced by Friedrich Jakob Soret. It was published in French, with the original German on facing pages. It contained that first "Attempt" of 1790, as well as the history of Goethe's botanical studies, the effect of his theory on his contemporaries, and something on de Candolle.

Chapter 5

Concluding Remarks
on Goethe's Morphology

When at the end of these thoughts on Goethe's theory of metamorphosis, I look back over the views I felt the need to express, I must admit that many outstanding representatives of various schools of scientific thought share a view contrary to my own. Their position on Goethe is completely clear to me, and their assessment of my attempt to represent our great thinker and poet is quite predictable. The opinions about Goethe's scientific endeavors are divided into two opposing camps.

The adherents of modern monism, led by Professor Haeckel, view Goethe as the prophet of Darwinism and one who thinks of the organic world as they do — that it is governed by the same laws that operate within inorganic nature. They would say that the only thing Goethe lacked was a theory of natural selection, which provided Darwin with a *foundation* for the monistic worldview, thus raising the theory of evolution to the level of scientific conviction.

This perspective is confronted by another that views Goethe's idea of the type as no more than a general concept, or idea in the sense of Platonic philosophy. Accordingly, they claim Goethe's inherent pantheism led him to make various assertions reminiscent of the evolutionary theory, and that he never felt any need to penetrate to its ultimate *mechanical foundations*. Consequently, it is impossible to attribute a theory of evolution in the modern sense to Goethe.

Through my attempt to explain Goethe's views *without assuming any positive standpoint,* based purely on Goethe's own nature and his whole spirit, it has become clear that neither of these two positions —

as significant as their contributions to an assessment of Goethe have been — has interpreted his views of nature altogether correctly.

The first view is certainly correct when it maintains that Goethe, in attempting to explain organic nature, opposed the dualistic assumption that there are insurmountable barriers between the organic and inorganic worlds. But Goethe never claimed that organic nature can be understood because its forms and phenomena can be explained mechanistically, but rather because he realized that the *higher* context in which they exist is in fact accessible to our knowledge. In fact, he conceived of the universe in a monistic way, as an undivided unity, from which he in no way excluded the human being; for this very reason, however, he saw that, *within* this unity, we can distinguish levels that obey their own laws. Even in his youth, Goethe rejected the tendency to picture this unity as *uniformity* and to think of the organic world — indeed, anything that manifests at a higher level within nature — as governed by the laws that operate in the inorganic world. Later, this rejection also led him to assume the validity of judgment through intuitive perception as a means of comprehending organic nature, and to distinguish it from the discursive intellect that comprehends inorganic nature. Goethe conceived of the world as a circle of circles, each with its own explanatory principle. Modern monists recognize only one circle — one governed by inorganic laws.[1]

The second view recognizes that in Goethe we are dealing with something other than modern monism. But because those who represent this view believe that science must explain organic nature in the same way as it does the inorganic, they recoil in horror from views such as Goethe's, and consider it completely useless to look more closely at his endeavors.

Goethe's high principles can thus never be *fully* validated by either camp. And it is precisely these principles that constitute the outstanding element in his endeavors. When it becomes clear that some of the *details* of Goethe's research need to be corrected, these principles lose none of their significance for those who recognize their full profundity. It thus becomes incumbent upon anyone seeking to expound

---

1. Materialistic monism is still the basis of mainstream science. Nobel laureate Ilya Prigogine, for example, explains the transition from the inorganic to the organic in terms of physicochemical fluctuations that produce irreversible advances toward more complex systems. He does not recognize a higher principle working from the whole into the parts in the development or behavior of organisms. (See *From Being to Becoming: The New Science of Connectedness.*) — ED.

Goethe's views to draw attention to what is *central* to the Goethean view of nature and not to become mired in a critical assessment of the details of his findings in some particular area of science.

Having attempted to carry out this task, I face the possibility of being misunderstood by those whose misunderstanding I would most regret — the pure empiricists. I am referring to those who explore every aspect of the factually demonstrable interrelationships of organisms (the material that presents itself empirically) and who today hold open the question of the primary principles of the organic world. My presentations cannot possibly be directed against them, because they do not relate to them. On the contrary, a part of my hopes are built on the empiricists precisely because all avenues remain open to them. They are the ones who will be able to set straight some of Goethe's assertions, for in the factual realm he occasionally erred; in this regard, even a genius cannot overcome the limitations of his time.

In the realm of principles, however, Goethe arrived at basic views that have the same significance for organic science as Galileo's basic laws have for mechanics.

To establish this fact was the task I set for myself. May those who remain unconvinced by my words at least recognize the honest intention with which I have endeavored — setting aside all consideration of persons and focusing entirely on the subject at hand — to solve the problem I have indicated: to explain Goethe's scientific writings out of the whole of his nature, and to express what is for me an inspiring conviction.

The fact that a happy and successful beginning has been made at interpreting Goethe's poetry in this way is in itself a challenge to re-explore all his works using the same approach. This is bound to occur sooner or later, and I will not be the last to rejoice when my successor succeeds better than I have. May youthfully striving thinkers and researchers — especially those whose views not only attain breadth but penetrate directly to *central* insights — give my reflections their attention, and follow in droves to present more perfectly what I have attempted to set forth.

Chapter 6

Goethe's Way of Knowing

Johann Gottlieb Fichte sent Goethe the first section of his *Theory of Science* in June 1794. On June 24, Goethe replied to the philosopher:

> For my part, I will owe you a tremendous debt of gratitude if you finally succeed in reconciling me with philosophers, whom I have never been able to do without but with whom I have never been able to feel united.

What the poet was asking of Fichte he had sought earlier from Spinoza, as he would later from Schelling and Hegel: a philosophical worldview that corresponded fully with his own way of thinking. But none of the philosophical approaches he encountered satisfied him completely.

This makes our task all the more difficult; for we intend to approach Goethe from a philosophical perspective. If he had claimed a scientific stance we could refer to it; but this is not the case. Thus, our task is to consider all of the poet's work that is available, discern its philosophical center, and sketch its salient features. We maintain that the correct approach to this matter is to follow a line of thought based on German idealistic philosophy, which tried in its way to satisfy the same, *highest* human needs to which Goethe and Schiller devoted their lives. It arose from the same cultural movement and is therefore much closer to Goethe than the views that generally dominate science today. From this philosophy we will be able to construct a view from which Goethe's poetic and scientific works can be derived. We would never be able to do this on the basis of contemporary tendencies in science. Today we are very remote from the way of thinking inherent in Goethe's nature.

It is indeed true that we have advanced in every area of culture, but it can hardly be maintained that this has also been an advance *in depth*. In the end, the significance of an era can be measured only by its progress in terms of depth. One is inclined to say, however, that our age is best distinguished by its wholesale rejection of the possibility of any real human deepening. We have become fainthearted in all areas, especially in our thinking and will. When it comes to thinking, there is an endless accumulation of information, but there is no courage to place it into the context of a comprehensive scientific view of reality. German idealistic philosophy, on the other hand, is accused of being unscientific because it had such courage. Today people want to *perceive* with their senses but not *think*. All confidence in thinking has been lost. Thought is considered incapable of penetrating into the mysteries of the world and of life. People have resigned themselves completely to living without any solution to the great riddles of existence. The only thing considered possible is *to create a system out of what is provided by sensory experience.*[1]

We forget that this perspective leads us to a position believed to have been overcome long ago. When deeply considered, the rejection of all thinking and the exclusive reliance on sensory experience are based on the same kind of blind faith in revelation that we find in religions. Ultimately, such faith rests merely on the fact that we are asked to believe what the churches hand down as ready-made truths. Thinking may strive to penetrate to their deeper meaning; but it lacks the capacity *to approach the truth,* to penetrate to the depths of the world through its own power.

What does a science limited to sense experience require of thinking? That it consider the factual information and then interpret and arrange it. The independent power of thinking to penetrate to the core of the world is denied by this science. Theology, on the one hand, demands blind subjection of one's thinking to the dictates of the church; science, on the other, demands blind subjection to the dictates of the senses. In either case, independent, deeply insightful thinking counts for nothing.

---

1. Since Steiner's time this scientific approach has been refined through systems theory and quantum mechanics, and an immense amount of empirical research has been done. There has been no progress *in depth*, however, because, as Steiner pointed out a hundred years ago, *the central, constitutive role of thinking in creating our insight into reality* has not been recognized. — ED.

Empirical science forgets that thousands upon thousands of people may have observed a sense-perceptible fact and passed it by without noticing anything remarkable about it. Then along comes someone who sees it and perceives within it the working of an important law. How do we explain this? The discoverer must have been able to look in a way that was different from those who came before. The discoverer perceived the fact with different eyes — had a certain thought about *how* to relate that fact to others, about what was significant in it and what was not. In this way, those who make scientific discoveries comprehend and order their experience through *thinking* and, consequently, see more than others do. *They see with the eyes of the spirit.* All scientific discoveries stem from the circumstance that the observer is able to observe in a way that is guided by the right thought. It is natural that *thinking* should guide observation. But it cannot do so when the researcher has lost confidence in it and does not understand its scope and significance. Empirical science helplessly roams the world of phenomena; the world becomes for it a confusing multiplicity of particulars because it lacks the energy of thought to penetrate its experience.

People speak of limits of knowledge today because they fail to understand the task of thinking. They lack a clear view of *what* they wish to achieve and doubt their ability to achieve it. If someone were to come today and show us the solution to the mystery of existence, we would gain nothing from it, because we would not know what to make of it.

It is exactly the same with our will and our actions. People are unable to set themselves a definite life task that they can actually accomplish. They merely fantasize about indefinite, vague ideals and then complain when they fail to achieve what they can barely envision. Just ask today's pessimists about what they really want and what they despair of accomplishing. They have no idea. Their nature is entangled in problems; they cannot cope with any situation, nor are they satisfied with any. Do not misunderstand me; it is not my intention to promote a superficial optimism that remains contented with life's trivial pleasures and yearns for nothing higher. I do not wish to condemn those who are painfully aware of our deeply tragic dependency on conditions that paralyze our every action, which we vainly struggle to change.

Let us not forget that pain is the precursor of joy. A mother's joy in her thriving children is that much sweeter when that joy has been won through worry, suffering, and effort. Every thinking person would in fact have to refuse any happiness offered by an external agent, because ultimately we cannot experience real happiness as the result of what is handed to us as an unearned gift. A creator who had intended to grant a heritage of happiness to humankind would have done better not to create us in the first place. Human dignity is increased when what we create is always cruelly destroyed; after all, as a result we must always build and create anew. Our happiness lies in doing and in our accomplishments. Revealed truth is like unearned happiness. Our human dignity depends on our seeking the truth ourselves, guided neither by sensory experience nor by revelation.[2]

Once this has been thoroughly recognized, revealed religions will have played themselves out. People will no longer look for revelations from God nor hope for freely bestowed blessings; they will want knowledge gained through their own thinking, and happiness created through their own efforts. Whether a higher power directs our destiny toward good or ill is of no concern to us; we ourselves must determine our own paths. The most exalted idea of divinity is still a god who, after creating human beings, withdrew completely from the world and left us entirely to our own devices.

Whoever attributes to thinking a perceptive capacity that goes beyond that of the senses, must also acknowledge that this capacity directs itself toward objects that lie beyond sense-perceptible reality. The objects of thinking, however, are *ideas*. When our thinking comprehends an idea, it unites with the foundations of universal existence. That which is actively at work in the outer world enters the human spirit; the human being *unites* with objective reality in its highest potency. *Beholding the idea in outer reality is the true communion of the human being.*

Thinking relates to ideas as the eye relates to light and the ear to sound; it is an *organ of perception*. This view can bring together two approaches currently considered completely incompatible — the empirical method and idealism as a scientific worldview.[3] It is generally

---

2. As a student of Goethe, Steiner was keenly aware of the importance of sensory experience, and he strongly defends its validity in the later sections of this work. Here, however, he is making the same point as in the above example of the discovery of a scientific law: *only* through our own thinking activity can we approach true reality. — ED.

3. Steiner uses *idealism* in the broad sense, which views ideas as the ultimate reality, as in the German idealism of Fichte, Schelling, and Hegel. This view also includes moral

believed today that the acceptance of the empirical method necessarily leads to the rejection of idealism. This is certainly not true. Of course, this must be our conclusion if we believe the senses are our only organs for perceiving objective reality. The senses provide only those relationships between things that can be reduced to mechanical laws.[4] Based on this, the mechanistic worldview would be the only true one. This view, however, makes the error of simply ignoring other, equally objective elements of reality that *cannot* be reduced to mechanical laws. What is *objectively* given does not in any way coincide with what is given *to the senses* as the mechanistic view maintains. What is given to the senses is only half of the given. The other half consists of ideas, which are also objects of experience — admittedly of a higher experience — and accessible to the organ of thinking. Ideas can thus also be attained through the inductive method.

Contemporary empirical science follows an entirely correct method; it adheres to the given but adds the inadmissible stipulation that this method must lead to sense-perceptible, factual results. Rather than limiting itself to the question of *how* we arrive at our views, it determines from the outset *what* the nature of these views must be. The only satisfactory scientific approach is an empirical method that leads to ideas as its results. This is idealism — not the kind that pursues a vaguely fantasized *universal oneness,* but one that attempts to apprehend the concrete idea of reality with the same certainty of experience with which today's extremely exact sciences seek facts.[5]

By approaching Goethe with these views, we believe that we are penetrating to the very nature of his being. We hold to idealism, but

---

idealism as implied by the English use of the word. By uniting empirical method with idealism, Goethe's scientific view bridges the gap between the two. — ED.

4. This sentence seems to contradict one of Steiner's main insights. He himself often points out that sensory perception alone does not provide any interrelationships whatsoever; these are established only through thinking. See chapter 9, "Goethe's Theory of Knowledge," pp. 93 and 101ff. This contradiction is resolved when we consider the following: We gain insight into organic nature to the extent that we apprehend the external particulars as manifestations of an inner lawfulness, or idea (we proceed from the whole to the parts). We do this through what Goethe called judgment through intuitive perception. When we observe the particulars in and of themselves, however, this relationship to the idea is lost, and we then resort to explaining their behavior as arising through mechanical cause and effect (we proceed to explain the whole in terms of the interaction of its parts). We do this through our intellect. (See also Steiner's characterization of intellect and reason pp. 110ff.) We can now understand the sentence in question to mean: "The senses, *combined with the intellect,* provide only those relationships between things that can be reduced to mechanical laws." — ED.

5. Steiner describes Goethe's scientific method more concretely in chapter 7, p. 83 and in chapter 10, part 1. — ED.

base its development not on the dialectic method of Hegel, but on a higher, more purified empiricism.

A similar view also underlies Eduard von Hartmann's philosophy.[6] He searched for the ideal unity in nature as it yields itself in a positive form to a content-filled thinking. He rejected the merely mechanistic view of nature and hyper-Darwinism, which clings to outer appearances. In science, he established a concrete monism. He looked for concrete ideas in history and in aesthetics. In all of this, he followed empirical, inductive methods.

Hartmann's philosophy differs from mine only with regard to the question of pessimism and his metaphysical emphasis on the "unconscious," which we will consider later. What Hartmann presents as the *grounds for* pessimism — the view that nothing in the world can fully satisfy, that dissatisfaction always outweighs pleasure — is precisely what I would call our *good fortune* as human beings. To me, what he offers merely proves that it is useless to pursue happiness. Indeed, we must give up all such efforts and find our life's purpose in selflessly accomplishing the idealistic tasks established by our reason. What else can this mean but that we should seek our happiness only in the unceasing activity of *creating?* The only people who ever manage to fulfill their destiny in life are those who are active — indeed, only those who are magnanimous in their actions, with no desire for reward. It is foolish to desire a reward for our activity; there is no real reward. These are the insights upon which Hartmann ought to build. He should point out that, under such circumstances, there is really only one possible motive for our actions. Once the prospect of attaining a desired goal falls away, the motivating force cannot be anything but selfless devotion to the object itself; *it can only be love.* Only action that arises from love can be moral. In science, our guiding star must be the *idea;* in our actions it must be *love.* And this brings us back to Goethe.

An active human being is concerned with doing the right thing, not about whether the right thing happens.... The art of living

---

6. Eduard von Hartmann (1842–1906), German philosopher who synthesized the views of Schopenhauer, Kant, and Hegel into a doctrine of evolutionary history based on conflict between the unconscious will and conscious reason; he is generally considered a pessimist, though he shared Hegel's broader sense of optimism. See also Steiner's discussion of Hartmann in his *Autobiography,* chapter 16 (chapter 6 in earlier editions). — Ed.

involves giving up our existence in order to exist. (*Verses in Prose*)

I did not arrive at my worldview only by studying Goethe — or Hegel, for that matter. I began with the mechanical, naturalistic worldview; then I realized that intensive thinking renders such a perspective untenable. Proceeding strictly according to scientific method, I found that objective idealism is the only satisfactory worldview. My *Theory of Knowledge* shows how thinking — when it comprehends itself and does not contradict itself — arrives at this view. Then I found that this objective idealism, in its fundamental thrust, fully permeates Goethe's worldview. Indeed, for years my own views have developed parallel with my study of Goethe, and I have never found my basic outlook to conflict *in principle* with Goethe's scientific work. If I have succeeded, at least in part — first in developing my point of view so that it comes to life in others as well, and second, in convincing them that this really is Goethe's position — then I consider my task fulfilled.

Chapter 7

The Arrangement of Goethe's Scientific Writings

In my responsibility as editor of Goethe's writings on natural science, my guiding idea has been to enliven the study of the details by showing the magnificent world of ideas that underlies them. I am convinced that Goethe's every assertion gains a whole new meaning — indeed, its *true* meaning — if we approach it with a full understanding of his deep and comprehensive worldview. We cannot deny that many of his scientific assertions appear insignificant in view of contemporary science, which since his time has advanced tremendously. But this is not at issue here; the important thing is the significance of such assertions *within the context of Goethe's own views.*

At the spiritual heights upon which the poet stood, scientific questions take on greater intensity. Without such questions, however, there is no science. *What were the questions Goethe asked of nature?* This is the important issue; whether and how he answered such questions are secondary considerations. Of course, with more adequate means and experience at our disposal today, we can also find more adequate answers to the questions he asked. But my exposition intends to show that, even with the greater means at our disposal, we can do no more than take the paths he indicated. Above all, we should learn from Goethe *how to ask questions of nature.*

We ignore what is most important by merely crediting Goethe with various observations that since his time have been rediscovered and now occupy a significant place in our worldview. In Goethe's case, the research results are not as important as the way he arrived at them. Appropriately, he himself states, "Venturing opinions is like moving pieces on a chessboard — they may be taken, but they have begun a game that will be won." Goethe developed a method that is completely in harmony with nature. With the means at his disposal, he tried to introduce this method into science. The individual results of his inquiries may have been transformed by the advances of science, but the scientific process thus introduced has itself been an enduring advance for science.

These perspectives necessarily influence the arrangement of the edited writings. Because I have departed from the usual way of arranging this material, it might seem justified to ask why I did not take this path, which seems to be the most sensible — with general science in volume one; biology, mineralogy, and meteorology in volume two; and physics in volume three. Thus, the first volume would contain the general views, and the rest would contain the specific elaborations of these essential ideas. As attractive as this may be, I would have never thought of adopting such an arrangement. Using that method, I would never have attained my goal — that is (returning to Goethe's analogy), *allowing the first moves of the game to reveal the underlying strategy.*

Nothing is more foreign to Goethe than to consciously proceed from general concepts. He always begins with *actual facts,* then compares and arranges them. While doing this, the fundamental ideas underlying the facts become apparent to him. It is very wrong to claim that ideas were not the driving force behind Goethe's creative work, on the grounds that he made that familiar remark about the idea of *Faust.* In his contemplation of things, after eliminating the unessential incidentals, what remained for him was the *idea* (in his sense of the word). The *method* Goethe used is always based on pure experience, even as he rises to the idea; he never allows a subjective element to slip into his research. He simply freed the phenomena of the incidental so that he could move toward their deeper foundations. His subject intends only to interpret the object in a way that discloses its innermost nature. "Truth is Godlike and does not appear directly; rather it must be apprehended through its manifestations." One must combine those manifestations in such a way that the "truth" can be seen. In observation, the truth, or *idea,* is already contained in the fact we confront; but we must remove the veil that conceals it. The removal of that veil is the true scientific method. Goethe took this path and we must follow him if we wish to fully access his mind.

In other words, we must begin with Goethe's biological studies, because this is where Goethe began. Here, for the first time, a rich content revealed its ideas to him — ideas that we later find as elements of his essays on general and methodological questions. If we wish to understand these writings, we must first have filled our minds with that content. The essays dealing with methodology are a mere spinning of thoughts for those who have not bothered to walk the path followed by Goethe. As for the studies of physical phenomena, they came about as a result of Goethe's view of nature.

Chapter 8

From Art to Science

When we wish to portray the spiritual development of a thinker, we must explain in a psychological sense how the particular direction of this development arises from the facts of that person's life. In presenting Goethe *the thinker*, however, we need not only to justify and explain his particular scientific direction, but, more importantly, to show how this genius became active as a scientist *in the first place*. Goethe suffered greatly from the false assumption of his contemporaries that poetic creativity and scientific research cannot be united in a single individual. What is most important here is to answer the question, What motives drove this great poet to take up science? Did the transition from art to science simply stem from his subjective inclinations, from personal whim? Or was Goethe's artistic bent such that *it* led him *of necessity* to science?

If the former had been true, then Goethe's simultaneous devotion to art and science would have resulted merely from an *incidental* personal enthusiasm for both aspects of human endeavor, and we would be concerned with a poet who also happened to be a thinker. Given a somewhat different course of life, Goethe might have taken up poetry in the same way without any interest whatsoever in science. Both aspects of this man would then have interested us separately; both might have contributed a good deal to human progress. But this would also have been true if these two spiritual directions had lived in two different individuals. Goethe the *poet* would have had nothing to do with Goethe the *thinker*.

But if the second supposition is true, then Goethe's artistic impulse would have demanded, out of its own inner necessity, to be complemented by scientific thinking. It would be simply inconceivable for the two impulses to have been divided between two personalities. Each of the two impulses would then interest us, *not just for its own sake,* but also because of its relationship to the other. There would then be an *objective* transition from art to science, a point where they meet in such a way that mastery in one field demands mastery in the other. If this is the case, then Goethe was not merely following a personal inclination; then it was the artistic impulse to which he was devoted that awakened needs within him that could be satisfied only through scientific activity.

Our age believes in keeping art and science as far apart as possible. They are thought to be polar opposites in human cultural development. Science, presumably, will give us the most objective picture of the world, show us reality as in a mirror — in other words, it is supposed to keep entirely to what is objectively given, and to exclude all arbitrary subjectivity. Its laws are determined by the objective world, to which it must subject itself. Science is supposed to find entirely in the objects of sensory experience the criteria for what is true and false.

When it comes to artistic creations, everything is supposed to be totally different. Their laws stem from the autonomous creative power of the human spirit. In science, every interference of human subjectivity is considered a falsification of reality, a transgression of experience; art, on the other hand, is thought to thrive on the subjectivity of genius. Its creations are products of the human imagination, not mirror images of the outer world. The origin of scientific laws lies outside us, in objective existence; the source of aesthetic laws lies within us, in our individuality. Therefore the latter are not considered to have any cognitive value whatsoever — they only create illusions without the slightest element of reality.

Those who view the matter in this way will never come to a clear understanding of the relationship between Goethean poetry and Goethean science. As a result, they will understand neither. Goethe's great historical significance lies in the fact that his art flows directly from the *primal wellsprings of existence,* that there is nothing illusory, nothing subjective about it, but that it appears rather as the herald of the lawfulness apprehended by the poet as he listens to the world spirit deep in nature's working. On this level, art becomes the interpretation of the world's secrets, just as science is in a different sense.

Indeed, Goethe always thought of art in this way. Art was for him *one* revelation of the primal lawfulness of the world, science the *other*. For him, art and science spring from a *single* source. Whereas researchers delve into the depths of reality to formulate its driving forces in the form of thoughts, artists seek to imbue their medium with these same driving forces.

> I think one could call science the knowledge of the general, abstracted knowledge; art, on the other hand, would be science applied in action; science would be reason, art its mechanism, wherefore one could also call it practical science. And finally, therefore, science would be the theorem, and art the problem. (*Verses in Prose*)

What science expresses as idea (theorem) is the same lawfulness with which art informs its medium — it becomes art's problem. "In human works, as in those of nature, what is most worthy of note are the intentions" (*Verses in Prose*).

Goethe looks everywhere not only for what is given to the senses in the outer world, but for the tendency through which it has come about. To grasp *this tendency* scientifically, to form it artistically, that was his mission. In forming her own works, nature gets herself "into specifications, as if into a dead-end street." We must go back to what might have come about if her tendency had been able to realize itself without hindrance, just as a mathematician never focuses only on this or that specific triangle, but is always mindful of the principles underlying all possible triangles. The essential question is not *what* nature has created, but according to what principle she has created it. The task then is to develop this principle as befits its own inner tendencies and not as it has occurred in nature, where it was dependent upon a thousand contingencies. The artist's task is "to develop out of the common the noble, out of the misshapen the beautiful."

Goethe and Schiller embraced art in its full profundity. The beautiful is "a manifestation of secret laws of nature, which, without its appearance, would have forever remained hidden from us" (*Verses in Prose*). A glance into the poet's *Italian Journey* is sufficient to realize that this was not an empty phrase but profound inner conviction, as when he says,

> The great works of art are at the same time the most sublime works of nature, brought forth by human beings according to

true and *natural* laws. Everything arbitrary, everything fanciful falls away; here is necessity, here is God. (September 6, 1787)

It is evident that, for him, nature and art have a common source. With regard to the art of the Greeks he says in this vein: "I have a hunch that they proceeded according to the same laws as nature herself, laws whose traces I have been following." And of Shakespeare: "Shakespeare joins company with the world spirit; he plumbs the world as it does, and nothing is hidden to either; but if it is the business of the world spirit to keep a secret before, often even after the fact, the poet is of a mind to give the secret away."

Here we should also recall the "joyful time" that the poet owed to Kant's *Critique of Judgment*, and that he actually owed only to the fact that here he

saw the creations of art and of nature, one treated like the other; that the capacities of aesthetic and teleological judgment each illuminated the other. . . . I was pleased that the art of poetry and comparative studies of nature were thought to be so closely related since both are subject to the same power of judgment.

In his essay "Significant Furtherance through a Single Ingenious Word," Goethe placed his objective [participatory) *poetry* alongside his objective [participatory] *thinking* with the very same intention.[1]

To Goethe, therefore, art and science appear to be equally objective; only their forms are different. Both appear as the expressions of *one* being, as necessary steps in a *single* development. Every view that relegates art or the beautiful to an isolated position *removed from* the whole picture of human evolution is repulsive to him. Thus he says,

In the aesthetic realm it is no good to speak of the idea of the beautiful; in so doing, we isolate the beautiful, which cannot be conceived of as separate. (*Verses in Prose*)

Style rests upon the deepest foundations of *knowledge,* on the essential nature of things, insofar as we are permitted to grasp it in visible and tangible forms. ("Simple Imitation of Nature, Mannerism, Style")

---

1. The adjective used here in the German original to characterize Goethe's thinking (as well as his poetry) is *gegenständlich*. This word can be variously translated as "concrete, object-oriented, representational, objective" and, in the spirit meant here, also "participatory." See p. 271 and n. 22 on p. 41. — ED.

Art is therefore based on knowing. Science has the task of recreating, in thought, the order according to which the world is constituted; art has the task of developing, in individual detail, the idea of this order. Artists incorporate into their works all of the world-lawfulness available to them. Works of art therefore appear as miniature worlds.

Herein lies the reason why the Goethean artistic tendency must be supplemented by science. Even as art, it is a form of knowing. What Goethe actually wanted was neither science nor art; *he wanted the idea.* And he either stated or portrayed it, depending on how it happened to present itself to him. Seeking to ally himself with the world spirit and to reveal its working, Goethe did whatever was required, working either through the medium of art or through that of science. Neither one-sided artistic nor one-sided scientific striving lay in Goethe's nature, but rather the never-resting urge to "behold all seeds, all active power" (*Faust,* line 384).

This does not make Goethe a philosophical poet, however, for his poetic productions do not make a detour through thought to their sense-perceptible formation; rather, they flow directly from the wellsprings of all becoming, just as his scientific research is not permeated by poetic imagination, but rests directly upon the perception of ideas. Still, while Goethe is not a philosophical poet, to the philosophical observer his fundamental tendency appears philosophical.

Thus, the question of whether Goethe's scientific works have a philosophical value takes on an entirely new form. It becomes a question of deriving the fundamental principles underlying these works from what we have of them. What must we posit so that Goethe's scientific assertions appear to flow from these premises? Our task is to express what Goethe left unexpressed, but which alone will make his views comprehensible.

Chapter 9

Goethe's
Theory of Knowledge

In the previous chapter we pointed to the fact that Goethe's scientific worldview was never formulated as a complete whole, or developed out of a single principle. We have before us only individual manifestations that show how this or that thought appears in the light of his way of thinking. This is true of his scientific works and of the brief indications he gives about one concept or another in his Verses in Prose and in letters to his friends. The artistic formulation of his worldview, finally, can be found in his poetic works, which also offer the most diverse clues to his basic ideas. But, in admitting without reservation that Goethe never expressed his basic principles as a coherent whole, we in no way intend to validate the claim that his worldview fails to spring from an ideal center that can be formulated in a rigorously scientific way.

Let us be clear about the matter before us. What worked in Goethe's spirit as the inner driving principle in all his creations, permeating and enlivening them, could not be manifested as such. Because it permeated all of his works, it could not, at the same time, appear in his consciousness as a separate entity. If this had been the case, then it would have had to appear before his mind as something complete and at rest, instead of being actively at work, as it actually always was. The task of Goethe's interpreter is to follow the diverse activities and manifestations of this principle in their constant flow in order to then sketch its ideal contours as a coherent whole. We will only see Goethe's exoteric works in their true light, when we succeed in a clear and precise formulation of the scientific meaning of this principle, and develop its various aspects with scientific consistency, because we will then be able to view them as they evolve out of a common center.[1]

This chapter will deal with Goethe's theory of knowledge, his epistemology. Before we consider Goethe's relationship to this science, we must briefly touch on a certain confusion regarding its task that has unfortunately persisted since Kant.

Kant believed that philosophy before him had strayed by seeking to know the essential nature of things without first asking how such knowledge is possible in the first place. He saw the fundamental malady of all philosophizing that preceded him in the fact that thinkers thought about the nature of an object before examining our human cognitive capacities. He therefore proceeded to examine this fundamental philosophical problem, thereby inaugurating a new trend in thought. Philosophy based on Kant has since focused untold cognitive power on this question; and in philosophical circles today, an approach to its solution is sought more than ever. As a result, however, epistemology — which has become the central scientific question of the day — is assumed to be no more than a comprehensive answer to the question, How is knowledge possible? Applied to Goethe, the question would then be, How did Goethe conceive of the possibility of knowledge?

On closer examination, however, we find that the answer to this question cannot possibly be the starting point for a theory of knowledge. For if I ask how something is possible, then I must have already examined the nature of the thing itself. But what if the concept of knowledge held by Kant and his followers — about which they ask whether it is possible or not — proved to be wholly untenable; what if it could not withstand penetrating criticism? What if our cognitive process were something quite different from Kant's definition of it? His whole work in this field would then be worthless. Kant simply took for granted the commonly accepted concept of knowing, and then inquired into its possibility. According to this concept, knowing is the depiction of a reality that exists in itself, outside our consciousness. We cannot, however, determine the possibility of knowing before we have found out what knowing is. Thus the question, What is knowing? becomes the primary concern for any theory of knowl-

---

1. Steiner is applying Goethe's method to Goethe's own works. Compare my discussion of Goethe's "genetic" method in section 5, pp. 258–259 and 266 of the concluding essay. — ED.

edge. It will therefore be our task to show how Goethe conceived of knowing.[2]

The formation of a particular judgment, or the recognition of a fact or series of facts — something that, for Kant, we can already call knowledge — is not yet knowing in Goethe's sense. Otherwise he would not have said that style [as the highest form of art] rests upon the deepest foundations of knowledge, and thereby distinguishes itself from the simple imitation of nature, wherein the artist turns to natural objects, faithfully and diligently imitates their forms and colors with the utmost exactness, and conscientiously avoids ever distancing himself from them. This distancing oneself from the sense world in its immediacy is characteristic of Goethe's view of genuine knowing. What is immediately given is experience. In our knowing, however, we create a picture of the immediately given, which contains significantly more than what the senses — the mediators of all experience — can provide. In order to grasp nature in the Goethean sense, we must not hold onto it in its immediate factuality; rather, nature must reveal itself through the process of cognition as something essentially higher than what appears at first sight.

The school of John Stuart Mill[3] assumes that all we can do with experience is simply to categorize various things into groups, and then retain them as abstract concepts. This, however, is not true knowing, for Mill's abstract concepts merely summarize what presents itself to the senses with all the qualities of immediate experience. True knowing must acknowledge that the immediate form of the given sense-perceptible world is not yet its essential form, which reveals itself to us only in the process of knowing. Knowing must provide us with what sense experience withholds, but which is nevertheless real. Mill's knowing is not true knowing because it is only an elaborated experience of the senses that allows things to remain as our eyes and ears convey them to us. It is not that we should go beyond the realm of experience and lose ourselves in a world of fantasy, as the metaphysicians of earlier and more recent times loved to do; rather we

---

2. This question, What is the nature of knowing (or cognition)? is probably most directly dealt with by Rudolf Steiner in his Intuitive Thinking as a Spiritual Path: A Philosophy of Freedom (previously translated as The Philosophy of Spiritual Activity). — ED.

3. John Stuart Mill (1806–1873), English empiricist philosopher and social thinker. — ED.

should progress from experience as given to the senses to a form of experience that satisfies our reason.

A new question now arises: What is the relationship between unmediated experience and the picture of experience that arises in the process of knowing? We will first answer this question independently, and then show that our answer also follows from Goethe's worldview.

Initially, the world presents itself to us as a multiplicity in space and time. We perceive particulars separated in space and time: this color here, that form there; now this tone, now that noise, and so on. Let us first take an example from the inorganic world and distinguish with great precision between what we perceive with our senses and what arises through the cognitive process. We see a stone flying toward a pane of glass, breaking through it, and finally falling to the ground. We ask, What is given here as immediate experience? A sequence of visual perceptions, proceeding from the places successively occupied by the stone, a series of sound perceptions as the pane shatters, the flying of glass fragments, and so on. Unless we want to deceive ourselves, we will have to say that nothing further is presented to our immediate experience than this incoherent aggregate of perceptions.

The same rigorous delimitation of the immediately perceptible (of sense experience) can also be found in Volkelt's excellent treatise on Kant's theory of knowledge, which is among the best that modern philosophy has produced.[4] But it is impossible to see why Volkelt regards discrete perceptual images as mental pictures, and thereby precludes the possibility of objective knowledge from the very start.[5] It is definitely a preconception to regard immediate experience as a totality of mental pictures. If I have some object before me, I see its form and color, I perceive a certain hardness, and so on. I do not know initially whether this aggregate of images given to my senses is something external to me, or whether it is a mere inner representation. Just as little as I know at first — without thoughtful consideration — that the warmth of a stone is the result of the warming rays of the sun, just as little do I know what the relationship is between the world given to me and my capacity to form mental images. Volkelt places

---

4. Johannes Immanuel Volkelt (1848–1939), *Kants Erkenntnistheorie ihren Grundprinzipien nach analysiert* (*Kant's Theory of Knowledge Analyzed According to its Basic Principles*), Hamburg, 1879. — ED.

5. The term *mental picture* is used by Steiner for what emerges from the process of cognition as the synthesis of percept and concept. — ED.

at the beginning of his epistemology the proposition "that we have a multiplicity of mental pictures of various kinds." That a multiplicity is given to us is correct; but how do we know that this multiplicity consists of mental pictures? Indeed, Volkelt does something quite inadmissible when he first asserts that we must ascertain what is given to us by immediate experience, and then presupposes something that cannot be a given: that the world of experience is a world of mental pictures. The moment we make such a presumption, we are forced to ask the epistemologically incorrect question characterized above. If our perceptions are mental images, then all our knowledge is of mental images and the question arises: How is it possible for a mental image to coincide with the object it is supposed to represent?

But does any real science ever deal with this question? Consider mathematics. Given a figure formed by the intersection of three straight lines: a triangle. The three angles α, β, and γ maintain a constant relationship; together they make a straight angle or two right angles (180°). This is a mathematical statement. What is perceived are the angles α, β, and γ:

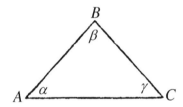

The above cognitive judgment is reached on the basis of thoughtful consideration. This judgment establishes a relationship between three perceptual images. There is no question of reflecting about any object behind the mental picture of the triangle.[6] So it is with all sciences. They spin threads from one mental image to another, creating order in what, from the point of view of immediate perception, is chaos; but nowhere does anything besides the given come into consideration. Truth is not the agreement of a mental picture with its object, but rather the expression of a relationship between two (or more) perceived facts.

---

6. Rudolf Steiner implies here that our mental picture of the triangle already includes our perceptions of the angles, and that we therefore feel no need to ask about a thing-in-itself beyond what we have apprehended as a mental picture. — ED.

Let us return to our example of the stone and the windowpane. We connect the visual percepts that proceed from the individual places through which the stone moves. This connection gives us a curved line (the trajectory); we obtain the laws of the trajectory; going further we perceive the material qualities of glass, then apprehend the stone as cause, the shattering of the pane as effect, and so on; we have so permeated the given with concepts that we come to understand it. All of this work, which pulls together the multiplicity of perceptions into a conceptual unity, occurs within our consciousness. The ideal interrelationship of the perceptual images is not given through the senses, but is rather simply grasped independently by our mind. For a being endowed only with faculties of sense perception, this entire process would simply not occur. For such a being, the outer world would remain the unstructured perceptual chaos that we have characterized as what first (immediately) confronts us.

Thus the place where the perceptual images appear in their ideal interrelationship — where the latter is held up to the former as their conceptual counterpart — is human consciousness. The fact that this conceptual (lawful) interrelationship, in its substantial aspect, is produced in our consciousness does not mean that it is subjective with respect to its significance. On the contrary; its meaning, or content, arises from the objective world just as certainly as its conceptual form arises from our consciousness. It is the necessary objective complement to the perceptual image. It is precisely because the perceptions of our senses are incomplete, unfinished in themselves, that we are compelled to add this necessary complement. If the immediately given were satisfying in itself and did not present us with problems at every point, we would never need to go beyond it. But the perceptual images do not by any means follow and arise out of one another in such a way that we can see them as resulting from one another; they result, rather, from something else that is inaccessible to the perception of the senses. Conceptual apprehension comes to meet them and grasps the aspect of reality that remains hidden to the senses. If sense experience provided us with something complete in itself, the process of knowing would indeed be useless. No combining, ordering, or grouping of sense-perceptible facts would have any objective value whatsoever. The activity of knowing is only meaningful if we do not regard the configuration given to the senses as complete, if we regard it as only half of a totality, bearing within itself something of a higher order still — something, though, that is no longer immediately perceptible to the senses. Now the human spirit becomes active. It perceives that higher element. Thinking should therefore not be conceived of as adding something to the essence of reality. It is no more and no less an organ of perception than the eye or ear. Just as the eye perceives colors and the ear hears sounds, thus thinking perceives ideas. Idealism is therefore perfectly compatible with the principle of empirical research. Ideas are not the contents of subjective thinking but the results of research. Reality comes to meet us when we approach it with open senses. It presents itself to us in a guise that we cannot regard as its true form; we can attain the latter only when we set our thinking in motion. Knowing means adding to the half-reality of sense experience what we perceive through thinking, so that our picture of reality becomes complete.

Everything depends on how we conceive of the relationship between ideas and sense-perceptible reality. By the latter I mean the totality of perceptions conveyed to us by our senses. Now the most widely held view is that concepts are merely a means for our consciousness to appropriate the data of external reality. The essence of reality is thought to lie only in the things themselves, so that if we were actually able to reach their primal nature, we would still be left with only its conceptual representation, and by no means this essence itself. This view, therefore, assumes the existence of two completely separate worlds: the objective outer world, which bears its essential nature — the foundations of its existence — within itself, and the subjective-ideal inner world, which is thought to be a conceptual copy of the outer world. This inner world is a matter of complete indifference to the objective world — it is not called for by the latter, it exists only for the cognizing human being. The epistemological ideal of this basic view would be to achieve the congruence of these two worlds. I include among its adherents not only the scientific mainstream of our time, but also the philosophy of Kant, Schopenhauer, and the Neo-Kantians, and equally the final phase of Schelling's philosophy. These schools of thought all agree in that they seek the essence of the world in a transsubjective realm, and in that they have to admit, from their perspective, that the subjective-ideal world — which for them is therefore a world of mere mental representations — has no meaning for reality itself, but only and exclusively for human consciousness.

As I have already indicated, this view leads to the assumption of a perfect correspondence between concept (idea) and percept. What is found in the percept would have to be replicated in its conceptual counterpart, only in ideal form. With respect to their essence, both worlds would have to coincide completely. The conditions of space-time reality would have to repeat themselves exactly in the idea, except that instead of the perceived spatial extension, shape, color, and so on, the corresponding mental pictures would have to be present. If, for example, I saw a triangle, I would have to follow its contours, size, the inclination of its sides, and so on, in my thoughts, and create a conceptual photograph of it for myself. When confronted with a second triangle, I would have to do exactly the same thing, and so likewise with every object of the external and internal sense world. Thus in my ideal picture of the world, each object would be found again with its exact location and characteristics.

We now ask, Do the consequences of this widely held view correspond with the facts? Not at all. My single concept of the triangle encompasses all individual, perceived triangles; no matter how often I bring it to consciousness, it always remains the same. My various mental pictures of the triangle are all identical.[7] I have only one concept of the triangle.

In reality, every single thing presents itself as a particular, fully defined "this" in contrast to equally well defined and thoroughly real "those." The concept, which is strictly a unity, comes to meet this multiplicity. In it there are no particulars, no parts; it does not proliferate; no matter how often it is pictured, it is always the same.

The question now arises, What is the actual source of the identity of the concept? It certainly cannot be its manifestation as mental picture, for Berkeley was completely justified in maintaining that my present mental picture of a tree has nothing whatsoever to do with the mental picture I will have of it a minute later if I close my eyes in the meantime, and that, if several individuals form mental pictures of the

---

7. The careful reader will not be able to accept this statement. Steiner himself clearly contradicts it in his reference to Berkeley in the second following paragraph. Our mental picture (Vorstellung) of an equilateral triangle is not identical with that of a right triangle, for example. Steiner does not distinguish here between concepts and mental pictures. In his *Intuitive Thinking as a Spiritual Path,* where he deals more thoroughly with the theory of knowledge, he makes this distinction clear. In chapter 6, "Human Individuality," he writes: "A mental picture is nothing but an intuition related to a specific percept. It is a concept, once linked to a percept, for which the relation to that percept has remained....Thus, a mental picture stands between a percept and a concept. A mental picture is the specific concept that points to a percept" (pp. 99–100). — ED.

same object, these will have just as little to do with one another. The identity can therefore lie only in the meaning of the mental images. It is their meaning, or essential content [the conceptual aspect], that attests to their identity.

Thus the view that denies all independent meaning to the concept or idea collapses. This view contends, specifically, that the conceptual unity, as such, is altogether without [its own] content — that it arises only through the omission of certain particulars in the objects of experience. The common elements, however, are emphasized and incorporated into our intellect so as to achieve a convenient grasp of the multiplicity of objective reality by embracing it with the fewest possible general terms — that is, according to the principle of the least expenditure of energy. Schopenhauer shares this point of view with the philosophy of modern science. It is represented in its most crass, and therefore most one-sided, consequences in Richard Avenarius' little pamphlet "Philosophy as Thinking about the World According to the Principle of the Least Expenditure of Energy. An Introduction to a Critique of Pure Experience."[8] This view, however, rests entirely upon a total misconstruing, not only of the content of the concept, but also of the percept.

To clarify this matter, let us go back to the fundamental insight that places the percept, in its particularity, over and against the concept in its universality.

We must ask ourselves, What actually distinguishes the particular? Can we define it conceptually? Can we say that a conceptual unity can be broken down into such and such particular perceptual multiplicities? Certainly not. The concept itself has nothing to do with particularity. This particularity, therefore, must consist of elements that are inaccessible to the concept as such. Since we know of no intermediary between percept and concept, these elements of the particular must belong to the percept itself (unless we wish to introduce something like Kant's fantastic mystical schemata, which can hardly be taken seriously today).[9] The reason for their particularity cannot be derived from the concept, but must be sought in the percept itself. What constitutes the particularity of an object cannot be grasped con-

---

8. "Die Philosophie als Denken der Welt gemaess dem Prinzip des kleinsten Kraft-masses. Prolegomena zu einer Kritik der reinen Erfahrung" (Leipzig, 1876). — ED.

9. Rudolf Steiner does not introduce the mental picture here as an intermediary between concept and percept as he does in his later work. — ED.

ceptually, but only perceived. Therein lies the reason for the inevitable shipwreck of every philosophy that attempts to derive the whole of perceived reality from the concept itself. Here also lies the classic error of Fichte, who wanted to derive the whole world from human consciousness.

Anyone who dismisses idealist philosophy out of hand for its inability to perform the impossible is indeed just as unreasonable as the philosopher W. T. Krug, a successor to Kant, who demanded that the philosophy of identity deduce for him a pen with which to write.

What actually distinguishes the percept from the concept is essentially just this element that cannot be conceptualized but must simply be experienced. Thus concept and percept stand juxtaposed as two different aspects of the world that are nevertheless identical in their essential nature. And because, as we have shown, the percept calls for the concept, it follows that its essence lies not in its particularity, but in its conceptual universality. With regard to its appearance, however, this universality must first be found in the subject; for while it cannot be derived from the object, it can indeed be found by the subject as the latter investigates the object.

The concept cannot draw its content from sense experience, for it does not take up into itself precisely what is characteristic of experience: its particularity. Everything particular is foreign to the concept. The concept must therefore provide its own content.

It is commonly said that the object of experience is individual, vivid perception, whereas the concept is abstract and, compared to the content-filled percept, poor, paltry, empty. The richness of these differentiated sensory particulars is sought in their number, which, because of the infinitude of space, can be infinitely great. But the concept is not therefore less fully defined, for here number is replaced by qualities. And just as quantities are not to be found in the concept, the percept lacks dynamic-qualitative character.[10] The concept is just as individual as the percept, its content just as rich. The only difference is that, to grasp the essence of the percept, nothing is required but open senses, a purely passive relationship to the external world, whereas the ideal significance of the world must arise through our own spontaneous spiritual activity if it is to appear at all. To say that

---

10. The dynamic-qualitative aspect of the concept arises through our inner participation. When this occurs, the concept loses its abstractness and is permeated with life and character. — ED.

the concept is the enemy of living perception is a thoughtless cliche. The concept is the essential being of the percept, its actual driving and active principle; it adds its own content to that of the percept without eliminating the latter, for it is not concerned with the perceptual content as such — and yet it is supposed to be the enemy of perception! The concept could become the enemy of perception only if a misguided philosophy wished to spin the entire wealth of the sensory world out of the idea. Such a philosophy would produce, instead of living nature, only a system of empty phrases.

Only in the way indicated here do we come to a satisfactory explanation of what actually constitutes knowledge based on experience. It would be impossible to explain why it is necessary to advance to a conceptual understanding unless the concept were to bring something new to the perception of our senses. Purely empirical knowledge could not take a single step beyond the millions of particulars placed before our perception. To be consistent, purely empirical knowledge would have to deny its own content. For why should we recreate conceptually what is already present in our percepts? In the light of these considerations, a consistent positivism would simply have to cease all scientific work and rely solely upon random occurrences.[11] Insofar as it does not do this, it actually carries out what it rejects in theory. In fact, both materialism and realism implicitly admit what we maintain. Their actual practice is justified only from our point of view, and stands in glaring contradiction to their own fundamental theories.

From our standpoint, the necessity of scientific knowledge and the need to go beyond sense experience can be explained without any contradiction. The sensory world appears to us as initially and directly given. It faces us like an immense riddle because we are simply unable to find within this world itself what drives, shapes, or animates it. Now reason enters, and with the ideal world that it conceives, holds up to the sensory world the governing principles that constitute the solution to the riddle. These principles are just as objective as the sensory world itself. The fact that they do not appear to the senses, but only to reason, has no bearing on their content. If there were no thinking beings, these principles would never appear; but this

---

11. In this sense, statistics and probability have come closest to consistent positivism. — ED.

would in no way detract from the fact that they are the essence of the phenomenal world.

Over and against the transcendental worldview of Locke, Kant, the later Schelling, Schopenhauer, Volkelt, the Neo-Kantians, and modern scientists, we thus put forward a worldview that is truly immanent.

Whereas they seek the primary principles of reality in a realm beyond our consciousness and foreign to it, immanent philosophy seeks those principles in what appears to reason. The transcendental worldview regards conceptual knowledge as a picture of the world; the immanent view sees it as the world's highest form of manifestation. All the former can produce is a formal theory of knowledge based on the question, What is the relationship between thinking and actual being? The latter places at the beginning of its epistemology the question, What is knowing? The former proceeds from the preconception that there is an essential difference between thinking and being; the latter enters without preconception into an investigation of what alone can give us certainty, of thinking, and it knows that, outside of thinking, it can find no being.

Summarizing the results of our epistemological reflections, we arrive at the following: We must proceed from the totally indeterminate, immediate form of reality as given to our senses — from what is only seen, only heard, and so on — before we set our thinking in motion. The point is that we distinguish between what the senses convey to us and what our thinking brings to it. The senses do not tell us that there are any particular relationships between things — for example that this is the cause and that the effect. For the senses, all things have equal importance for the structure of the world. Thoughtless observation does not indicate that a seed is at a higher level of complexity than a grain of dust on the road. As far as the senses are concerned, if they look alike, they are both of equal significance. At this level of observation, Napoleon is no more important to world history than a peasant in some backwater village.

This is as far as present-day epistemology has progressed. That these truths have by no means been thought through exhaustively is demonstrated by the fact that virtually every epistemologist makes the mistake of immediately designating as mental picture what confronts us on the first level of perception as initially undefined and indeterminate appearance. This, however, is nothing but a gross violation of the very insight we have just gained. As long as we remain at the level of pure sense perception, we know just as little about a falling stone being a mental picture as we know about its being the cause of the depression in the ground where it falls. We can arrive at this latter judgment only through thoughtful consideration, and only through reflection could we arrive at the insight that the world given to us is a mere mental picture — assuming this is true. My senses give me no clue as to whether what they convey is an actual being or merely a mental picture. The sensory world bursts in upon us instantaneously — as though fired from a pistol. If we want it in its purity, we must refrain from attaching to it any qualifying attributes. We can only say one thing: that it confronts us, it is given to us. This says nothing at all about this sensory world itself. Only by proceeding in this manner can we avoid interfering with an unbiased assessment of what is given. This freedom from prejudice is lost if from the very start we attach a particular characterization to what is given. If, for example, we say that the given is a mental picture, then our entire inquiry will be based on this presupposition. We would not thereby be providing an unbiased theory of knowledge, but would rather be answering the question, What is knowing? under the presupposition that what is given to the senses is a mental picture. This is the fundamental error of Volkelt's epistemology. At the beginning he establishes the rigorous requirement that all theory of knowledge be free from presupposition. But he then goes on to assert that we have a multiplicity of mental pictures. Thus his theory of knowledge is only an answer to the question, How is knowing possible, if we assume that the given is a multiplicity of mental pictures?

Our approach is quite different. We take the given as is: as a multiplicity of — something or other, which will reveal itself to us if we allow ourselves to be carried along by it. By allowing the object itself to speak, we thus have the prospect of gaining objective knowledge. We can hope that the phenomenon that presents itself to us will reveal everything we need, providing we do not allow some obstructive prejudice to block the free access of its proclamations to our power of judgment. For even if reality should forever remain a riddle to us, knowing such a truth would have value only if it were gained by reference to actual things. It would be totally meaningless, on the other hand, to maintain that our consciousness is constituted in such a way that we are unable to reach any clarity regarding the things of the world. Whether our spiritual capacities are adequate to grasp the nature of things — this we must test ourselves in connection with these things themselves. I may possess the most perfect mental capacities, but if things reveal nothing about themselves, my gifts are useless. And conversely, even if I know that my powers are slight, this in itself does not yet tell me that they are not nevertheless sufficient to know things.

We have also come to see that what is immediately given, in the form characterized above, leaves us unsatisfied. It presents a challenge, a riddle that needs to be solved. It says to us, I am here; but I do not appear to you in my true form. As we hear this voice from without with growing awareness that we arc facing a half-reality, an entity whose better side remains concealed from us, there announces itself from within us the activity of the organ through which we attain knowledge of the other side of reality, through which we are able to complement the given half and thus create a whole. We realize that what we do not see, hear, and so on, must be supplemented through our thinking. Our thinking is called upon to solve the riddle presented by perception.

We will only understand this relationship when we investigate why we are dissatisfied with perceptible reality, yet satisfied with the reality attainable through thinking. Sensory reality confronts us as something finished. It is simply there; we have contributed nothing to its being as it is. We therefore feel ourselves confronted with something foreign that we have not produced — indeed, we were not even present at its production. We stand before an already existing entity. Yet in order to fully comprehend something we need to know how it came to be what it is, to follow the steps leading to the thing before us. This is different with our thinking. A thought-configuration does not present itself to me unless I myself participate in its coming about; it enters the field of my perception only when I myself raise it out of the dark abyss of imperceptibility. A thought does not appear within me as a finished entity, as does a sense perception; on the contrary, when I hold it fast as a finished configuration, I am conscious of the fact that I myself have brought it into this form. What lies before me appears to me not as a foreign entity, but as the completion of a process so intimately bound up with me that I have always stood inside it.

This is precisely what I must accomplish with whatever appears on the horizon of my perception, if I am to understand it. Nothing should remain obscure to me; nothing should confront me as already finished; I myself must follow it to its completion. This is why the immediate form of reality we usually call experience induces us to work it through scientifically. When we bring our thinking into movement, we uncover the initially hidden factors that determine the given; we raise ourselves from the product to its production; we arrive at the stage where the sense-perceptible becomes transparent to us in the same way that thought is transparent. Thus our inner need for knowledge is satisfied. Our scientific understanding of something is complete only when our thinking has fully and thoroughly penetrated the sense-perceptible. A world-process appears completely penetrated by us only when this process is our own activity. A thought appears as the conclusion of a process within which we stand. The only process into which we can fully place ourselves, completely immerse ourselves, is thinking. For scientific observation, experienced reality must appear as arising out of a developing thought process in the same way that a pure thought itself does.

To explore a thing's essential nature means to proceed from the center of our thought-world and to work our way outward until there arises before our soul a thought-configuration that appears to be identical with our outer experience. When we speak about the essential nature of a thing or of the world, we can therefore mean nothing other than apprehending its reality as thought, as idea. In the idea we come to know that from which we must derive everything else: the principle of things. What philosophers call the absolute, eternal being, the foundations of the world, what the religions call God, this we call — based on the theory of knowledge presented here — the idea. Everything in the world that does not directly appear as idea will eventually be recognized as proceeding from it. What seems to superficial consideration to have nothing to do with the idea is derived from it by a deeper thinking. No other form of existence can satisfy us except what is derived from the idea. Nothing should remain isolated outside it; everything must become part of the greater whole encompassed by the idea. The idea, however, requires no going beyond itself. It is the essential being, built upon and firmly founded in itself. The reason for this does not lie in the fact that the idea is immediately present in our consciousness. It lies in the idea itself. If the idea did not express its own being, it would seem to us in need of explanation just like the rest of reality.

This seems to contradict what was said above: that the idea appears in a form that satisfies us because we actively participate in its coming into existence. But this does not stem from the organization of our consciousness. If the idea were not built upon its own foundations, we could have no such consciousness [of satisfaction] at all. If something does not have within itself the center from which it springs, but has its center outside itself, then, when it presents itself to me, I cannot declare myself satisfied with it; I must go beyond it to find that center. Only when I come upon something that does not point beyond itself do I attain the consciousness, Now you are standing inside the center; here you can remain. My consciousness that I am standing inside a thing is only the result of its objective nature, of the fact that it contains its own principle. By taking possession of the idea, we gain entry into the center of the world. What we grasp here is the source from which everything springs. We become one with this principle; therefore the idea — what is most objective — appears to us, at the same time, as most subjective.

Sense-perceptible reality is, in fact, such a riddle to us for the very reason that we do not find its center within it. It ceases to be so enigmatic when we realize that it has the same center as the thought-world, which comes to manifestation within us.

Such a center must be a unified one. Indeed, it must be of such a kind that all other things point to it as to their source of explanation. If there were several centers to the world — several principles through which it could be known — and if one area of reality pointed to this world principle, another area to that one, then, as soon as we found ourselves in one such area, we would be directed to its center only. It would not occur to us to inquire about still other centers. One area would know nothing about the other. They would simply not exist for one another. Therefore it makes no sense at all to speak of more than one world. The fact that there are different kinds of consciousness and that each has its own image of the idea does not at all change the fact that the idea is one and the same anywhere in the world and in any type of consciousness. The idea-content of the world is based on its own foundations, it is complete and perfect within itself. We do not create it; we only seek to comprehend it. Our thinking does not create it; it perceives it. Thinking is not a producer but an organ of apprehension.

Just as various eyes all see the same object, various kinds of consciousness think the same thought-content. They think the same thing; but they approach it from different sides. It therefore appears to them in various modifications. These modifications, however, do not stem from a difference in objects, but rather from different angles of vision.

Differences in human views are just as explicable as the differences in the way a landscape presents itself to two observers standing in different places. If we are at all capable of penetrating to the world of ideas, we can be sure that in the end this world is common to everyone. It can of course still be the case that we see it in a very one-sided way — for example, from our point of view it may appear in a most unfavorable light, and so on.

We are probably never faced with a sensory world completely devoid of thought-content. We perhaps come closest to pure sense perception in earliest childhood, when there is as yet no trace of thinking. Our ordinary life experience is halfway permeated by thinking; it already appears more or less lifted out of the obscurity of perception into the clear light of spiritual comprehension. The sciences work toward the goal of fully overcoming this obscurity and leaving nothing in experience that has not been permeated with thought.

Now what has the theory of knowledge achieved for the other sciences? It has clarified the purpose and task of all science. It has shown us the significance of every particular science. Our theory of knowledge is the science that determines the nature and task of all the other sciences. It has made it clear that what the individual sciences attain is the objective foundation of world existence. The sciences arrive at certain concepts; epistemology throws light on the actual task of these concepts. Through this characteristic result, our theory of knowledge, formulated in accordance with Goethe's way of thinking, diverges from all other epistemologies of the present. It does not wish merely to establish a formal relationship between thinking and being; it does not wish to solve the epistemological problem through logic only, it wants to come to a positive result. It shows what the content of our thinking is; and it finds that it is at the same time the objective world-content.

This makes epistemology the most significant science for the human being. It clarifies our role as human beings, and shows us how we stand in relation to the world; it thus becomes for us a source of satisfaction. It shows us our true calling. When in possession of its truths, we feel ourselves uplifted; our scientific research appears in a new light. Only now do we know that we are connected with the innermost core of world-existence in the most immediate way, that this core, which remains concealed to all other beings, is uncovered by us, that the world spirit manifests in us, that it dwells in us. We see that the world process is brought to completion within us; we see that we are called upon to accomplish what the other powers of the world are incapable of achieving and that this achievement is the crowning of creation. If religion teaches that God created human beings in his own image, our theory of knowledge teaches us that God took creation only to a certain point. It was at this point that he brought the human being into existence, and as we come to know ourselves and to look about us, we set ourselves the task of carrying the work forward, of bringing to completion what the primal power began. We immerse ourselves in the world and realize what can be built upon the foundations that have been laid; we learn to see the intentions of the primal spirit and carry them out. In this way the theory of knowledge is also the science of the significance and vocation of humanity; and it resolves this question (of the "vocation of humanity") in a much more definite way than Fichte did at the turn of the eighteenth into the nineteenth century. In no way can we gain from the book of that powerful mind the same full satisfaction that can be derived from a genuine theory of knowledge.

It is our task to work upon individual existence so that it appears to proceed from the idea, so that its particularity is fully sublimated and merges with the idea, into whose element we feel ourselves transported. Our spirit has the task of forming itself in such a way that it acquires the ability to see through all given external reality so that this reality appears to proceed from the idea. We must endeavor to become tireless workers in transforming every object of our experience until it presents itself as a part of our ideal world-picture.

We have now arrived at the point where Goethe's way of viewing the world takes its start. Let us apply what has been said in such a way that we imagine the relationship between idea and external reality presented here as actual deed in Goethe's research. Goethe penetrated to the heart of things in the way that has been justified here. He himself saw his inner way of working as a living heuristic capacity that, acknowledging an unknown rule (the idea) of which he has a presentiment, seeks to introduce it into the external world (*Verses in Prose*). When Goethe admonishes us to educate our organs,[12] he can also only mean that we should not simply surrender to what our senses convey, but direct our senses so that they show us things in the right light.

---

12. "Animals are educated by their organs; human beings educate theirs and master them" (*Verses in Prose*). — ED.

Chapter 10

Knowledge and Action
in the Light of Goethe's Ideas

1. Methodology

We have established the relationship between the world of ideas attained through scientific thinking and unmediated "given" experience. We have become acquainted with the beginning and the end of a process: experience devoid of ideas, and a conception of reality filled with ideas. Between those two, however, lies human activity. Our task is to actively unfold the end out of the beginning. *How* we do that is our method. It goes without saying, of course, that how we conceive of the relationship between the beginning and the end of the scientific process will call for a particular method. On what do we base this method? Step by step scientific thinking must overcome the shadowy form of reality we have described as the immediately given, and raise it into the luminous clarity of the idea. In other words, our method will consist in repeatedly asking of every fact: How does it contribute to a unified world of ideas? What is its place in my conceptual image of the world?

When I have understood this and have recognized how a thing relates to my ideas, my cognitive need is satisfied. There remains only one potential source of dissatisfaction: when a thing appears that refuses to connect with the concepts I stand for. I feel the need to overcome the intellectual discomfort caused by anything about which I must say: I see that it is present, and when I encounter it, it confronts me as a question mark; yet, nowhere in the harmony of my ideas can I find a place for it; no matter how I twist and turn my conceptual system, the questions it raises within me remain unanswered.

This suggests what we need when we consider an object. When I first approach it, the object faces me in isolation. My thought world strives toward the point where its concept lies. I cannot rest until what first confronted me as an isolated phenomenon appears as an integral part of my conceptual system. Then the isolation of the object dissolves and reappears in a larger context. It is now illuminated by the combined thoughts of all other objects; it now contributes to the whole, and I fully understand its meaning within this larger harmony. All this takes places within us whenever we thoughtfully approach an object of experience. All scientific progress depends on this becoming aware of the point where a phenomenon can be integrated into the harmony of the world of ideas.

Let us not misunderstand this; it does not mean that every phenomenon should be explainable in terms of preexisting concepts, as if the world of ideas were closed and everything new had to be understood in terms of an old concept already in our possession. As our world of ideas expands, we may come to a point that has never been thought by anyone. Indeed, the historical progress of science depends precisely on the emergence of new ideas. Every one of them is connected by a thousand threads to all other possible thoughts. Each of these connections assumes its own form. In each case, the connection is different. *And it is precisely this that is the scientific method — that we show the concept of a particular phenomenon in its connections with the rest of the world of ideas.* We call this process the deduction (or proof) of the concept. Scientific thinking of any kind consists only in finding links between concepts, in allowing one concept to arise from another. The scientific method involves this shuttling back and forth between concepts.

The reader may wonder whether I am describing just another version of the old story of the correspondence between the intelligible world and the sensory world. According to its tenets, if we are to believe that this shuttling back and forth between concepts can lead us to an accurate image of reality, we must assume that a correspondence exists between the objective world and our concepts. This, however, is an erroneous view of the relationship between individual objects and concepts. When I am first confronted by a particular object or phenomenon in the world of experience, I have no idea at all *what* it is. Only after I have penetrated it, and its concept has become clear to me, do I know *what* I am looking at. This does not imply that the particular object and the concept are two *different* things. No, they are the same thing. What presents itself to me in the particular object is nothing but the concept itself. The reason I see this object as separate and cut off from the rest of reality is that I have not yet perceived it in its essence, that it has not yet presented itself to me as it is. This consideration allows us to specify further the nature of the scientific method; each individual object represents a particular content in the system of thought. It is rooted in the totality of the world of ideas and can be understood only in relation to this totality.

Thus every object necessarily presents our thinking with a double task. First, we must establish firmly the contours of the corresponding thought, and, second, we must establish all the threads that lead from this thought to the whole idea world. Reality demands clarity in the individual details and depth in the whole. One is the task of the intellect, the other the task of reason. The intellect creates thought forms for individual aspects of reality. The more precisely it delineates them, the more sharply it draws the contours, the more faithfully it does its work. Reason then assigns these thoughts their places in the harmony of the world of ideas. This assumes, of course, that this unity already resides in the content of the thoughts created by the intellect, that one life pervades the content of all our thoughts while the intellect artificially keeps them separated. Reason overcomes the separation without losing the clarity. The intellect leads us away from reality, and reason brings us back to it. This can be represented graphically:

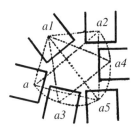

All parts are connected in the overall composition; the same principle is at work in all the parts. The intellect separates the individual forms, because in the given outer world we encounter them separately [as indicated by the solid lines], and reason recognizes their unity [indicated by the dotted lines].

If we assume two experiences — 1) the sun shining down, and 2) a warm stone — our intellect holds the two apart because they present themselves as *two* phenomena. One is thought of as the cause, the other as the effect. Then reason steps in, breaks down the partition, and sees the *unity in the duality.* All concepts created by the intellect — cause and effect, substance and property, body and soul, idea and reality, God and world, and so on — are merely ways of artificially holding apart what is a unified reality. The role of reason, on the other hand, is to look for the inner unity in the multiplicity without erasing the content created or mystically obscuring the clarity of the intellect. In this way we are returned to the unitary reality from which the intellect had distanced us. A more precise nomenclature would term *concepts* products of the intellect and *ideas* the creations of reason. Now we can see that the path of science leads to ideas through concepts.

This consideration offers a clear distinction between the subjective and the objective elements of knowing. It is clear that our division of reality is purely subjective and created by our intellect. I can divide the same objective unity into individual thoughts that are different from those of others. Through its connections, however, reason can restore the objective unity from which we departed.

Fig. 1   Fig. 2   Fig. 3

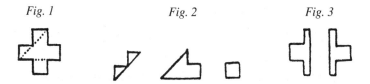

The unified image of reality (*Fig. 1*) can be broken down for the sake of understanding it. I may divide it one way (*Fig. 2*) and someone else another way (*Fig. 3*). Our reason pulls it together, and we return to the same unified image. This helps us understand why human beings have so many different concepts and diverse views of reality, even though reality must remain the same. *The differences reside in the differences between our intellectual approaches.* This sheds light on the development of various scientific points of view and helps us understand the origin of the multiplicity of philosophical worldviews, none of which need to be certified as the truth.

In considering the multiplicity of human concepts, the question is not merely whether the concepts are true or false. We will always try to understand how a particular thinker's intellectual world arises from the world's harmony; we will try to understand rather than denounce as error those opinions that happen to disagree with our own. This difference in scientific viewpoints is related to the fact that each person has a different realm of experience. Each of us encounters only a small part of the whole reality. Each person's intellect processes this part, and it is this sample that mediates the way to ideas. Thus, even though we may all be cognizant of the same idea, it is always in different realms. Only the *final result* can be the *same;* the *paths* leading to it may be *different.* The individual judgments and concepts that constitute our knowledge do not have to agree.

It is important, however, that those judgments and concepts eventually lead us to swim in the flowing stream of ideas. When all is said and done, all human beings meet in this stream when active thinking takes them beyond their separate points of view. Limited experience or an unproductive mind may, of course, lead to *one-sided,* incomplete views. But even the most limited experience must finally lead us to the realm of ideas. For we rise to this realm not through the breadth of our experience, but through our inherent capacities as human beings. Limited experience merely results in a one-sided *expression* of the realm of ideas. It limits our means to bring forth the light shining within us, but it cannot prevent us completely from letting this light arise within us. Whether our scientific or general views are exhaustive is not at all a matter of their spiritual depth.

Returning to Goethe, many of his statements will be seen as following from the thoughts described in this chapter. And I might add that I find this the only right relationship between author and commentator. Thus Goethe writes, "If I know my relationship to myself and to the outer world, I call it truth. And thus, each person can have his or her own truth and still it is always the same" (*Verses in Prose*). This can be understood only on the basis of the foregoing considerations.

2. Dogmatic and Inherent Method

A scientific judgment is formed either by connecting two concepts or by connecting a percept and a concept. The judgment "No effect without a cause" is of the former kind; "The tulip is a plant" is an example of the latter. In daily life there are also situations when we connect one percept with another — for example, "The rose is red." Whenever we pass a judgment, we do so on a certain basis. Now there are two ways of looking at the basis for a judgment.

According to the first school of thought, we assume that the objective basis for the truth of a judgment lies beyond the evidence provided by the concepts and percepts that contributed to the judgment. In this view, *the basis for the truth of a judgment does not necessarily coincide with the subjective basis that led to the judgment.* The *logical* basis, in this view, should not be confused with the *objective* basis. Whereas this school of thought may suggest a way to reach the objective foundations of our insights, the means attributed to our cognizing mind are insufficient for the purpose. The objective reality underlying my claims lies within a world unknown to me. The claim itself, together with its *formal* basis (inner consistency, the support of various axioms, and so on) is the only aspect within my knowledge.

Any kind of science based on this kind of view is *dogmatic.* Theological philosophy based on revelation is an example of dogmatic science, as is contemporary science. Just as there is a *dogma of revelation,* there is also a *dogma of experience.* The dogma of revelation transmits truths about matters completely removed from the human perspective. The human being does not know the world about which ready-made articles of faith are prescribed. We can never find the grounds upon which our beliefs rest. It is impossible to ever know *why* something is true. What can be attained is a *belief, not knowledge.* But the claims of experimental science are mere dogmas as well, insofar as it asserts that we should limit ourselves to pure experience, merely observing, describing, and systematizing its changes, never rising to the conditions, which are *not yet given* in the immediate experience. In this case also, truth is not attained through insight into the object, but is imposed upon us from outside. I see what happens and what is there, and I register it. The reason why this is the way it is is considered to lie within the object. I see the consequences, never the cause. At one time science was dominated by the dogma of *revelation;* now it is dominated by the dogma of *experience.* In the past, thinking about the causes of revealed truth was considered presumptuous; today it is considered impossible to know anything other than what the facts express. The question of *why* the facts speak in this way and not in another is considered beyond the purview of experience and therefore unanswerable.[1]

---

1. Higher organizational principles — the metamorphosis of plants and animals or the essential nature of a particular species — cannot be grasped through an intellectual analysis of sensory experience. We apprehend such principles only through what Goethe calls reason. Compare Steiner's distinction of intellect and reason, pp. 110ff. — Ed.

We have shown that beyond recognizing the truth of a judgment, it makes no sense to presume why the statement is true. When we push through to the point where the essence of a thing arises in us as idea, we come to see the idea as entirely self-contained, self-supporting, and self-sustaining, requiring no further external explanation; we can come to rest in it. Given the necessary capacities, we can recognize that the idea contains in itself all its constituent parts, that we have in it all we could ever ask for. The whole ground of being has emerged in the idea, has poured itself into it without any reservation, and we need not look any further. We do not find in the idea an *image* of what we are looking for in things; rather, we find what we are looking for itself. To the extent that the parts of our idea-world flow together in our judgments, this result is achieved by their own content and not through any external reasons. In our thinking, the concrete grounds for our statements are immediately present, not just their formal grounds.

We therefore reject the view that, beyond all ideas, there is an absolute reality that sustains all things, including thinking itself. That worldview is completely unable to find the grounds of existence in the attainable world. For this view, the ultimate cause of existence has not entered the world as it is manifested to us. It is rather a being for itself and separate from the present world. This view, which can be called *realism,* takes two forms; either it postulates a multiplicity of real beings underlying the world (Leibniz, Herbart), or it assumes a unified reality (Schopenhauer). This *reality* cannot be known to be identical with the idea in either case; its very nature is presumed to be fundamentally different.

It is impossible to be a realist once the question of the essential nature of phenomena fully enters our consciousness. For what is the purpose in asking about the *essential nature* of the world? It really comes down to my seeing a thing, and a voice within telling me that, ultimately, it is really much more than what I see before me. In fact, however, even as I look at the thing, this greater reality is already actively trying to manifest within me. If I look for explanations, it is only because the world of ideas active within me demands my explanation of the surrounding world. A being in whom ideas do not arise would not be motivated to explain things more deeply; such a being would be fully satisfied with sensory appearances. The drive to explain the world arises when our thinking urges us to unite the idea-content available to it with the world of appearances and to penetrate all things in a conceptual way — to make what we *see, hear, and so on into things we understand.*

If we give these matters our most serious consideration, it is impossible to be an adherent of realism as we have described it. Any attempt to explain the world through some reality that is not an idea is a self-contradiction, and it is difficult to understand how that notion gained any followers at all. We cannot have a need — nor is it even possible — to explain perceptible reality through something not found in thinking itself, let alone something fundamentally different from thinking. For one thing, what would motivate us to explain the world in terms of something completely alien to us, even hidden from us? Assuming we were to encounter this hidden agent, we would have to ask, In what form and where? It cannot be found in thinking. If not in thinking, should we expect to find it in some outer or inner perception? But what purpose can it possibly serve to explain the world of sensations through something of the same nature?

We are left with a third possibility — the assumption that we are able to reach an unthinkable yet very real world by means other than thinking or perception. This assumption leads us directly to mysticism. We do not need to concern ourselves here with this, because we are interested only in the relationship between thinking and being, *idea* and *reality.* Let the mystic write the epistemology of mysticism. It was the matured Schelling's view that our reason can only develop *what* the world-content is, but can never attain the fact *that* it exists in the first place. To us, this seems most absurd. For us, the *existence* of a thing is the precondition for *what* it is, and we would have no way of attaining the *what* of a thing unless we had established *that* it exists in the first place. According to our reason, the fact that a thing exists is a part of the very fact that I grasp its meaning. Schelling assumed that it is possible to experience a positive meaning of the world without even being convinced that it exists. This and his conviction that we can know of existence only through *higher experience* seems inconceivable to self-reflective thinking; we are led to assume that in his later years Schelling could no longer understand his earlier views, which had such an impact on Goethe.

It is not permissible to presume higher forms of being than those accessible to the world of ideas. People look for yet another reality only because they are often unable to grasp that the being of an idea is much nobler and fuller than is perceived reality. If we are dissatisfied with ideas, it is because we consider them to be insubstantial fabrications of the mind, empty of any concrete reality. It is because we are in fact unable to grasp the positive nature of ideas. We think of them as mere abstractions and have no experience of their fullness, perfection, and soundness. We need to lift ourselves through culture and self-development to a higher perspective, from which we can apprehend the concrete *reality* of a being that is invisible to the eye and unavailable to the hand's touch, and which only reason can encompass.

In other words, we are establishing an *idealism* that is at the same time *realism*. By this we mean that thinking yearns to understand reality through ideas. This yearning is hidden in the question, *What is the essence of reality?* The answer to this question emerges only at the end of the scientific process. We do not proceed as do the realists who postulate a true reality from which they derive the world of their experience. We distinguish ourselves from the realists through our full awareness of the fact that ideas are the only means we have to explain the world. Realists also have only this means, but they do not realize it. Realists derive their world from ideas, while convinced they are deriving it from another reality. Leibniz's world of monads is nothing but a world of ideas. But Leibniz believes he has gotten hold of a reality more fundamental than the world of ideas. All realists make the same mistake: they contrive realities, never realizing that they remain in the realm of ideas.

We reject this realism, because it deceives itself about the fact that ideas are actually the foundation of its world-conception. We reject with equal firmness the false idealism that believes we cannot transcend our consciousness, because we never escape the world of ideas, and thus all our conceptions and the whole world itself are a subjective illusion, a dream of our consciousness (Fichte). Such idealists fail to understand that, while we cannot get beyond the world of ideas, they are themselves an objective reality whose foundation lies in itself and not in the subject. They forget that, although we cannot escape the universal nature of thinking, rational thinking takes us right into the heart of objectivity. *Realists fail to understand that the objective is the idea; idealists fail to understand that the idea is objective.*

We still need to consider the empiricists, who maintain that all attempts to explain reality through ideas are indefensible philosophical deductions. They assert that we should limit ourselves to what is immediately accessible through our senses. Our response to this viewpoint is simply that its requirements can only be *methodological* and *formal* in nature. If we must stop with the given, it can mean only one thing — that we must appropriate the things that come to meet us. *What* comes to meet us, however, cannot be predetermined by *this* viewpoint, because that *what* would first have to be found in the given itself. It is hard to conceive how one could argue for pure experience and simultaneously demand that one remain within the limits of the sensory world, because ideas can also meet the criteria of being given.

Positivism is forced to leave unanswered the question of *what* is given and is thus easily compatible with idealistic results of research. In this case, the demands of empiricism coincide with our own. We unite all points of view in ours *inasmuch as they are justified.* Our viewpoint is idealism, because it finds the foundations of the world in ideas. It is realism, because it treats the idea as concrete reality. And it is positivism, or empiricism, to the extent that it works toward the content of ideas as given rather than by means of a priori constructs. Ours is an empirical method that penetrates to the real and, ultimately, finds satisfaction in ideal results. It is inadmissible, in our view, to conclude on the basis of what is given, or known, the existence of something not given that underlies and determines it. We reject any conclusion in which one of the elements is not given. Drawing a conclusion is no more than moving logically from given elements to other equally given ones. In the end we link *a* to *b* by way of *c;* but each of these must be given.

When Volkelt says that thinking forces us to assume realities other than the given and to transcend it, we say that what we wish to add to the immediately given is already active in our thinking. We reject all metaphysics, which consists in explaining the given through a nongiven, or something postulated (Wolff, Herbart). To us, a conclusion is merely a formal act; it leads not to something new but makes connections among elements that are actually present.

3. The System of Science

What form does a fully developed science take in the light of Goethe's way of thinking? First of all, we must be clear about the fact that the entire *content* of science is a given — partly given externally from the sensory world, partly from within, from the world of ideas. All our scientific activity involves overcoming the particular form in which this entire content of the given presents itself and giving it a satisfying form. This is necessary, because the inner unity of the given is hidden from us when we first encounter it, and only its surface appears to us. The method that will establish these unifying relationships differs according to the phenomenal field in which we are active.

Let us first consider a realm in which we are dealing with a multitude of sensory elements, related in varying ways. As we begin to contemplate these elements with our thinking, their interrelationships become clear to us. One element or another may appear conditioned to some degree by the others in a particular way. The conditions determining one become clear as we consider the others; we derive one manifestation from another. The manifestation of the warm stone, for example, can be derived as the effect of the warming sun rays, which are consequently seen as the cause. What we perceive in one thing is explained when we derive it from another perceptible thing. We see how ideal laws appear in this realm. They encompass the sensory events and stand above them. They determine the lawful response of one thing insofar as it is determined by another.

Our task here is to assemble a series of phenomena in such a way that their necessary connections become evident, so that we can see them function as a thoroughly lawful whole. The realm that can be explained in this way is *inorganic nature*. But, in our experience, things do not appear to us in such a way that the nearest in time or space is always the nearest in terms of its inner nature. We must progress from what is nearest in time and space to what is nearest conceptually. We must look for phenomena that are immediately adjacent in the conceptual realm. We must endeavor to assemble a series of facts that complement and mutually support one another. In this way, we arrive at a group of interacting sense-perceptible elements. The phenomenon unfolding before our eyes follows, in a transparent way, from the factors involved. Following Goethe, we will call such a phenomenon an archetypal phenomenon, or fundamental fact. *This archetypal phenomenon is identical with objective natural law.*

On the one hand, the connections we are describing can be established mentally, as when I think, for example, of factors that affect a stone when thrown horizontally: First the kinetic force; second, the

Earth's gravitational force; third, air resistance. I can then derive the trajectory of the stone from these factors. Alternately, I can physically bring together the individual factors and wait for the resulting phenomena. This is what we do when we make an *experiment*. Whereas a natural phenomenon may be baffling to us, because we know the effects (or manifestations) but not the causes (or necessary conditions), the phenomenon produced by an experiment is clear, because we assembled the causal factors ourselves. *This is the path of scientific research — we begin with experience to see what is actually involved; we then continue, through observation, to determine why it actually is so; and then we proceed to the culminating experiment to see how [the lawful relationships involved] actually express themselves.*

Unfortunately, we seem to have lost the essay from Goethe that best supports these views. It came after his essay "The Experiment as Mediator between Subject and Object." Beginning with this essay, we will attempt to reconstruct the presumed content of the lost essay from the only source available to us — the correspondence between Goethe and Schiller.

The essay "Experiment as Mediator between Subject and Object" arose from the studies that Goethe conducted to justify his research on optics. The essay then was left lying until, in 1798, the poet resumed the study with renewed vigor and, together with Schiller, began a thorough and scientifically serious investigation of the fundamental principles of the natural scientific method. On January 10, 1798, Goethe sent Schiller the essay mentioned for comments, and on January 13 he wrote to his friend that he was willing to expand on the views presented in it in a new essay. He went to work on it and on January 17 a short essay was sent to Schiller, outlining one of the characteristics of the scientific method. This essay is not included in the catalogue of his works. It would certainly be invaluable for a full appreciation of Goethe's basic views on scientific methodology. We can, however, find the thoughts presented there in Schiller's detailed letter of January 19, 1798. What this letter indicates is confirmed and complemented by Goethe's *Verses in Prose*.[2]

---

2. [Later, Steiner added this footnote:] In my introduction on p. xxxviii of volume 34 of Goethe's complete works I say that unfortunately we seem to have lost the essay from Goethe that best supports his thoughts on experience, experiments, and scientific knowledge. It has not been lost, however, but found its way into the Goethe Archive in the form mentioned here. The essay is dated January 15, 1798, and was sent to Schiller on the seventeenth. It is the continuation of the essay 'The Experiment as Mediator between

Goethe distinguishes three methods of scientific research. These in turn rest on three different approaches to the phenomena. The first method is *common empiricism,* which does not go beyond the empirical phenomena, or immediate facts. It is absorbed by individual appearances. If common empiricism is to be of consequence, it must limit its activity to detailed descriptions of the phenomena it encounters — that is, it takes an empirical inventory. Science, in the empiricist's view, would be nothing but a sum of individual, factual descriptions.

In contrast to empiricism, *rationalism* represents the next step. It strives to establish *scientific phenomena.* Not limiting itself to the mere description of the phenomena, it attempts to explain them by discovering causes, formulating hypotheses, and so on. This is the step where the intellect, departing from the phenomena, goes on to draw conclusions about their causes and connections. Goethe considered both of these stances one-sided. Common empiricism is crude and unscientific, because it never escapes the mere recitation of chance occurrences. Rationalism, on the other hand, interprets into the phenomenal world causes and connections that are not contained within it. Common empiricism is unable to rise from the fullness of the world of facts to free thinking, and rationalism loses the phenomena as the solid, factual ground under its feet, succumbing to the power of wishful thinking and subjective fancy.

Goethe forcefully condemns the passion for rushing from observations to conclusions. Thus, he says in his *Verses in Prose:*

It is a bad thing, and one often encountered, to immediately tie a conclusion to an observation and then give both equal weight. ...Theories are usually the hasty product of an impatient intellect that would like to be rid of the phenomena and eagerly replaces them with images, concepts, or sometimes only words. One suspects, one even clearly sees, that it is just a makeshift; but do not passion and partisanship always love a makeshift? And rightly so, because they need them so much.

Subject and Object.' I took the thoughts expressed in the essay from the correspondence and presented them in the introduction on p. xxxix in exactly the same way it is now available. In terms of content, the essay adds nothing to what I wrote there. Indeed, the insights into Goethe's method and mode of knowledge gained through my study of his other writings are confirmed in every point. — R. Steiner.

Goethe is especially hard on the misuse of causal reasoning. Rationalism in its unbridled fantasy continually looks for causality where the facts do not warrant it. In *Verses in Prose* he states, "The most innate and most important concept — that of *cause and effect* — is used in ways that lead to countless, endlessly repeated errors." The mania for simplistic connections in particular leads one to think of phenomena as links in a chain of causes and effects following one another in a strict linear fashion. In truth, however, any phenomenon that is conditioned by an earlier one is at the same time dependent on many other influences. In this case, the *length* of nature is taken into consideration, but not its *breadth*. According to Goethe, both paths — that of common empiricism and that of rationalism — are *intermediate* stages on the way to the highest scientific method, but only stages that must be transcended.

This is achieved by *rational empiricism,* which deals with *pure phenomena* that are identical with objective, natural laws. Common empiricism, unmediated experience, gives us only disconnected, individual facts, an aggregate of outer appearances. It gives them to us not as the conclusion of a scientific process but as its initial experience. Science requires us to look for connections and view individual facts as interconnected. In this sense, there seems to be a separation between the need to conceptualize and the given facts.

For the cognizing spirit, there are only relationships; in nature there is only separation. The spirit strives for the species (or type); nature creates only individuals. We escape this contradiction by reflecting on the fact that, on the one hand, the connecting power of the spirit is without content and therefore cannot, in itself, grasp anything concrete, and that, on the other hand, the separation of natural objects is not a matter of their essence but of their manifestation in space. Indeed, when we get to the essence of the individual, our attention is drawn to the species, or type. Because natural objects manifest as separate, we need the synthesizing power of the spirit to show us their *inner* unity. And because the unity of reason is itself empty, it needs natural objects to fill it. Thus, in the *third stage,* phenomena and spiritual capacities meet and become *one.* Only now is the spirit fully satisfied.

There is another area of research in which the manifestation of an individual fact does not appear as the consequence of another discrete fact. Thus, we cannot understand it by calling on the aid of another similar fact. Here, a series of sense-perceptible elements appear as a direct expression of a unifying principle. If we wish to understand the individual fact at all, we need to penetrate to this principle. We cannot explain the phenomenon as the result of outer effects but must develop it from the inside outward. What had played a determining role is now merely an influence or stimulus. In the [inorganic] realm discussed earlier [beginning on p. 118], I could understand everything if I could see a fact as the effect of other facts — that is, deduce it from external conditions. But now I am being forced to ask different questions. If I know the external influences, I still have no certainty as to exactly how the phenomenon will respond. I must derive the response from the central principle of the phenomenon affected by the external influence. I cannot say what effect this external influence will have, but only that the inner principle of the phenomenon responds in a certain way to a particular external influence. Anything that happens is the consequence of an *inner* lawfulness. What I need to comprehend, therefore, is this inner lawfulness. My research must discover what shapes itself from the inside out. The *type* is the self-structuring principle at the foundation of every phenomenon in this realm, and I must look for it in each one. We are now in the realm of organic nature. What we term archetypal phenomena in relation to inorganic nature is the *type* in organic nature. The type is a *general image,* or idea, of the organism — the animality in the animal.

Because of their significant relevance to our consideration of the type, we have reiterated the main points discussed earlier [in chapter 4]. In the ethical and historical sciences, however, we are concerned with ideas in a narrower sense. As sciences, ethics and history are driven by ideas, which are the reality they investigate. The task of each science is to work through the given material far enough to reach the archetype, the type, or, in the case of history, the guiding idea.

Once . . . physicists have come to understand what we have called the archetypal phenomenon, they are safe, and philosophers with them. They become convinced that they have arrived at the frontier of their science and have come to an empirical high point, from which they can look back down and survey all the stages of experience, and from which they can also look forward into, if not enter, the realm of theory. The philosophers are also safe, because they take the physicists' results and make it the starting point of their own work. (*Theory of Color*)

This is where the work of philosophers truly begins. They take the archetypal phenomena and bring them into a satisfying inner relationship. We now see, from Goethe's point of view, what must replace metaphysics: observation guided by ideas; the combination and derivation of the archetypal phenomena. Goethe speaks repeatedly in this way about the relationship between empirical science and philosophy, and with particular clarity in his letters to Hegel. In the *Annals,* he speaks again and again of a schema of natural science. If this were to be found, we would be able to see how he conceived of the relationships among individual archetypal phenomena and how he assembled them in a lawful sequence.

We can get an idea of this for ourselves by looking at his list of the various kinds of effects:

> accidental
> mechanical
> physical
> chemical
> organic
> psychic
> ethical
> religious
> arising from genius

This hierarchical list can help us to order the archetypal phenomena.[3]

4. On the Limits of Knowledge and the Formation of Hypotheses

People talk a great deal these days about the limits of knowledge. It is said that our ability to explain existing reality can reach only so far, at which point we must stop. We believe that this question cannot be answered correctly unless it is asked correctly. By asking the right questions, we can often dispense with a whole army of errors.

---

3. This list was published in vol. 4, section 2, p. 294 of the edition of Goethe's scientific works edited by Steiner. — ED.

If we consider the fact that the object to be explained is a given, it should become clear that the given itself cannot limit us in any way. Before it can demand explanation or understanding, it must present itself to us within the world of given reality. Whatever remains outside the realm of the given does not need explaining. Any limit would arise only when, confronted by a given reality, we lacked the means to examine it.

Our need to explain arises precisely because the way we wish to define the given — the explanation we wish to give to it — appears on the horizon of what our thinking presents to us. It is not that the explanation — the essence of the thing to be explained — is unknown to us; far from it — it is its emergence in our mind that requires the explanation. The thing that demands the explanation and our means to explain it are both available to us. We only need to establish the connection between the two. The explanation is not a quest for an unknown but a clarification of the interrelationship between two knowns. It should never occur to us to explain a given in terms of something that we do not already know. In principle, this means that there can be no limits to explanation.

Having said this, one thing does give a semblance of justification to the theory that there is a limit to knowledge. It may happen that we have an inkling that some external reality exists, but that it is removed from our field of perception. We perceive its traces, its effects, and we presume that it exists. In this sense, we can speak of a limit of knowledge. The unattainable in this case, however, is not of such a kind that it will provide principles of explanation; it is rather something perceptible, but not yet perceived. Such obstacles to my perception do not constitute a fundamental limit to knowledge, but are accidental and external and may be surmounted. Something I only suspect today may become a complete experience tomorrow. A principle, however, knows no external obstacles, which are usually spatial or temporal; it is given to me inwardly. Unless I observe it myself, I cannot assume its existence through my knowledge of other things.

This is where the theory of hypotheses comes in. A hypothesis is an assumption whose truth we do not know directly but only through its consequences. We see a series of manifestations that is explained only when we assume an underlying factor that cannot be experienced directly. Can such a hypothesis extend to the assumption of a principle? Obviously not, because it would be a contradiction to assume an inner principle without experiencing it. A hypothesis can assume only what I do not perceive yet, but would if I removed external obstacles. *A hypothesis can indeed assume something not perceived, but it must assume something that potentially can be perceived.* Thus, we must be able to verify every hypothesis through future experience. A hypothesis is justified only when it has the potential to go beyond being hypothetical. Hypotheses about *central scientific principles* have no value. When a thing cannot be explained through a known, concrete principle, it is not explicable, nor does it call for an explanation.

5. Ethical and Historical Sciences

We have gained some clarity about our relationship to the world by answering the question, What is knowing? The view we have developed in dealing with this question is certain to shed light on the value and significance of human actions as well. The way we conceive of our role as human beings will determine the significance we attach to our achievements in the world.

Our first task will be to investigate the nature of human activity. How do the effects of human actions compare with the effects of other events within the universal process? Let us consider two things: a product of nature and a human creation — for example, a crystal and a wagon wheel. Both objects appear to us as the results of laws that can be expressed as concepts. The only difference is that the crystal must be considered to be the *immediate* product of the natural laws that determine it, whereas in the case of the wagon wheel, the human being intervenes between the concept [laws] and the object. What we think of as underlying the reality of the natural object is introduced into reality through human activity.

Through the act of knowing, we experience the principles that determine sensory experience; our thoughts reveal the world of ideas that already lie within reality. We complete the world process by invoking the agent who continually generates products, yet would remain forever hidden within them if not for our thinking. Through our activities, however, we complement this process by introducing the unrealized world of ideas into reality. We have come to realize that ideas are the foundation of all existence, its determining condition and nature's intention. Our knowing leads us to the point where we can apprehend the tendency of the world process, the intention of creation, in the indications contained in our natural environment. Having done that, we are called upon in our actions to work as individuals toward the realization of that intention. Consequently, our actions appear as the direct culmination of the kind of productivity that fills all nature; they flow directly from the world's foundations.

And yet, how different our actions are from that other, natural activity! The products of nature do not by any means carry within themselves the ideal lawfulness that seems to govern them. They call for a meeting with something higher — human thinking. The governing principle then appears *to this thinking*. It is different for human activity, in which the idea dwells directly within the active object [that is, in the human being]. And if a higher being were to meet it, this being could find in our activity only what we ourselves have put there; a perfect human action is the result of our own intentions and nothing else.

When we see one natural product influencing another, we see an effect. That effect is determined by laws that can be expressed as concepts. But to understand the effect, it is not enough to connect it with one law or another; we must have a second perceptible thing — which we must also be able to resolve completely into concepts. If we observe a depression in the ground, we look for the object that made it. This leads us to the concept of an agent that is active when the cause of a phenomenon appears as another external perception — that is, to the concept of a *force*. We encounter force only when an idea first appears in an object of perception and, in that form, affects another object.

In contrast to this, there are instances when such mediation falls away, and the idea approaches the sensory world directly. In these situations, the idea itself appears as the causal agent. It is here that we speak of *will*. *Will is the idea itself, apprehended as force.* It is completely inadmissible to speak of will as an independent agency. When a human being performs an action, we cannot say that will is added to the idea. Whoever speaks in this way has not come to a clear understanding of the concepts involved. After all, what is the human personality if we disregard the world of ideas that fills it? It is active existence, of course. To conceive of it otherwise — as a dead, inert product of nature — would be to place it on the level of a lifeless stone. This active existence is an abstraction, however, not concrete reality. It cannot be grasped and is without substance.

If we try to grasp it and give it content, we are simply returned to the world of ideas engaged in activity. Eduard von Hartmann makes this abstraction into a second world-constituting principle, next to the idea. But it is nothing but the idea itself, in a form of manifestation. Will without idea would be *nothing*. This cannot be said of the idea, because activity is one of its elements, whereas the idea is its own self-sustaining being.

Now let us consider another characteristic of human activity that follows with necessity from what has been said. When we explain a natural event, we trace it back to its conditions; we try to discover the "producer" of the given product. When I observe an effect, it is not enough to look for its cause. These two perceptions alone do not satisfy my need for an explanation. Rather, I must return to the laws according to which *this* particular cause has *this* particular effect. With human actions this is different. Here the determining lawfulness itself takes action; the causal agent that forms the product appears on the scene. In the case of this manifesting entity, we do not need to look any further for underlying determining factors. When we know the idea that is embodied in a work of art, we understand the work; we do not need to look for any further lawful connections between the idea (cause) and work (effect). We understand the actions of a political leader if we know the intentions (ideas) behind them; we need not inquire any further. *We may therefore distinguish between natural processes and human actions; in natural processes, the law is the underlying determining factor behind what comes into manifest existence, whereas in human actions existence itself becomes the law, and is determined solely by itself.* Consequently, in every natural process we can distinguish between what determines and what is determined. What is determined follows with *necessity* from the determining factor. But human actions are determined only by themselves; this is *freedom* of action. When the intentions of nature (which exist behind appearances and determine them) enter the human being, they themselves manifest, but as appearances that are not determined by hidden causes. If all the processes of nature are manifestations of the idea, then human activity is the idea itself in action.

In our theory of knowledge, we concluded that our consciousness is not merely a means to form an image of the world foundation, but that this fundamental lawfulness itself manifests in its most primal form in our thinking. Consequently, we will see the unconditioned activity of this primal lawfulness in human actions as well. We do not need a world guide to give our actions purpose and direction. The world guide has renounced his power and handed everything over to human beings; he has relinquished separate existence and assigned us the task of continuing the work. We find ourselves in the world, we observe nature, and we recognize in it the indications of something deeper — of hidden laws and intentions. Our thinking allows us to recognize those intentions, which become our spiritual possessions. Having penetrated to the world's foundation, we now take action toward realizing its intentions.

Thus, the philosophy presented here is a true *philosophy of freedom*. In the realm of human activity, it acknowledges neither natural necessity nor the influence of an external creator or world guide, because in either case the human being would not be free. If natural necessity were functioning in ourselves as it does in other beings, we would act under compulsion. To understand such actions, we would have to look for external factors that determine them, and freedom would be out of the question. Of course, we are not excluding the fact that there are innumerable human activities that fall into this category, but here we are not considering those. Human beings, to the extent that they are beings of nature, may also be understood in terms of natural laws that govern natural processes. But considering human existence strictly from the perspective of natural laws does not account for our activity as knowing or truly ethical beings. That is the point where we actually step beyond the realm of natural events. What has been established here holds true for our highest potential, which is more an ideal than a reality. The course of human life involves our evolution from a being of nature to one such as we have described. It is our task to liberate ourselves from all natural laws and to give ourselves our own laws.

We must also reject the influence of an otherworldly guide of human destinies. Once we assume the existence of such a guide, we can no longer speak of true freedom. Such a power determines and directs the activities of human beings, who must then do as directed. Thus we no longer experience the motivation of our actions as the ideal we have set for ourselves, but as a *commandment* of that power. Again our actions are determined rather than free. We would not feel free of external compulsion, but dependent — mere intermediaries for the intent of a higher power.

Dogmatism, as we have seen, involves trying to discover why something is true by looking for an agent outside our subjective consciousness and inaccessible to it. Our view, on the other hand, confirms the truth of a judgment because its reasons lie in the concepts that are contained in our consciousness and that flow into the judgment. Those who conceive of a world foundation beyond the compass of our ideas must believe that the reason we recognize something as true is different from the objective reason for its truth. Truth is thus conceived as dogma. A *commandment* in the realm of ethics is the same as *dogma* in the realm of science. Those who base their actions on commandments act according to laws that they have not formulated; they look for externally prescribed norms for their actions and act out of *duty*. This is the only context in which it makes sense to speak of duty. When we experience the motive as external, we bow to *necessity* and follow it, acting out of duty.

Our theory of knowledge cannot accept the validity of this kind of action where human nature has reached moral maturity. We recognize the infinite perfection of the world of ideas; we know that the impulses for our actions emanate from this world within us, and that, consequently, the only ethical actions are those that emanate directly from their corresponding ideas within us. According to this viewpoint, we perform an action only because we feel an inner need for its realization. We act because our own volition motivates us, not an external power. Once we have formed a concept of it, the object of our action fills us inwardly so that we actively strive to carry it out. The only motive for our actions should be the urge to realize an idea, the drive to achieve a purpose. Whatever impels us to act should first unfold its life within us as idea. We then act not out of duty or blind instinct, but out of *love for the object* toward which our action is directed. The object, when we conceive of it, evokes within us the desire to act in accordance with its nature.

This, and only this, is a free deed. If there were another motive beyond interest in the object, we would not act only for the sake of the action, but to achieve *something else*. The action would be something that we really did not want; it would be an action *against our own will*. This is true when we act egoistically. Then we are uninterested in the action itself but feel the need for what it brings us. But we then feel a sense of compulsion, because to achieve the desired benefit we must perform the action. We feel no need for the action itself and would not do it if no benefit followed. However, an action not performed for its own sake is not a free deed. *Egoistic actions are not free.* We act unfreely when we act for any reason other than the objective content of the action itself. When we perform a deed *for its own sake,* we act out of *love. Only when guided by the love of our action, by devotion to the objective world, are we truly free.* If we are incapable of such selfless devotion, we will never experience freedom in our actions.

If human activity is to be nothing other than the realization of our own ideas, then those ideas must, of course, exist within us. We must be inwardly productive. After all, what else could fill us with motivation except an idea taking shape in our mind? The clearer, the more sharply delineated the idea appears to us, the more fruitful it will be. We are powerfully driven toward realizing those actions that are fully formed as an idea. Vaguely conceived, indefinite ideals are unsuitable motives for action. How can they fire our enthusiasm if they are not vivid and clear? The motives for our actions must therefore always arise as individual intentions. Everything fruitful that human beings do originates in individual impulses. Universal "moral laws" and ethical norms applied to all are completely worthless. If morality according to Kant consists only of what everyone can accept as the law, then our response must be that, if everyone were to do only what is suitable for all, positive action would have to cease and greatness disappear. No, action should not be guided by vague, general ethical norms but by the most individual ideals. There is nothing that everyone can aspire toward; aspirations vary from person to person, depending on the calling of each. In his essay "Ethical Freedom in Kant" (Berlin, 1882), J. Kreyenbühl has this to say:

> If in fact freedom is to be *my* freedom; if a moral action is to be *mine;* and if goodness and justice are to be realized through *me* — through the actions of *this* particular individual — then I cannot possibly be satisfied with a general law that disregards all individuality and specificity of the concurrent circumstances and demands that I test every action ahead of time as to whether its guiding motive conforms to an abstract norm of universal human nature, and whether, as it lives and works within me, it could become a general standard of behavior.... Adapting to what is commonly acceptable in this way would render impossible any individual freedom; any progress beyond the

ordinary and parochial; and any significant, outstanding, and groundbreaking, ethical achievement.

This illuminates the questions that any system of ethics must answer. They are usually addressed as though ethics were a collection of norms for the guidance of human actions. From this point of view, ethics is placed in opposition to the natural sciences — indeed, to all science that deals with reality. Whereas science endeavors to demonstrate the laws of existence, ethics is supposed to teach us the laws of what should be. Ethics is expected to be a code that encompasses all human ideals, a detailed answer to the question, *What is good?*

That kind of science is impossible. There can be no universal answer to this question. Ethical activity is a product of what arises in each individual. It always arises in a particular case, never in general. There are no universal laws about what one should or should not do. One should never view the laws of various nations in this way; they, too, are no more than the expression of individual intentions. What one person perceived as moral was transferred to a whole nation to became the "law of the land." A universal natural law intended to be valid for all people at all times is a monstrosity. Legal philosophies and concepts of morality come and go with nations, even with individuals. Eventually, it is always the individual that decides. Consequently, it is not feasible to speak of ethics in this way.

There are other questions, however, that a science of ethics can answer, ones that have been mentioned in passing, specifically those that concern the difference between human activity and natural events, the nature of will and freedom, and so on. All these questions can be summed up in one: To what extent are human beings intrinsically ethical? This is simply a question about insight into the moral nature of the human being. The question is not, What should a human being do? It is rather, What *is* it that human beings do when they follow their inner nature?

The wall is thus removed that separates all science into two separate spheres: a science of all that is and a science of what should be. *Like all sciences, ethics is a science of what is.* In this sense, there is something that is common to all the sciences: they proceed from a given and progress to the conditions that determine it. But there cannot be a science of human activity, because such activity is indeterminate, productive, and creative. Jurisprudence is not a science but a *collection of memoranda* about the legal habits proper to one nation's individuality.

As individuals, human beings belong not only to themselves but also to two greater wholes. First, as members of a nation, individuals are united by social mores and have in common a culture, a language, and shared views. But as individuals we are also citizens of history and participate in the great process of human evolution. This dual allegiance to greater wholes seems to restrict our free human activity. Our actions do not seem to be only the product of an individual but seem conditioned by what we have in common with our nation. Our individuality seems to be annihilated by the national character. Am I free, then, if it is possible to explain my actions not only as an expression of my individual nature but also largely as an expression of my nationality? Do I act a certain way because nature happened to make me a member of this particular national community? The same is true of my place in human history. As a child of my time, I am dependent on the cultural era into which I was born.

But if we view ourselves as beings of both knowledge and action, the contradiction resolves itself. The capacity for knowledge allows us to penetrate the character of our national identity and see where our fellow citizens are headed. The very factors that seem to determine us are those we must transcend and take into ourselves with full awareness; thus, they become individual in us and acquire the personal character of free actions. The same is true of the historical evolution within which I take my place. I gain insight into the governing ideas and moral forces of my time; and once I do so, they no longer determine me but become individual motives.

We need to actively penetrate our time and culture so that we will not be led but lead ourselves. We must not allow ourselves to be led blindly by our national character; we must instead come to understand it so that we can work *consciously* in the spirit of our nation. We cannot allow ourselves to be carried along by cultural progress; rather, we must appropriate the ideas of our time. This requires us, first of all, to understand the culture in which we live. Then, in freedom, we will assume the tasks of our time and apply our efforts in the appropriate context. This is where we need the humanities (history, cultural and literary history, and so on). In the humanities, we look at human achievements — the accomplishments of culture, literature, the arts, and so on. Here the spirit takes hold of spiritual matters. The purpose of the humanities must be to allow us to recognize where chance placed us as individuals; we must recognize what has been achieved and what we need to accomplish. The humanities help us to find the right place to participate in the world's work. We must know the cultural world and determine our contribution accordingly.

In the first volume of his *Images of the German Past* (Leipzig, 1859), Gustav Freytag says:

> All great creations of national powers — traditional religions, mores, laws, and government — can no longer be seen as the achievement of individual human beings. They are organic creations of a higher life, which at any given time can become visible only through individuals, and which at any given time unifies individual spirits into a powerful whole.... Thus, without being mystical about it, one can speak of a folk-soul.... Unlike the will of an individual, however, the life of a nation does not work consciously. What is free and rational in history is represented by individuals; the national force works untiringly with the dark compulsion of a primal force.

If Freytag had investigated the life of nations, he might have found that it resolves itself into the sum of the actions of its individuals. They overcome this dark compulsion by raising what is unconscious into their consciousness. He would have seen how the very thing he calls the folk-soul and describes as a dark compulsion proceeds from individual impulses of the will — from the free actions of human beings.

We must, however, consider yet another aspect of the work of individual human beings within a nation. Each person represents a spiritual potential, a sum of forces, looking for a possibility to unfold its activity. Consequently, as individuals we must each find the place where our work can be incorporated meaningfully into the national organism. Whether we find our place cannot be left to chance. The purpose of a state's constitution is to ensure that each person finds a suitable sphere of action. The state is the form in which the national organism lives.

The task of anthropology and political science is to discover how people can realize their potential as individuals within the state. The constitution must arise from the nations's innermost being. The best constitution will express the national character in specific formulations. Political leaders cannot force a constitution upon the people. They must investigate the deepest characteristics of their nation and channel latent tendencies through an appropriate constitution. It can happen that the majority of a nation is drawn in a direction that goes against its own nature. According to Goethe, national leaders are then obligated to let themselves be guided by that nature and not by the momentary demands of the majority. They then have to represent the deepest qualities of the nation against the nation (*Verses in Prose*).

We should add here a word about the method of historical research. History must always bear in mind that the causes of historical events may be found in the individual intentions, plans, and so on of individuals. It is always a mistake to interpret historical events according to underlying plans. One must always ask about the goals of certain individuals, what path they followed, and so on. History must always be based on human nature, human will, and human tendencies.

We can now substantiate what has been said about ethical science with Goethe's own words:

> The rational world must be considered a great, immortal individual, which unceasingly does what is needed and in this way gains mastery even over random occurrences. (*Verses in Prose*)

We can understand this only in terms of the relationship between individuals and historical evolution as we have described it. By implication, Goethe refers to the positive activity of individuals in history when he says:

> Absolute action of any kind leads to bankruptcy.... The least of us can be perfect if they act within the limits of their capacities and skills.... [Regarding the need to elevate oneself to the leading ideas of one's people and time:] Let each of us ask ourselves which organ we have available and will use to work upon our time.... We need to know where we ourselves stand and where the others want to go.... [Our view of duty is confirmed in:] *Duty:* when one loves what one has commanded oneself to do. (*Verses in Prose*)

We have consistently established the independence of the individual as a being of knowledge and action. We have shown how our ideas coincide with the foundations of the world and have recognized that everything we do can emanate only from our own individuality. We seek the core of existence within the individual human being. No one can reveal a dogmatic truth to another person and no one can force another to act. As individuals, we are rooted in ourselves. Whatever we are as individuals, we must become through our own powers, not through those of others. We must create everything out of ourselves, including the source of our own happiness. We have seen that there can be no question of a power guiding us, determining the direction and substance of our existence, and condemning us to dependency. If I am to find happiness, I am the only one who can bring it about. An external power cannot prescribe the norms of my actions; likewise, such a power cannot endow things with the capacity to awaken a feeling of contentment in me — I must do it myself. Pleasure and displeasure are present for me only when I have first attributed to objects the power to awaken those feelings in myself. A creator that would determine externally what gives us pleasure and what gives us none would be leading us about on a leash.

All optimism and pessimism are thus refuted. The optimist assumes that the world is perfect, that it must be the source of the greatest satisfaction for a person. If I assumed this were true, I would first have to develop *in myself* the needs to be fulfilled and thus satisfied. I would have to gain what I demand from objects of the world. The pessimist, on the other hand, believes that the world is such that it always leaves us dissatisfied, that happiness is impossible. What pitiable creatures human beings would be if nature were to grant us happiness from outside. All complaining about an existence that fails to satisfy us or a world that is hard must end when we consider the fact that no power on Earth can give us pleasure unless we first lend it the magic ability to lift us and make us happy. Happiness must arise for us from what we ourselves make of things, from our own creations. Only this is worthy of free beings.

Goethe's Way of Thinking Compared to Other Views

The theories of earlier thinkers or of those contemporaries who influenced Goethe's intellectual development did not serve as the basis for his views. Goethe's form and manner of thinking and, indeed, the very way he viewed the world were shaped by his inherent disposition. This was true from his earliest youth and remained so throughout his life.

Two of Goethe's main characteristics deserve notice here. One is his thirst for the wellspring and depths of all existence. In the final analysis it was his faith in the idea. Goethe was always filled with an inkling of something higher and better. One might call it a deeply religious side of his character. What so many find necessary was foreign to him: the urge to pull things down to their own level, to strip them of anything sacred. *He had another need: to sense something higher and to work his way up toward it.* In everything, he looked for some aspect he could revere. Karl Julius Schröer demonstrated this in a charming way in regard to Goethe's love life. Goethe cast out all that was frivolous or superficial, and for him love became a form of devotion. He expressed beautifully this fundamental quality of his being in his own words:

> In our bosom surges a pure longing
> To give ourselves freely, in gratitude,
> To something *Higher, Purer, Unknown* —
> We call it: *devotion!*
>
> (*Trilogy of Passion,* "Elegy")[1]

---

1. In unsers Busens Reine wogt ein Streben / Sich einem *Höhern, Reinern, Unbekannten* / Aus Dankbarkeit freiwillig hinzugeben — Wir heißen's: *fromm sein!* (*Trilogie der Leidenschaft / Elegie*). — Ed.

This side of Goethe's being is inseparably connected with another; he never attempts to approach that higher presence directly, but instead through nature. "The True is like the divine; it never appears directly, we must intuit it through its manifestations" (*Verses in Prose*). In addition to his faith in the idea, Goethe believed that we attain the idea by observing outer reality. It never occurred to him to look for the divine anywhere but in the works of nature, where he always attempted to find the divine element. Even as a young boy, Goethe erected an altar to the great god *"directly connected with nature"* (*Poetry and Truth,* part 1, book 1). That ritual arose from the belief that the highest we can reach may be attained by faithfully cultivating our relationship with nature. Thus, what we have elaborated as a theory of knowledge was Goethe's inherent mode of observation. He approached reality with the conviction that all things are manifestations of the idea, which we attain only by raising our sensory experience to spiritual contemplation. This conviction began in childhood and remained a part of him; it became his fundamental assumption in his view of the world.

No philosopher could have given Goethe such a conviction; he was not looking to them for that, but for something else. His way of observing was anchored in the depths of his being, but he needed a language with which to formulate it. His nature worked in a philosophical way and expressed itself in philosophical formulae, which could be explained only on philosophical premises. And he looked to the philosophers to become fully aware of what he *was* — to *realize* the *activity* living in him. He looked to them to explain and justify his own being. To that end, he studied Spinoza and discussed science with the philosophers of his time.

In Goethe's youth, Spinoza (1632–1677) and Giordano Bruno (1548–1600) seemed to express his inner being most strongly. It is remarkable that in both cases he first encountered their works through attacks against them, yet nevertheless recognized that their teachings related to his own nature. This is especially true of Giordano Bruno's teachings. He encountered Bruno in Bayle's *Dictionary of History and Criticism,* in which Bruno is violently attacked.[2] This affected Goethe

---

2. *Dictionnaire historique et critique* (1697) by Pierre Bayle (1647–1706), French philosopher and critic. — ED.

to the degree that, in the parts of *Faust* conceived around 1770 when he was reading Bayle, we find verbal echoes of Bruno's sentences.

In his diaries and notebooks (*Tag-und Jahresheften*), the poet tells us that in 1812 he returned to Bruno. This time, the impression was even more profound, and many of the poems he wrote that year echo the philosopher from Nola. This is not to say that Goethe borrowed or learned anything specific from Bruno. Rather he found in his writings a way to formulate what had always lived within his own nature. He found that he could express himself most clearly when he used Bruno's words. Bruno considered universal reason to be "the creator and guide of the universe." He called reason the *inner artist* that forms matter (*materia*) *from the inside outward*. Reason gives rise to all that exists, and there is no being in which reason will not lovingly participate. Bruno said that "no matter how small and fragile a thing may be, it contains a part of the spiritual substance."[3]

This coincided with Goethe's view that we cannot judge a thing properly unless we can see the way universal reason has placed it just where it is and how it has become what we encounter. Sensory perception is not enough, because our senses fail to explain how the thing relates to the universal idea in terms of its meaning for the larger whole. We must therefore observe in such a way that our reason builds an ideal foundation upon which to see what the senses communicate. As Goethe put it, we must *"look with the eyes of the spirit."* Here, too, he borrowed a formula from Bruno:

> We use different sensory organs to recognize colors and sounds; similarly, we do not use the same eyes to see the substrate of the arts and that of nature [because] we see one with our sensory eyes and the other with our eyes of reason. (Ibid.)

This is also true of *Spinoza*. His teaching is based on the idea that the divine has fully entered the world. Human beings can hope to know God only by plunging into the world. From a Spinozistic viewpoint, any other way seems impossible, because God has renounced his own existence and cannot be found outside of the world. Rather, we must look for him where he is. Any real knowledge of the world must be such that it delivers us some knowledge of God. All higher

---

3. See *Cause, Principle, and Unity: Essays on Magic*, New York: Cambridge University Press, 1999. — ED.

insight is therefore a meeting with God. We call it *knowledge in beholding.* We know things *sub specie aeternitatis* (as emanations of God). The laws in nature that our mind recognizes are God's being, not just made by God. All that we see as logical necessity is thus because God's being, or eternal lawfulness, is inherent in it.

This view struck a chord in Goethe. He firmly believed that nature in all its activity reveals the divine, and here this belief was expressed in the clearest way. "I am holding fast, and increasingly so, to the atheist's [Spinoza's] veneration of God," Goethe wrote to Friedrich Jacobi, who at that point was trying to show Spinoza in a different light. Herein lies the kinship between Spinoza and Goethe. This deep, inner harmony between Goethe's being and Spinoza's teaching is often overlooked by those who emphasize a superficial reason for Goethe's attraction to Spinoza — that is, that neither could tolerate an explanation of the world through ultimate causes. In fact, this rejection by both Goethe and Spinoza was a result of even more fundamental views.

Let us consider the theory of final causes [teleology]. The way it explains the existence and characteristics of something is to establish its usefulness to another thing. One shows that a thing is constituted in a certain way because of the particular characteristics of something else. This assumes that a world creator exists above the two things and makes them so that each meets the needs of the other. If the creator lives within all things, however, this explanation makes no sense, because then the properties of a thing must follow from the active principle *within* it. We look into the nature of a thing for the reason it is one way and not another. If we believe that the divine lives within each thing, it will never occur to us to look for an external principle to explain its lawfulness. Goethe's relationship with Spinoza needs no explanation other than the fact that he found in his work the formulas and scientific language to express his own inner world.

If we now consider Goethe's relationship with his contemporaries, we must speak primarily of Immanuel Kant (1724–1804), who is generally considered the founder of modern philosophy. In his own time, he created such a stir that every well-educated person was required to come to terms with him. This intellectual encounter became necessary for Goethe as well. But, for him, it proved unfruitful, because there is a deep contradiction between Kant's theories and what we may speak of as Goethe's way of thinking. Indeed, we can say without hesitation that all of German thinking runs along two parallel lines, one permeated by Kant's way of thinking and the other closer to Goethe's thinking. But as contemporary philosophy continues to approach that of Kant, it moves further from Goethe. Thus it is becoming less and less possible to understand and appreciate Goethe's worldview.

We shall describe here the main points of Kant's philosophy to the extent that they are relevant to Goethe's views. According to Kant, the point of departure for human thinking is experience — the world as revealed to the senses, including what our inner sense conveys in the way of psychological and historical facts and so on. The world consists of a multiplicity of things in space and processes in time. It is a matter of indifference that a particular object faces me, or that I experience this particular process; it could have been something else completely. In fact, I can even eliminate in thought the whole multitude of things and processes. I cannot, however, imagine the world without *space* and *time*. For me, there can be nothing that is neither spatial nor temporal. Even if such things exist, I cannot know it, because I cannot picture anything without space and time. I cannot know whether things themselves exist in space and time. I know only that, for me, this is the form in which I must encounter things. *Space and time,* therefore, are the conditions of *my* sensory perceptions. I know nothing of things *as such*. I know only how they must *appear* to me if they are to exist for me at all.

With this, Kant introduces a new problem; he introduces a new kind of question into science. Earlier philosophers had wanted to know the properties of things, but he wants to know how a thing must appear to become the object of our knowledge. Philosophy for Kant is the science of the conditions under which human experience of the world becomes possible. We know nothing about "the thing in itself." But our task is not fulfilled when we merely perceive a multitude of objects in time and space. We try to create unity in that multiplicity, and that is the task of the intellect, which is the sum of those activities whose purpose is to organize the sensory world that confronts us into prearranged forms. The intellect connects two sensory perceptions by establishing one, for example, as a cause, the other as an effect, or one as the substance and the other as a property. Again, the task of philosophical science is to show under which conditions the intellect succeeds in creating a system of the world.

So the world is, in the Kantian sense, a subjective manifestation that arises in the forms of the sensory world and the intellect. All I can know for sure is that there is a thing in itself; its appearance depends on our organization. Obviously, it makes no sense to assume that this sensory world formed by the intellect has any significance other than for our own cognitive capacity. This becomes clearest when Kant speaks of the meaning of the world of ideas. According to him, ideas are simply higher vantage points of reason under which the lower entities created by our intellect can be subsumed. Our intellect, for example, establishes connections among psychological manifestations. Reason — our capacity for ideas — then grasps these connections *as though* they all emanated from a soul. But this has no significance for the actual reality itself; it is merely a means of orientation for our cognitive capacity.

This is Kant's theoretical philosophy inasmuch as we are interested in it here. The polarity between it and Goethe's philosophy is obvious. According to Kant, we determine given reality; it is the way it is because we conceive it that way. Kant actually skips over the real epistemological question. At the beginning of his *Critique of Pure Reason,* he takes two steps that he doesn't justify, and his whole philosophical edifice suffers as a result. He simply distinguishes between subject and object without investigating the significance of the fact that our intellect makes such a distinction between two realms of reality — in this case, the knowing subject and the object to be known. He then attempts to formulate *conceptually* the mutual relationship between these two domains, again without inquiring into the meaning of such a formulation.

If Kant hadn't viewed this central epistemological question from a skewed perspective, he would have noticed that the distinction between subject and object is only an intermediate step in the process of cognition, that underlying them both is a unity perceptible by reason, and that the qualities we ascribe to a thing are not merely subjective. A thing is a unity constituted by reason, and it is the intellect that distinguishes between the "thing in itself" and the "thing according to us." It is simply inadmissible to say that what we attribute to the thing in one case can be denied it in another. Whether I see the same thing from one point of view or from another, it nevertheless remains a unified whole.

An error that permeates Kant's philosophical edifice is his belief that the multiplicity of the sense-perceptible world is something fixed, and that science constitutes the systematization of that multiplicity. He never realized that this multiplicity is not something ultimate that we must overcome if we are to understand it. Consequently, according to Kant all theory is merely added onto experience by our reason and intellect. The idea for him is not what reason recognizes as the deeper ground of the given world after penetrating the multiplicity on the surface. Rather, to him the idea is a methodological principle that makes it easier to organize phenomena. According to Kant, we would go astray if we were to believe it possible to conceptually derive things from the idea; we can organize our experiences only *as though* they all arose from a unity.[4] According to Kant we have no concept of the foundation of things as they exist in themselves. Our knowledge of things is present only for our sake, is valid only for our individuality.

Goethe was unable to gain much from this worldview. In his view, our observation of things in terms of ourselves always plays a subordinate role that involves responses of pleasure and displeasure. He expected science to do more than tell us how things are in relation to ourselves. In his essay "The Experiment As Mediator between Subject and Object" he describes the task of researchers. They are not to impose their own standards and criteria, but to take them from within the sphere of the things observed. This one sentence is enough to show how very different the Kantian way of thinking is from that of Goethe. Kant considered all judgments about things to be merely the product of subject and object, telling us only how the subject sees the object. According to Goethe, on the other hand, the subject selflessly enters into the object, taking the criteria for judgment from the context of the things themselves. Goethe himself said of Kant's students that "they could indeed hear [me] but could not respond nor could they be of any help." The poet felt he had gained much more from Kant's *Critique of Judgment* [see p. 88].

Goethe had a more philosophically rewarding relationship to Schiller. Through Schiller, Goethe's insight into his own way of seeing progressed a step further. Until his well-known conversation with Schiller, Goethe had practiced a certain way of looking at the world. He observed plants and established an archetypal plant from which individual forms could be derived. The archetypal plant (and likewise

---

4. The distinction between the Goethean and Kantian concepts of unity is well articulated by Henri Bortoft in *The Wholeness of Nature*. — ED.

a corresponding archetypal animal) took form in his mind and served to explain related phenomena. But he had never thought about what the essential nature of the archetypal plant might be. Schiller opened his eyes by calling it an *idea*. After that, Goethe was aware of his idealism. Until then he had called the archetypal plant an experience, because he believed that he saw it with his eyes. In the introduction written later for his essay "The Metamorphosis of Plants," Goethe says, "Thus I endeavored to find the archetypal animal, which means, ultimately, the *idea* of the animal." Nevertheless, we must bear in mind that Schiller did not convey to Goethe something foreign to him; rather, it was only by observing Goethe's way of knowing that Schiller found his way to an *objective idealism*. Schiller contributed only the terminology to describe the way of knowing that he recognized and admired in Goethe.

Goethe received little from Fichte, whose realm was too far removed from Goethe's to have any real effect. Fichte had established a science of consciousness in the most brilliant way, whereby he traced the activity through which the human I transforms the given world into a thought world. He could have stopped with his description of the human I as giving a satisfying form to the given and creating relevant connections between disconnected givens. But he made the mistake of believing that this activity is the creation of everything that takes place in the I. Therefore, his views come through as a one-sided idealism that takes its entire content from consciousness. Goethe, who always looked for the objective, was unable to find much that attracted him in Fichte's philosophy. Goethe had no understanding for what was valid in it, and the poet certainly found fault with the way Fichte expanded it into a universal science.

With the young Schelling, who was Fichte's student, there were many more points of contact. He not only proceeded to analyze the activity of the I, but also studied the activity within consciousness through which consciousness comprehends nature. Schelling saw the objective reality of nature — its actual principle — as playing itself out in our I through our cognition of nature. To him, external nature was merely the solidified form of our concepts of nature. What lives in us as an ideal view of nature appears again outside us, only separated out in space and time. What we encounter outside of us as nature is a finished product, the determined, hardened form of a living principle. This principle cannot be attained through external experience but must be created first in our soul. Schelling says in his *Ideas for a Philosophy of Nature:*

> To philosophize about nature means to create nature.... Nature as mere product (*natura naturata*) is what we call nature as object (the concern of all empiricism). Nature as productivity (*natura naturans*) is what we call nature as subject (the concern of all theory).... The contrast between empiricism and science lies in the fact that empiricism views its object as existing, as finished and accomplished, whereas science sees it in a state of becoming and still being brought about.

Through these views of Schelling, with which Goethe became acquainted partly as a result of personally meeting the philosopher, the poet was brought another step forward. Now he came to see that his tendency was to progress from the finished product to what is in a state of becoming, or being produced. We hear this resonance with Schelling in his essay "Judgment Through Intuitive Perception," where he writes that "by observing an ever-creating nature" he endeavored to make himself "worthy of spiritual participation in her productions."

Finally, Hegel helped Goethe to become clear about the place of the archetypal phenomenon from a philosophical point of view. Hegel deeply understood the meaning of the archetypal phenomenon and characterized it in his letter of February 20, 1821:

> You place the simple and abstract at the top, and you aptly call it the archetypal phenomenon. You then show how concrete phenomena result from the effects of further influences and conditions. And finally you organize the whole process so that the series proceeds from the simple conditions to the more complex, and as a result of this ranking and gradual elaboration the complex appears in full clarity. To track down the archetypal phenomenon, to free it from other, accidental surrounding conditions, and to apprehend it in the "abstract," as we say, to me this is the accomplishment of a great and spiritual understanding of nature, and I am convinced that it represents the truly scientific aspect of knowledge in this field.... May I also mention to you the special interest we philosophers take in this archetypal phenomenon that is raised for our view; we can certainly

make use of such a distillate! We have our Absolute — initially so oysterlike, grey, or quite black — which we have struggled to bring into the light and air, for which it is now beginning to long, and we need to cut windows to bring it completely into the light of day. Our schemes would vanish into thin air if we introduced them too quickly into the colorful, chaotic company of the world's unpleasantness. It is here that Your Honor's archetypal phenomena come in handy; in this double light — spiritual and conceptual in its simplicity, visible and palpable in its sensuality — the two worlds meet, our abstruse one and that of manifest existence.[5]

Hegel thus clarified for Goethe the thought that the empirical scientist must go all the way to the archetypal phenomena, and that from there the paths of philosophy lead onward. This makes it clear, however, that the fundamental thought of Hegelian philosophy is a consequence of the Goethean form of thinking. Both Goethe and Hegel consider it fundamental to transcend external reality by penetrating deeply into it, thus rising from the created to the creative, from the determined to what determines. In his philosophy, of course, Hegel only wishes to uncover the eternal process from which all things proceed. He wants to see the given as resulting from what he recognizes as the absolute.

Consequently, Goethe's acquaintance with philosophers and philosophical tendencies helped him to understand what was already present in him. He gained nothing new as far as his own views were concerned. But he gained the means to speak of them and say what he was doing and what was taking place within his soul.

As a result, Goethe's worldview offers numerous points for further philosophical elaboration. Initially, they were seized only by Hegel's students. The rest of philosophy remained at a polite distance. Only Schopenhauer, who held the poet in high esteem, based some aspects of his own philosophy on Goethe's work. In a later chapter, we will speak of Schopenhauer's praise for the color theory. Here we will confine ourselves to the more general relationship between Schopenhauer's ideas and Goethe's. He comes close to Goethe in one point: he rejects any attempt to derive the given phenomena from exter-

---

5. Steiner may have had this letter in mind when he formulated the "house analogy" described on p. x of the editor's introduction to this book. — ED.

nal causes and recognizes only the activity of an inner lawfulness, only a step-by-step process from one appearance to the next. This is reminiscent of Goethe's principle of finding the elements of an explanation within the things themselves; but this resemblance is deceptive. Schopenhauer wants us to remain in the phenomenal realm, because we are unable to attain the "thing in itself," which is external to it and beyond our reach, since all phenomena, as given to us, are really mental representations, and those representations can never take us beyond our own consciousness. Goethe, on the other hand, wants to remain with the phenomena because he actually expects to find the elements that explain them in the phenomena themselves.

Finally we will compare Goethe's worldview with that of Eduard von Hartmann (1842–1906), whose scientific views are the most important of our time. This writer's *Philosophy of the Unconscious* has great historical significance. Later writings elaborated what was only outlined in that first book and added new material on a number of points. This work, taken in its entirety, reflects the whole spiritual nature of our time. Hartmann distinguishes himself through his admirable depth of mind and his remarkable mastery of the various sciences. He is on the cutting edge of contemporary intellectual achievement. One need not agree with him to fully appreciate his stature. The reader who knows only the *Philosophy of the Unconscious* may be unable to see how close the views of Hartmann and Goethe are to each other. The point where they meet is visible only in Hartmann's *conclusions* drawn from his principles, which he developed later.

Hartmann's philosophy is idealism. He wants to be *more* than an idealist, but whenever his explanation of the world calls for something absolute, he resorts to ideas. Most important, he thinks of the idea as the fundamental reality underlying all things. His assumption of an unconscious is based on the fact that not every idea in our consciousness is necessarily tied to its conscious form. Ideas are not present (active) only where they are conscious but in other forms as well. Ideas are more than subjective phenomena; they are significant in and of themselves. Far from being present only in the subject, ideas are objective, world principles. When Hartmann includes the will along with ideas as a world-forming principle, it is nevertheless difficult to understand those who view him as just another follower of Schopenhauer, who carried to the extreme the belief that all concepts are merely subjective manifestations of consciousness. With him it is out of the question that the idea might have participated as a real principle in the constitution of the world. In Schopenhauer's view, the will is *exclusively* the ground of the world.

This is why Schopenhauer never managed to develop the various specialized sciences in relation to his philosophy, whereas Hartmann followed his principle into every scientific domain. Schopenhauer said nothing about history's richness, except that it is a manifestation of the will. Hartmann, on the other hand, finds ideas at the core of every historical phenomenon, which he incorporates into the larger process of human evolution. Schopenhauer is uninterested in individual beings, or phenomena, because the only important thing he has to say about them is that they are expressions of the will. Hartmann takes hold of each particular and shows how the idea can be found everywhere. The essential characteristic of Schopenhauer's worldview is uniformity and that of Hartmann's is unity. Schopenhauer views the world as driven by an empty, uniform impulse. Hartmann sees the world driven by the rich content of the idea. Schopenhauer posits an abstract unity; Hartmann posits the concrete idea as a principle, of which unity, or rather self-consistency, is only one characteristic.

Schopenhauer could never have created a philosophy of history, a science of religion, as Hartmann did. Hartmann says, "Reason is the formal, logical principle of the idea, inseparably united with the will and, as such, controls and determines the world process without exception." This allows him to look for the logical core that can be grasped by our thinking (if not by our senses) in every manifestation of nature and history. Only those who accept this premise will be able to justify their desire to understand the world through thinking in terms of ideas.

Hartmann's objective idealism stands entirely on the foundation of Goethe's worldview. Goethe says, "Everything we become conscious of and everything we can speak of is simply a manifestation of the idea" (*Verses in Prose*). And he demands that people develop their capacity for knowledge to the degree that ideas become visible to them — as visible as the external world is to the senses. Thus, he stands on the ground where ideas are not merely manifestations of consciousness, but objective, world principles. The world is formed objectively by what lights up in our thinking like flashes of lightning. The important thing about an idea is not what it means for us consciously, but what it is in itself; it is an underlying principle of the world through its own being. Consequently, thinking is becoming aware of what exists in and of itself. Although the idea could not appear without consciousness, it must nevertheless be understood in such a way that its primary characteristic is not its appearance in consciousness, but what it is in itself in terms of its intrinsic nature, to which our awareness of it contributes nothing. Following Hartmann, therefore, we must see the idea — aside from its manifestation in consciousness — as the active unconscious underlying the world. It is Hartmann's essential contribution that we must look for the idea in all that is unconscious.

But to distinguish what is conscious from what is unconscious is not enough. This distinction is significant only for *my consciousness*. But we must pursue the idea in its objectivity and fullness, and we must recognize not only *that* the idea is effective, but also *what* the nature of that effective agent is. If Hartmann had been content to assert that the idea is unconscious, and if he had then explained the world in terms of this unconscious — which is only one attribute of the idea — then he would have merely added another unified theory to the many that explain the world on the basis of an abstract formula. In fact, his first main work was not entirely free of this. But Hartmann's thinking is too concentrated, far-reaching, and deep not to have seen that a definition of the idea as unconscious is inadequate. We must instead penetrate more deeply into what we recognize as unconscious; we must go beyond this characteristic and determine its concrete content and, from it, derive its particular manifestations. In this way, Hartmann evolved from an abstract monist (which he still was in his *Philosophy of the Unconscious*) into a concrete monist. It is the *concrete* idea that Goethe addresses in its three forms: archetypal phenomenon, the type, and the "idea in the stricter sense."

The aspect of Goethe's worldview that we find in Hartmann's philosophy is our becoming aware of the objective nature of the world of ideas and our devotion to it in response to that awareness. It was Hartmann's philosophy of the unconscious that motivated him to pursue the objective idea. Once he recognized that the essence of the idea is not based on its consciousness, he should also have acknowledged the idea as something that exists for itself as an objective reality. He differs from Goethe in that, next to the idea, he also sees the will as a formative principle in the world. But this motif of the will has no bearing on the truly fruitful aspect of Hartmann's philosophy. His assumption concerning the will arises from his notion that the idea rests in itself and must be prompted by the will to become active. According to Hartmann, the will alone can never be creative, because it is an empty, blind drive toward existence. Before the will can bring *something* into existence, the idea must come into play, because only it can provide its *content*.

But what should we do with this will? It escapes us the moment we try to grasp it, because it is impossible to get hold of an empty, meaningless impulse. Consequently, the idea is the only thing we can grasp as world principle. *Only what is filled with content and meaning can be grasped*, not something void of meaning. To get hold of the concept of *will*, it must appear as ideal meaning; only with and through the idea can it appear, never alone. Whatever exists must have *content;* all existence must be filled — it cannot be empty. This is why Goethe conceived of idea as *active,* effective, and not requiring further impetus. Something that is full of meaning cannot receive the impetus to manifest from something that contains no meaning. Consequently, the idea, in Goethe's sense, should be understood as *entelechy* — that is, as active being. And we must first abstract it from its active form to reintroduce it as will. The idea of pure will is meaningless for empirical science as well. Hartmann does not use it when he deals with concrete phenomena.

Hartmann's closeness to Goethe is even more noticeable in his ethics. Eduard Hartmann finds that all striving for happiness — all the pursuits of egoism — are ethically worthless, since they cannot lead to satisfaction. To act out of egoism, according to Hartmann, is to act out of an illusion. We should take hold of the task assigned to us by the world and work selflessly for its sake alone. Our goal should be to devote ourselves to the object, without attempting to gain anything for ourselves. This is also the fundamental characteristic of Goethe's ethics. Hartmann should not have suppressed the word that expresses the character of his moral theory: *Love.*[6]

---

6. We do not claim that Hartmann does not consider the concept of love in his ethics. He has dealt with it from the phenomenal and metaphysical point of view. But he does not consider love to be the ultimate goal in ethics. Self-sacrificing, loving devotion to the world process does not appear to Hartmann to be an end in itself but only a means of deliverance from the troubles of existence and of regaining our lost state of blissful peace. — R. STEINER.

When we make no personal claims, when our actions are motivated only by the objective task, when we find the motive of our doing in the act itself, our actions are moral. Then, however, *we are acting out of love*. All selfishness, everything that is merely personal, disappears. It is characteristic of Hartmann's sound, powerful mind that, though he grasped the idea in a one-sided way in its unconscious form, he nevertheless found his way to concrete idealism, and that, though he began with an ethics of pessimism, this distorted point of view led him to the morality of love.

Hartmann's pessimism, however, is different from that promulgated by those who like to complain about the uselessness of our actions only to excuse their own passivity. Hartmann does not indulge in complaint but rises above any such affectation to pure morality. He shows that the pursuit of happiness is worthless by revealing its fruitlessness. In this way he points to the importance of our activity itself. That he is a pessimist at all is his own error, which may also be a remnant of earlier stages in his thinking. But from where he stands now, he should see that one cannot base pessimism on an empirical proof that dissatisfaction predominates in the real world. What is highest in us cannot want anything other than to create its own happiness. It does not want to receive it as a gift from outside. What is highest in us seeks happiness in its own activity. Hartmann's pessimism dissolves in the light of (his own) higher thinking. *Because the world leaves us dissatisfied, we create the most beautiful happiness for ourselves through our own activity.*

Hartmann's philosophy provides one more proof that it is possible to reach the same place from different points of departure. His premises were different from those of Goethe, but in their elaboration we encounter Goethe's train of thought at every turn. We have depicted this here to show the deep inner integrity of the Goethean worldview. It is so deeply rooted in the being of the world that we are certain to encounter its main features wherever energetic thinking penetrates through to the sources of knowledge. In Goethe everything was so original and not at all merely the fashionable view of his time that even his opponents were bound to think like him. The eternal mystery of the world reveals itself through individuals, and in the modern age it spoke most meaningfully through Goethe. One can indeed say that *the significance of a person's views today can be measured by their relationship to Goethe's worldview.*

Chapter 12

Goethe and Mathematics

One of the great obstacles to a fair assessment of Goethe's significance for science is the bias regarding his relationship to mathematics. This is a double bias: first, it is believed that Goethe was an enemy of mathematical science and had greatly underestimated its significance for human knowledge; second, it is asserted that the poet, lacking a background in mathematics, had avoided any sort of mathematical approach to the physical aspects of natural science because of his incompetence.

In response to the first point, we must emphasize that Goethe repeatedly expressed such unambiguous admiration for mathematical science that it makes little sense to say that he held it in low esteem. In fact, he would have preferred that all natural sciences be conducted with the rigor characteristic of mathematics.

> We must learn from mathematics the conscientious placement of matters in their proper sequence, always grasping how one thing follows from what came before, so that even when we are not using calculations we go about our work as though we had to account for it to the strictest of geometers.[1] ... I have been called an opponent and enemy of mathematics, whereas no one could hold it in higher esteem than I do.[2]

The second accusation can hardly be taken seriously by anyone who has any insight into Goethe's nature. Goethe repeatedly voiced his concerns about the work of problematic people who assume tasks and never consider whether such tasks are within the scope of their

---

1. "On Mathematics and Its Misuse." — ED.
2. "The Experiment as Mediator between Object and Subject." — ED.

abilities! Are we to believe that Goethe himself would have violated this precept, that he should have developed his scientific views without considering his own limitations as a mathematician? Goethe knew that there are an infinity of paths to the truth, and that each of us can travel the one best suited to his or her individual capacities.

> We must each think in our own way; for along the way we will always find something true or a kind of truth that will help us in life. The main thing is not to get carried away, to maintain self-control. . . . The least of us can be complete by operating within the limits of our individual capacities and skills; but the finest qualities are darkened, invalidated, and destroyed when we deviate from this indispensable moderation. (*Verses in Prose*)

It would be ridiculous to claim that, in order to achieve anything at all, Goethe should have engaged in a field beyond his ken. The main point is to determine the task of mathematics and where its contribution to natural science begins. Goethe gave the most scrupulous attention to that. When it came to defining the boundaries of his creative power, his precision was surpassed only by the depth of his genius. We would like to point this out in particular to those whose only comment on Goethe's scientific thinking is that he lacked a logical turn of mind. The way Goethe made the distinction between his own method of natural science and that of mathematicians reveals a deep understanding of the *nature* of mathematics as a science. He knew precisely the source of mathematical certainty; he had formed a clear concept of the relationship between the laws of mathematics and other laws of nature.

Before a science can have any value for knowledge, it must provide insight into a particular realm of reality. It must develop a particular aspect of the world. *How* that is done depends on the spirit of each particular science. Goethe would have had to know the spirit of mathematics to determine what could and could not be accomplished by natural science without the use of calculation. This is really the point, and Goethe stressed it most forcefully. The way he did this reveals his understanding of the nature of mathematics.

Let us consider the nature of mathematics more closely. Mathematics deals with magnitude; it determines quantities. But magnitude does not exist in and of itself. Nowhere in the whole realm of human experience is there anything that is *only* magnitude. Among all the characteristics of a thing, there are some that may be described in numbers. Because mathematics is concerned with the quantitative element, its objects are never the complete phenomena but only those aspects that can be measured or counted. It isolates everything that can be submitted to these operations from the phenomena. In this way it obtains a whole world of abstractions with which it then goes to work.

Thus, mathematics deals not with things, but with those aspects of things that lend themselves to measurement. And it must acknowledge that this is only *one side* of reality and that there are many others over which it has no control. Mathematical judgments do not fully encompass real objects; they are valid only within the intellectual realm of abstractions that we ourselves have conceptually isolated from the full reality as *one* of its aspects. Mathematics abstracts the magnitude and quantity of things; it establishes ideal relationships between magnitude and number, and in so doing rises to a realm of pure thought. Real objects allow for the application of mathematical truths to the extent that they can be quantified.

It would be a great error, however, to believe that mathematical judgments can encompass nature in its wholeness. Nature is not merely quantity but also quality, and mathematics limits itself to the quantities. The treatment of mathematics and the treatment of qualities must work together; they meet in the phenomenon, each approaching it from one side. Goethe expressed this relationship by saying:

> Mathematics, like dialectics, is an organ of our higher capacities; its practice is an art, like rhetoric. In both cases, form is the only criteria; the content is indifferent.... Whether mathematics adds pounds or guineas, [whether] rhetoric defends truth or falsehood is of no consequence to them whatsoever. (*Verses in Prose*)

And in his *Outline of a Theory of Color,* Goethe says, "Who would deny that mathematics — one of the most wonderful of human capacities — has served physics very well from *one particular side?*" Recognizing this, Goethe saw that it is possible for a mind that is uncultured mathematically to nevertheless deal with problems in physics — if that mind restricts itself to its qualitative aspects.

Chapter 13

Goethe's Fundamental Geological Principle

People often look for Goethe where he cannot be found at all. This has been especially true in evaluations of Goethe's geological research. Here even more than anywhere else, it would be necessary to allow everything he wrote in particular to recede and let his intentions come to the fore. He must be assessed according to his own dictum: "When looking at human works, as well as those of nature, it is the intentions that deserve our special attention" (*Verses in Prose*); and "The spirit out of which we work is the highest" (*Wilhelm Meister's Apprenticeship*). What is worthy of emulation is not what he achieved so much as how he worked to accomplish it — that is, his method and not his specific theories. Goethe's specific achievements depended on the scientific instruments of his time and are now outdated. Goethe's method arose from his greatness of spirit and remains valid, even though scientific instruments have been perfected in the meantime and experience has been broadened.

Goethe was led to geology through his involvement with the Ilmenau mines, which had become an aspect of his official duties. When Duke Karl August came to power, he earnestly devoted himself to the long-neglected mine. First, experts were to establish the reasons for its decline, after which everything was to be done to get it running again. Goethe, as assistant to Karl August, energetically began the work, which often took him into the Ilmenau mine to gather information himself. After May 1776 he could often be found there.

Amid these *practical* concerns he also felt a *scientific* need to better understand the natural laws pertaining to what he was able to observe there. The comprehensive view of nature that was shaping itself with increasing clarity in his mind forced him to find his own explanations for what he saw spread out before him (see his essay "Nature").

From the very beginning, we notice a peculiarity of Goethe's nature. His concern is different from that of many researchers. Others are most interested in knowing the particulars and are interested in an edifice of ideas, a system, only to the extent that it helps them observe the particular; to Goethe, however, the particular is merely a point through which he moved toward an all-embracing concept of existence. In his essay "Nature," we read, "She [nature] lives in many children; and the mother, where is she?" And we find in his *Faust* this same striving to understand not only the directly existent but its deeper foundations — for example, when Faust speaks of his longing to "behold all seeds, all active power." What he observes on the Earth's surface and underground is thus one more means to penetrate the mystery of the world's formation. All his research is animated by what he describes to Duchess Louise in a letter of December 28, 1789: "Nature's works are always like words freshly spoken by God." Sensory experience becomes for him the script in which he can read the word of creation. Goethe writes in this vein to Frau von Stein on August 22, 1784: "*The great and beautiful script* is always legible and becomes undecipherable only when people try to transfer their petty notions and limitations to infinite beings." We find the same tendency expressed in *Wilhelm Meister:* "Would you mind if I were to treat these cracks and crevices as letters that I must decipher — if I were to make them into words and learn to read them?"

Thus, beginning in the late 1770s, we see the poet ceaselessly working to decipher this script. He strove to develop a view that enabled him to see the necessary inner connections between the separate things he observed. His method was "to develop and unfold, not to assemble and order." To him, it was not enough to see granite, porphyry, and so on, and to arrange them according to outer characteristics; he was looking for the law underlying all rock formation, which he would only need to call before his mind to understand how granite, for example, formed here or porphyry there. After first making distinctions, he looked for the unifying aspect. On June 12, 1784, he wrote to Frau von Stein, "The simple thread that I have spun for myself leads me nicely through all these underground labyrinths, and it gives me an overview even where there is confusion." He looked for the common principle that gives birth to one kind of rock here and that kind there, according to the various conditions under which it manifests. He considered nothing in his experience as final; the only unchanging element is the *principle* that underlies everything. Consequently, he was always preoccupied with finding the *transitions* from one kind of rock to another, because it is much easier to recognize the intention, or generative tendency, in those transitions than in the distinctively formed products, where nature reveals only one specific side of her being "and occasionally comes to a dead end."

It is a mistake to think that we prove Goethe wrong by pointing out that contemporary geology knows nothing of such transitions between types of rock. Goethe never claimed that granite actually changed into something else. Once it becomes granite, it is a finished, completed product and no longer has the inner generative force to become something else. But Goethe was looking for something that geology lacks today — the *idea,* or principle, that forms granite before it becomes granite. And this is the same idea that underlies all formations. When Goethe speaks of a transition from one rock to another, he does not mean an *actual* transformation but the development of the objective idea that expresses itself in various ways, at one time assuming *this* form and becoming granite, then expressing *another* potentiality and becoming slate, and so on. Goethe's view is concrete idealism, not some wild theory of metamorphosis.

However, it is only in the Earth as a whole that this principle of rock formation fully expresses all that lies within it. Thus, the main thing for Goethe is the Earth's formation, in which each particular must find its place. He is interested in how each rock formation finds its place within the Earth as a whole; he is interested in the particular only as a part of a whole. Ultimately, the geological system of mineralogy that seems right to Goethe imitates the processes of the Earth; it shows why things come about in one particular place or another. The decisive factors for him are *where* and *how* a certain rock formation is formed. Although he otherwise greatly respected Werner's work, Goethe reproached him for arranging minerals according to accidental external characteristics rather than according to their occurrences, which tells us how they came about.[1] *The perfect system is not made by the scientist but by nature herself.*

---

1. Abraham Gottlob Werner (1750–1817), geologist and mineralogist known for arranging and systematically classifying minerals. — ED.

We must remember that Goethe saw the whole of nature as one grand, harmonious kingdom. He claimed that all things in nature are animated by one single tendency. According to him, if things are similar it must be because they obey the same laws. He was unable to accept that factors other than inorganic forces are at work in geological phenomena, because they are nothing but inorganic in nature. *Goethe's first act in relation to geology was to extend the activity of inorganic laws to that science.* This was the principle that helped him understand the mountains of Bohemia and the phenomena observed at the Serapis Temple in Pozzuoli. He was trying to introduce principles into the dead crust of the Earth by thinking of it as having arisen according to the same laws we see at work in other physical phenomena.

Goethe was inwardly repelled by the geological theories of James Hutton (1726–1797) and Elie de Beaumont (1798–1874). What could he make of those explanations he considered to be in violation of all natural order? It has become banal to say that Goethe's *peaceful nature* contradicts such theories as that of the rising and sinking of the Earth's crust. No, it contradicted his sense of a *unified* law of nature. He was unable to fit them into a view that corresponds with nature. Through this sense he had already (1782) arrived at a view that was not accepted by professional geologists until several decades later — that fossilized animals and plants must have a relationship with the stones in which they are embedded. Voltaire still spoke of them as nature's "playful productions," because he lacked a concept of the consistency of nature's lawfulness.

According to Goethe, something found in a particular place is understandable only when we can find a simple, natural connection with its environment. The same principle also led Goethe to the fruitful idea of an ice age ("Geological Problems and Attempts to Resolve Them"). As he looked for a simple, natural explanation for the masses of granite distributed over large areas, he felt he had to reject the explanation that they had been hurled there by a tumultuous uplift of distant mountains, because it explained a natural fact as resulting from an *exception* to — indeed, the abandonment of — existing, known laws of nature. Instead, he assumed that all of northern Germany had at one point been covered by a body of water a thousand feet deep, that much of it was frozen, and that blocks of granite were left behind as the ice melted. This explanation was based on familiar laws that we can experience for ourselves. This recognition of the consistent working of natural laws is Goethe's contribution to geology. How he explained the Kammerberg and whether he was right about the Karlsbad mineral springs is irrelevant. "I am not trying to impose opinions but offering a method as a tool that anyone can use as he chooses" (Goethe to Hegel, October 7, 1820).

Chapter 14

Goethe's
Meteorological Ideas

As we have seen in his geology, it would be a mistake to see Goethe's actual achievements as his primary contribution to meteorology.[1] He never completed his meteorological experiments; we have only his viewpoints. His thinking always looked for the *pregnant* point, in the light of which a series of phenomena would naturally arrange themselves (see "Significant Help from a Single, Ingenious Word"). His mind could not be satisfied with any explanation that drew on external, incidental factors to explain an orderly sequence of various phenomena. When he encountered a phenomenon, he looked for all similar and related facts belonging to the same sphere, so that he would have a complete whole before him. Within that circle, there had to be a principle through which the inner necessity of everything regular — indeed, that of the whole circle of related phenomena — became apparent. To him, it seemed unnatural to explain manifestations *within this* circle by dragging in conditions that lay beyond it.

This is the key to the principle he established for meteorology:

I became increasingly aware that it is not enough to ascribe the causes of such a constant phenomenon[2] to the planets, the Moon, or some unknown tide of the atmosphere.... We re-

---

1. See the section of his "Outline of a Weather Science" entitled "Self-Evaluation." — R. Steiner.
2. The constant phenomenon he refers to here is *the regular rising and falling of the barometer* observed by him and others (see the end of his "Outline of a Weather Science"). — Ed.

ject all such influences. We assume that weather occurrences on Earth are neither cosmic nor planetary events; we must explain them, according to our premises, as purely *telluric* phenomena. ("Outline of a Weather Science")

Goethe wanted to trace atmospheric phenomena back to their earthly causes. First he needed to find the particular point that expressed the fundamental lawfulness that determined everything else. The barometer provided such a phenomenon. Goethe regarded it as the archetypal phenomenon and tried to connect everything else with it. He tried to follow the rising and falling of the barometer and thought that he observed a certain regularity in it. By studying Ludwig Schrön's tables, he found that "the rising and falling of the mercury followed *"an almost parallel course"* in different places, unaffected by the differences in latitude, longitude, and altitude where observations were made." Since he considered this rising and falling a manifestation of gravity, he believed he had found a direct expression of the quality of gravity in the barometer's fluctuations.

There is no point in projecting anything further into this explanation; Goethe rejected the formation of hypotheses. He wanted to express only the observed phenomenon; he was not looking for an actual, causal factor as would contemporary natural science. Other atmospheric phenomena were supposed to align with *this* particular phenomenon.

Goethe was most interested in cloud formations. In the theories of Luke Howard (1772–1864), he found a way to distinguish within their constantly changing forms certain essential configurations, thus "holding fast in enduring thoughts what lives in fluctuating appearances." He was still looking for a way to understand the transformations of cloud formations, just as he had found — in the "spiritual ladder" of the plant — a way to explain the transformation of the typical shape of a leaf. In the realm of meteorology, the "spiritual ladder" with which he connected the various formations was the qualitative difference of the atmosphere at various altitudes. In neither the case of the plant nor of the clouds did Goethe dream of assuming that his "spiritual ladder" was the actual entity. He was fully conscious of the fact that, as far as the senses are concerned, only the individual cloud formations can be seen as actual realities in space, and that any higher explanatory principles are intended only for the eyes of the spirit. Contemporary attempts to refute Goethe are thus often a quixotic tilting at windmills. By ascribing to his principles a form of reality that he himself denied them, people think they have defeated him. But the form of reality he took as his foundation — the objective, concrete idea — remains unknown to contemporary natural science. Consequently, in this regard, Goethe himself must seem alien to science today.

Chapter 15

On the Subjectivity
of Sensory Perceptions

I am not writing this account just because an edition of Goethe's works must include his theory of color along with a suitable introduction. Instead, it arises because of my own deeper need for clarity. I myself also began by studying mathematics and physics, but the numerous contradictions involved in our modern views of nature have forced me to undertake a critical investigation of their methodological foundations. My earlier studies led me in the direction of strictly empirical knowledge; my awareness of those numerous contradictions, however, called for a rigorous, scientific epistemology. My empirical starting point safeguarded me from reverting to Hegel's purely conceptual constructions. Finally, with the help of my epistemological studies, I found that the source of many errors in modern natural science is the erroneous function attributed to simple sensory perception. Science today attributes all sensory qualities (sound, color, warmth, and so on) to the subject and assumes that, beyond the subject, the only thing that corresponds to such qualities are material movement. These processes of movement — alleged to be the only thing that exists in this "realm of nature" — can of course no longer be perceived, but they are inferred from the subjective qualities.

Yet, when we consider this conclusion carefully, its inconsistency becomes obvious. The concept of motion was borrowed initially from the sensory world — that is, we encounter it only in things that have sensory qualities. We have no experience of motion except through sensory objects. If we extend this assumption to entities that are not sense-perceptible (as the elements of discontinuous matter, or atoms, are supposed to be), we must become truly aware that, by extending this concept, we are transferring an attribute known through the senses to a very different (imperceptible) form of existence. We face the same contradiction when we attempt to find actual meaning in the initially empty concept of the atom. We have no choice but to endow it with sensory qualities, no matter how sublimated. One scientist describes the atom as impenetrable or as a force, another describes it as having extension in space, and so on — always some characteristic borrowed from the sensory realm. And without these attributes, our concepts would be completely meaningless.

Herein lies the inconsistency. We draw a line through the center of the perceptual world and declare one side objective and the other subjective. To be consistent, we would have to say that, if atoms exist at all, they must simply be particles of matter and have material qualities, and the only reason we fail to perceive them is their minute size, which makes them unavailable to our senses.

This eliminates the possibility of juxtaposing the motion of atoms as something objective to subjective qualities such as sound and color. It also guarantees that, in the relationship between a motion and the sensation of, for example, red, we would simply find two events completely within the realm of the senses.

Consequently, it also became clear to this author that the motion of the ether,[1] the position of atoms, and so on belong to the same category as sensory perceptions themselves. To characterize sensory perceptions as subjective is merely the result of fuzzy thinking. If we assert that sensory qualities are subjective, then we must also say this of the movement of the ether. If we fail to perceive the motion of the ether, it is not because of a principle but simply because our senses are not organized finely enough. This, however, is contingent only on external circumstances. It is quite possible that, through an increasing refinement of the sense organs, human beings may eventually be able to perceive the ether directly. If people in that distant future were to accept the doctrine of the subjectivity of sensations, they would also have to declare the motion of the ether subjective, just as people today do color and sound and so on. As we can see, this physical theory leads to an impossible contradiction.

The view that sense perceptions are subjective is further supported

---

1. *Ether,* here, refers to an all-pervading, infinitely elastic, massless medium, formerly postulated by physics as the medium for the propagation of electromagnetic waves. — ED.

by *physiological considerations.* Physiology tells us that perception arises as the result of a mechanical process outside of our body that is communicated to nerve endings in the sense organs; from there it is transmitted to the central nervous system, where it finally triggers a sensation. I have described the contradictions of this theory elsewhere in this book [chapter 17]. The only aspect in this process that can be called subjective is the form of movement within the substance of the brain. No matter how far we may go in investigating the processes in the subject, we always remain in the mechanical realm. And sensations will never be found in the brain.

Therefore, we have no choice but to resort to *philosophical* considerations to become clear about the subjectivity and objectivity of sensation. These considerations lead to the thoughts that follow.

What exactly does *subjective* mean in terms of perception? We will not get anywhere unless we come up with a precise analysis of *subjective* as a concept. Subjectivity, of course, can be determined only by itself. We cannot call anything subjective that is not proven to be determined by the subject. We must now ask, What can we describe as belonging to the human subject? Only what a person can experience personally through inner or outer perception. Through outer perception we can investigate our bodily constitution, and through inner perception we can apprehend our thinking, feeling, and willing. In the case of outer perception, what would we classify as subjective? Our whole bodily constitution, including the sense organs and the brain, which probably vary somewhat from person to person. What we discover in this way are the particular arrangements and functions of the substances as they mediate our sensations. The subjective aspect in this case involves only the path that the sensation must follow before it can be called my sensation. Our organization transmits the sensation, and these pathways are subjective; the sensation itself, however, is not.

Now let us consider inner experience. What do I experience internally when I describe a sensation as my own? I observe that I make the connection between the sensation and my individuality through thinking and that I expand my awareness to include that sensation. But I am not aware of producing the *content* of the sensation. I only establish a connection with myself; the quality of the sensation is a factor that is grounded in itself.

No matter where we start, whether inside or outside, we never reach the point where we can say, Here we have the subjective character of sensations. The concept of subjectivity cannot be applied to the content of a sensation.

These are the considerations that forced me to consider any theory of nature to be impossible that, on principle, goes *beyond* the realm of the perceived world, and that have led me to embrace the sensory world as the only object of natural science. I then had to look for what we call natural laws in the interdependency of this sensory world.

This is what led me to the view of the scientific method that lies at the foundation of Goethe's color theory. Those who agree with these considerations will read this color theory with eyes very different from those of conventional scientists today. They will see that it is not really a matter of conflict between the hypotheses of Goethe and Newton, but a question of whether contemporary theoretical physics is acceptable. If it is not, then neither is its view of the theory of color. In the following chapters, readers will become acquainted with what we see as the theoretical foundations of physics. This will provide a basis for viewing Goethe's work in the proper light.

Chapter 16

Goethe As Thinker and Researcher

1. Goethe and Modern Science

The following pages might never have been written if a feeling of obligation to speak honestly did not arise when one has the sense of having recognized the truth. Given the current direction of natural science, I have no doubt about how they will be judged by professionals in the field. These pages will be described as a dilettante's attempt to reopen an issue long ago resolved by those "in the know." When I consider the derogatory opinions of those who have a say in the matter, I must admit that the prospect is not very tempting. Nevertheless, I cannot shrink from the anticipation of such arguments, because I could make them myself. Consequently, I know how little validity they have. Thinking "scientifically," in the sense of modern science, is really not that difficult. A rather remarkable case in point was the recent publication of Eduard von Hartmann's *Philosophy of the Unconscious*. The spirited author of this book would be the last one to deny its imperfections. But the quality of thinking we encounter there gets right to the bottom of matters. Consequently, it left a strong impression on all those who feel the need for deeper insight. It proved frustrating, however, to the more superficial scholars of natural science, who generally opposed it. When those attacks remained relatively unsuccessful, an anonymous author published *The Unconscious from the Perspective of Philosophy and the Theory of Descent* (1872). Its author strongly criticized the new philosophy, raising every argument that could be used against it from the perspective of contemporary natural science. The book created a stir, and scholars were quite satisfied. They claimed both the author and his arguments as their own.

But then, to their great disappointment, the author turned out to be none other than Hartmann himself.

This provides convincing proof of one thing: When seriously striving people still find it impossible to ally themselves with the latest trends, it is not through ignorance of scientific research or because they are amateurs; it is because they understand that the paths those trends follow are the wrong ones. It is not difficult for philosophy to consciously adopt the position of contemporary science. Hartmann has irrefutably demonstrated this to anyone willing to look. I mention this to corroborate my previous statement that I would have no trouble formulating the very objections others might raise to what I have said.

Presently, it seems that anyone who gives serious consideration to philosophical thinking on the nature of things is considered a dilettante. Simply having a worldview at all is seen as an idealistic whim by our contemporaries of a mechanistic (or better yet, a positivistic) conviction. It is easy to understand this opinion when we see how hopeless the ignorance of these positivist thinkers is when we hear them speak of the "nature of matter," the "frontiers of knowledge," the "nature of the atom," and so on. Such discourse provides ample opportunity to study their amateur approach to fundamental scientific matters.

We must have the courage to admit all this vis-à-vis contemporary natural science, despite the powerful, admirable achievements of that same natural science in the realm of technology. Such technical achievements have nothing to do with any real desire to understand nature. We have seen this in our contemporaries whose inventions have a significance for the future we can barely begin to assess, but who also lack a deep *scientific* yearning. It is one thing to observe the processes of nature with the purpose of utilizing its forces for technology, and it is quite another to study those processes with the purpose of understanding their nature more deeply. True science exists only when the inquiring spirit seeks the satisfaction of its *own* needs, *with no external purpose.*

True science, in the highest sense of the word, deals with objective ideas; *it can be nothing but idealism,* because it is rooted ultimately in spiritual needs. Nature awakens questions in us that demand resolution, but it cannot deliver the answers itself. Such new challenges arise when nature is confronted by a higher realm through our capacity for knowledge. Such questions would not even arise for a being not possessed of this higher nature. Consequently, answers can be obtained only through this higher nature itself. Scientific questions are thus primarily a matter that the inquiring spirit has to settle with itself. They do not lead this spirit beyond its own realm. But the realm in which the spirit is at home and where it lives and weaves is the world of ideas and thinking. Scientific activity in the highest sense of the word means dealing with questions that arise in thinking through answers conceived in thought. Ultimately, the function of any scientific endeavor is to serve this higher purpose.

Consider scientific observation; it is supposed to lead us to an understanding of a natural law, which is itself of a purely ideal nature. The urge to look for a governing lawfulness behind the phenomena arises from the spirit. Only a spiritual being would feel this urge. As for observation, what are we really trying to accomplish through it? Can sensory observations actually find answers to questions forged by the spirit? Not at all. After all, why should a second observation give us more satisfaction than the first if spirit could actually be satisfied with the observed object; one observation should be enough. But it is not really a question of a second observation; rather it is one of finding the ideal basis for the observations. The question is, What ideal explanation does the observation allow? How do I need to *think* so that it seems possible? These are the questions that come to us when we encounter the sensory world. I must pull up from the depths of my spirit what I find lacking in the world of the senses. When I encounter the sensory realm, I must myself create the higher nature toward which my spirit strives; nothing else can do it for me. Because the results of science can come only from the spirit, they must be *ideas*. This arises from its own necessity and is indisputable; it confirms the idealistic character of all science.

Modern natural science, by its very nature, cannot believe that knowledge is characterized by ideas. It views ideas not as the first, most original, creative agencies, but rather as the final *product* of material processes. Science is unaware that those material processes belong to the world we can observe through our senses, which nevertheless resolves itself into idea when understood more deeply. The process to be observed is as follows. Through our senses, we perceive facts which proceed according to mechanical laws, then manifestations of warmth, light, magnetism, electricity, and finally life processes and such. At the highest level of life, we find that it rises to forming concepts, or ideas, carried by the human brain. Emerging from this realm of thought, we find our own I. This seems to be the highest product of a complicated process mediated through a long sequence of physical, chemical, and organic events. But when we investigate the world of ideas — the essence of the I — we find much *more* than merely the end product of this process. We find that the individual aspects of this thought world are related in a completely different way than are the parts of the process we merely observed. As a thought arises in us and in turn calls for another, we find that there is an ideal relationship between those two thoughts which is of a very different nature from the relationship I observe, for example, between the dyeing of a piece of cloth and the chemical agent that causes it.

It is completely natural that the successive stages of the neural process in the brain have their sources in the metabolism, and that it is the metabolism itself that sustains my thought. In that metabolism, however, we will not discover why one thought *should follow* from another. This can be found only in the logical relationship between the thoughts themselves. The realm of thoughts, therefore, is governed not only by *organic necessity* but also by a necessity of a *higher, ideal nature*. The spirit, however, looks for the same ideal necessity that it finds in its world of ideas in the rest of the universe as well. This necessity arises for us only because we do not merely *observe*, but also *think*. In other words, whenever we apprehend things not only through observation but also through thinking, they no longer appear to us merely in terms of their factual relationships; they are also related through an inner, ideal necessity.

One cannot object to this by asking whether there is any point in trying to comprehend the sensory world through thinking if the things of this world, by their very nature, do not allow such comprehension. This question can be asked only when we have failed to get to the core of the matter. The world of ideas springs to life within us, encounters the objects we perceive through the senses, and asks, What is the relationship between me and the world facing me? What is that world in relation to me? Here I am with my ideal necessity that rises above transient reality; within me I have the power to explain myself, but how can I explain what I encounter outside of me?

This is where we find an answer to the significant question repeatedly brought up, for example, by Friedrich Theodor Vischer (1807–1887), who described it as the pivotal point of all philosophical thinking; it is the question of the relationship between spirit and nature. What is the relationship between these two forms of being that seem separate? If this question is asked in the right way, it is not as difficult to answer as one might think. After all, what can it mean? It is not as though the question were asked by a third party who is trying to understand from a vantage point above both spirit and nature. Rather, it is asked by one of those two beings — by the spirit itself. The spirit wants to discover the relationship between itself and nature. This is the same as asking how I can establish a relationship with the nature that I encounter. And how can I express this connection in a way that accords with the needs that live in me? I live in ideas; what kind of idea corresponds to nature, how do I express as idea what I contemplate as nature? It is as if we often blocked the way to a satisfactory answer by asking the wrong question. But the correct question is half the answer.

The spirit searches everywhere for a way to transcend the sequence of facts given by mere observation and tries to penetrate to the *ideas of things*. Science begins where thinking begins. What appears to our senses as a sequence of facts is expressed as ideal necessity by the results of science. Those results only appear to be the final product of the process described above; in fact, we must consider them to be the foundation of everything in the entire universe. Where they appear for our observation is a matter of indifference, because their significance is independent of where we observe them. The net of their ideal necessity spreads over the whole universe.

We can begin anywhere; ultimately we will get to the *idea* if we have enough spiritual strength. Inasmuch as modern physics fails to recognize this, it is led into a whole sequence of mistakes. Let me point out one such error as an example.

Consider the definition of what is typically described by physicists as one of the "common characteristics of bodies" — the principle of *inertia*. It is usually stated as follows: no object can change its current state of motion except as the result of an external cause. This definition creates the impression that the concept of an inert body has been abstracted from the world of the senses. And John Stuart Mill (who never investigates this question but turns everything on its head to prove an arbitrary theory) would not for a moment hesitate to explain it this way. Nevertheless, it is incorrect.

The concept of an inert body arises purely through a conceptual construct. In calling anything that extends in space a "body," I can think of some bodies that undergo changes through external influences, and others that move on their own initiative. Consequently, if I find something in the external world that fits my definition of "bodies that cannot change without an external cause," I call it *inert* — that is, subject to the law of inertia. My concepts are not abstracted from the sensory world but constructed autonomously from an idea, and only with the help of this idea can I orient myself in the sensory world. The definition would therefore have to be stated this way: A body that cannot itself change the state of its movement is inert; once I have found a body that fits this definition, I can apply everything that applies to an inert body to the one I have found.

2. The Archetypal Phenomenon

If we were able to follow the whole series of events that take place whenever there is a sensory perception, from the peripheral nerve ends in the sensory organ all the way to the brain, we would still not reach the point where the mechanical, chemical, and organic (the time-space) processes cease and where something occurs that we can call sensory perception — sensation of warmth, light, sound, and so on. Nowhere do we find a point of transition from causal movement to its effect, the perception. Can we then describe the relationship between these aspects as cause and effect?

Let us look objectively at the matter. Let us assume that a particular sensation arises in our consciousness. It arises in such a way that it calls our attention to an object from which it originates. When I have the sensation of red, the content of my mental representation of red allows me to immediately connect it with a particular spatial coordinate — that is, a space or surface — to which I then ascribe the sensation. The only time this does not occur is when the sensory organ itself responds in its own way to an external influence, such as the sensation of light in response to a sudden pressure on the eye. We need not be concerned here with such instances, because they lack the characteristics of normal perception, and such exceptions will not show us anything about the nature of this perception.

If I have a sensation of red in connection with a particular location, my attention will initially be directed to some object in the outer world as the source of that sensation. I might ask about spatial-temporal processes taking place in the thing I associate with the color

red. And it will turn out that mechanical, chemical, and other processes present themselves as answers to my questions. I can proceed
to investigate the processes that mediate the color red for me on the
way from the thing to my sensory organ. Here, too, the only mediators I will be able to find are movement processes, electrical currents,
and chemical changes. The results would be no different if I were able
to investigate the further transmission from the sensory organ to its
corresponding center in the brain. *What* is transmitted along this entire path is the perception of red. *How* this perception presents itself
in any particular thing that happens to lie along the way from stimulation to perception depends, of course, on the nature of that thing.
The sensation is present in each place, from the initial stimulus to the
brain, though never explicitly as such, but in the way that corresponds
to the nature of the object that happens to be in that place.

This reveals a truth well suited to illuminate the whole theoretical
foundation of physics and physiology. What do I learn by investigating something involved in a process that enters my consciousness as
a sensation? All I really learn is how that particular thing responds
to the action that proceeds from the sensation. In other words, the
way a sensation *expresses itself* in a particular object of the world of
space and time. Far from being the *cause* that initiates the sensation
within me, the spatial-temporal process is the *effect* of the sensation
in a thing that exists in space and time. I could include any number
of things along the path from the stimulus to the organ of perception;
each will respond in a way that is both determined and limited by its
own nature. It is thus the *sensation itself* that expresses itself in each
of the processes.

The transmission of sound involves longitudinal vibrations of the
air; the transmission of light involves hypothetical ether vibrations.
Both forms are simply the particular way those specific sensations
are able to manifest in a medium that, by its very nature, is capable
only of rarefaction and condensation, in other words, of oscillation.
The sensation itself cannot be found in this medium, because *it cannot exist there*. Such processes, however, cannot be said to embody
the objective nature of the sensation, but rather a form in which it
manifests.[1]

---

1. In a later section, Steiner compares the transmission of sense perceptions to the
transmission of a telegram (see p. 189). — ED.

Now let us ask, What is the nature of those mediating processes? Besides through our senses, is there any other means by which we can investigate them? Can I really study my senses using anything but the senses themselves? Are the peripheral nerve endings or brain convolutions anything other than sensory perceptions? All these things are at the same time both subjective and objective — assuming, of course, that the distinction is even tenable. We can now approach the matter somewhat more precisely. As we follow perception from stimulus to an organ of perception, we are really studying a continuous transition from one perception to another. The perception of red caused us to begin the whole process in the first place, and it points us toward the stimulus. Once we look there, we find other sensations related to red. They are movement processes, and these in turn appear as other movement processes between the stimulus and the sensory organ, and so on. All of these, however, are perceived sensations as well. All of it is a metamorphosis of events that — insofar as they are accessible to sensory observation at all — reveal themselves as nothing but perceptions. *The perceived world is nothing other than an aggregate of metamorphosed perceptions.*

For the sake of convenience, we have expressed ourselves in a way that cannot be reconciled completely with these conclusions. We said that each "thing" that inserts itself into the gap between the stimulus and the perceptual organ evokes a sensation that corresponds to its nature. Strictly speaking, of course, the "thing" is really the sum of the processes that constitute its appearance.

People will now argue that these conclusions preclude any sense of permanence in the ongoing world process. Like Heraclitus, we claim that the sole principle of the world is the continuous flow of things where nothing is permanent. Surely, there must be a "thing in itself" behind all appearances; there must be "permanent matter" behind this world of changes. We must therefore take another look at the question of "permanent matter," or "duration in change."

When my eye is confronted by a red surface, a sensation of red appears in my consciousness. We can distinguish the beginning, middle, and end of that sensation. In contrast to this transient sensation, we wish to find an enduring, objective process, one that is likewise objectively limited in time — that is, one with a beginning, middle, and end. But this process is supposed to be happening in relation to a material basis which has neither beginning, nor end, which is indestructible and eternal. This matter is supposed to be the truly permanent element in these fluctuating processes.

Such a conclusion might be valid if the concept of time were applied correctly to the sensation. But perhaps we need to distinguish clearly between the essence, or content, of the sensation itself and its appearance. They are one and the same for my perception, of course, because without its essence, the sensation would not appear to me at all. Now, from the perspective of this essence, does it make any difference whether it enters my consciousness at a particular moment and then leaves it seconds later? The essence of the sensation (its objective existence) is independent of all that. What sense then does it make to claim that something [permanent matter, — Ed.] is fundamental to the existence of a sensation if it has nothing to do with its essential nature?

Neither is our application of the concept of time correct in relation to an objective process that begins and ends. If something acquires a new characteristic that develops for a while in various ways then disappears, the *content,* or quality, of that characteristic would in this case also have to be regarded as its essence. This essential quality would in itself have absolutely nothing to do with the concepts of beginning, duration, and end. By "essential" we are speaking of what actually makes something what it is or the way it presents itself. The important thing is not the fact that something emerges at a particular moment in time, but *what* it is that actually emerges. All the particular qualities that express themselves through this "what" make up the essential being of the world. Now this "what" manifests under manifold conditions and in the most diverse forms. All these forms are interrelated; they create the conditions for one another. The nature of their relationship thus becomes one of separation in *space* and *time.*

The concept of *matter* arose only because of a very misguided concept of time. The general belief is that the world would evaporate into a mere apparition without being if we did not anchor the totality of fleeting events in a permanent, immutable reality that endures in time while its various individual configurations change. But time is not a container within which changes occur. Time does not exist *before* things or *outside* of them. It is the tangible expression of the fact that events — because of their specific nature — form sequential interrelationships.

Let us imagine a complex of sense-perceptible facts, a^1, b^1, c^1, d^1, e^1; and another complex — a^2, b^2, c^2, d^2, e^2 — that depends on the first by virtue of internal necessity. I can understand the specific nature of the second complex by deriving it conceptually from the first. We have thus far described these complexes according to their essence — irrespective of time and space. Now let us imagine that both complexes actually appear. If a^2–e^2 is to appear, then a^1–e^1 must also appear, but in such a way that their necessary relationship is visible. This means that the phenomena a^1–e^1 must be present first and allow for the phenomena a^2–e^2, after which the latter can appear. From this we see that time arises only when the *being* of something *manifests externally.*

Time thus belongs to the world of appearances and has nothing to do with the being, or essence, of a thing. Such being can be apprehended only as an idea. Only those who are unable in their own thinking to trace the appearance back to its essential being will conceive of time as preceding the facts. But then they require some kind of existence that endures throughout all changes, which they find in the concept of indestructible matter. Thus they create something impervious to time that persists unchanged by fluctuations. But this merely emphasizes their inability to penetrate from the time-bound appearance of a fact to its essential, timeless being. Can I truthfully say of the essence of a thing that it arises and then ceases? I can say only that its essence relates to the essence of something else, and that the resulting relationship appears as a chronological sequence. The essence of a thing is indestructible; it is beyond all time and, in fact, determines time.

We have thus elucidated two rarely understood subjects: manifestation, or appearance, and being, or essential nature. When we understand what has been explained here, we will not try to prove the indestructibility of the essence of a thing, because destruction implies the concept of time, which has nothing to do with the essential nature of things. Consequently, we can say that *the sense-perceptible world as it presents itself to us is an aggregate of metamorphosing perceptions without an underlying material substratum.*[2]

Our remarks here have also shown that we cannot speak of a subjective nature of perceptions. When we perceive something, we can

---

2. Based on these considerations, it should be clear now that the essential nature of phenomena may be seen as their enduring element and true foundation. Consequently, there is no need to look further for such a foundation in a hypothetical material substratum. — ED.

follow the process from stimulus to central organ, but nowhere do we find a point at which we can observe a leap from the objectivity of what has not yet been perceived to the subjective perception. This refutes the idea that the sense-perceptible world is subjective. The world of perception is rooted in itself and is initially unrelated to either subject or object.

These considerations pertain only to the concept of matter as the foundation of physics identified with the old, equally incorrect, metaphysical concept of substance. It is one thing to view matter as the actual reality underlying phenomena, and another entirely to apprehend matter as phenomenon, or appearance. Our considerations are directed only toward the first and do not pertain to the second. If I consider matter to be merely something that occupies space, then for me it refers only to a phenomenon with no greater reality than any other phenomenon. I just have to keep this characteristic of matter in mind. The object of all science is the world that presents itself to us through perceptions — that is, as extension, movement, rest, force, light, warmth, color, sound, electricity, and so on.

If the perceived world were such that its essence was expressed fully through its sensory appearance — in other words, if everything that appeared to us were a perfect, undisturbed manifestation of its inner being — we would not need science at all, because understanding would arise in the very act of perception. Indeed, there would be no difference at all between essential being and phenomenal appearance; they would coincide completely. This is not the case, however.

Imagine that element *A* in the world of facts has a certain relationship to element *B;* according to our considerations both are phenomena, and nothing more. Their relationship thus also manifests as a phenomenon, which we will call *C.* What we can ascertain in the factual world is the relationship between *A, B,* and *C.* But there are countless other elements just like *A, B,* and *C* in the perceptible world. Let's take a fourth at random, *D;* once it is added, everything else is modified by its presence. Instead of *A* and *B* producing *C,* the presence of *D* will lead to the appearance of yet another phenomenon, *E.*

The main point here is that, whenever we approach a phenomenon, we see it as it has been modified by numerous conditions. Before we can understand it, we must look for all of these relationships. There are all sorts of connections — some closer, some more remote.

If phenomenon E is to appear to me, other more or less connected phenomena must come into play. Some are essential to the existence of the phenomenon; the absence of others could not prevent some such phenomenon from arising, but they would affect the particular way it arises. Accordingly, we must distinguish between the necessary and incidental conditions of a phenomenon. Phenomena that arise only through the effects of necessary conditions can be called *primal* phenomena, the others *derived* phenomena. If knowing their conditions allows us to understand the primal phenomena, then by including other conditions we can understand the derived phenomena as well. Thus, the task of science is to gain such a deep understanding of the phenomenal world that it finds phenomena that depend only on necessary conditions. The conceptual expressions of those necessary relationships are *natural laws*.

Whenever we approach a particular field of phenomena, we must first describe and record them, and then we must establish which elements have a necessary connection. These elements are the archetypal phenomena. Then we must find the conditions that are related in a more remote way to those elements and discover how they modify the original phenomena.

Science views the phenomenal world as follows: all phenomena are actually derived and thus initially incomprehensible. To understand the interrelationships among phenomena, science views archetypal phenomena as leading the way and derived phenomena as following from them. The scientific system is different from nature's system to the degree that science establishes the relationships among phenomena, thereby making them intelligible. Science need not contribute anything to the phenomenal world but only uncover its hidden relationships. Use of the intellect should be limited to this work. The intellect and all scientific endeavors reach beyond their rightful domain when they resort to the imperceptible to explain the perceptible.

Before we can understand Goethe's theory of color, we must understand the absolute correctness of these concepts. There could be nothing farther from Goethe's mind than to speculate on what the nature of a phenomenon — warmth, light, and so on — might be other than the essence of its appearance; he recognized the appropriate task of thinking. According to Goethe, light was given as a sensation. When he was trying to explain the connection between light and color, he could not do so through speculation, but only through an *archetypal phenomenon* by looking for the necessary conditions that light must encounter before color can arise.

Newton, too, saw that color arises in relation to light, but he went on to speculate, How does color come from light? To do so lay in his speculative way of thinking, but not in Goethe's thinking, which immersed itself in the phenomena and correctly understood its own task. To Goethe, Newton's assumption that "light is made of colored lights" seemed to be a product of invalid speculation. He felt justified in speaking of the *relationship* between light and color only when certain conditions were given, but not in speaking of light itself by introducing a speculative concept. Hence his statement, "Light is the simplest, least fragmented, most homogeneous being known to us. It is not by nature a composite."[3] Anything said about the *composition* of light is a statement of the intellect about a phenomenon. But the proper domain of the intellect is limited to statements about the *interrelationships* of phenomena. This reveals more deeply why Goethe, when he looked at light through a prism, *could* not accept Newton's theory. The prism should have been the *first condition* for the appearance of color. But another factor, the presence of darkness, proved to be a more primary condition for its occurrence. The prism was only a secondary condition.

I believe this should remove all obstacles for the reader who wishes to understand Goethe's work on color. The great scientific value of Goethe's theory of colors would have been recognized long ago if people had not repeatedly assumed that the difference between these two theories involved conflicting interpretations, the validity of which merely needs to be tested. Those who continue to accept the contemporary view of physics on this issue have been completely won over by the fundamentally false notion that it is necessary, through intellectual reasoning, to trace perceptions back to their underlying cause. But the moment one sees that the way to explain phenomena is to *observe* them in a context established by understanding, one must accept Goethe's theory of color *in principle*, because it begins with a correct view of the relationship between our thinking and nature. Newton did not share this view.

---

3. Compare Steiner's statements on Goethe's conception of light in his discourse on "Goethe, Newton, and the Physicists," pp. 188–89.

Of course, I do not intend to defend every aspect of Goethe's theory of color. I do, however, want to uphold its *principle*. But it also cannot be my task here to use Goethe's principle to deduce color phenomena that were unknown during his time. I would undertake such a task only if I was one day fortunate enough to have the time and means to write a theory of color along the lines of Goethe's principle and based entirely on the most recent research. I would consider it one of the most rewarding works of my life. This introduction has to restrict itself to a scientific justification of Goethe's *way of thinking* in his theory of color. In the next section, I will clarify its inner architecture.

3. The System of Natural Science

It might seem as though, by limiting the task of thinking to the ordering of perceptions, our investigations are now calling into question the very autonomy of concepts and ideas which we advocated so strongly to begin with. Further reflection will show that this is not the case; after all, what is the goal of thinking when it establishes connections between perceptions?

Imagine perception *a* and perception *b*. Initially, they are given to us as entities devoid of concepts. The qualities offered to my senses cannot be transformed into anything else through conceptual thinking. Nor can I find any conceptual quality that would allow me to construct what is given by sensory experience if I could not access it through perception. For example, there is no way for me to communicate the quality "red" to a color-blind person, no matter how I describe it conceptually. *There is an aspect of the sensory perception that never enters into the concept — something that must be experienced before it can become an object of cognition at all.*

So what is the role of the concept that we attach to a sensory perception? Clearly, it must contribute something entirely new, something that stands on its own yet also belongs to that sensory perception, but without ever appearing in the perception itself. Now, it is certainly true that this new "something" that the concept brings to the sensory perception is precisely what meets our need for explanation. Only then can we understand an element of the sensory world when we have a concept of it. We can always point to whatever sensory reality offers us; and anyone who has the ability to perceive it will know exactly what it is. The concept allows us to say something about the sensory world that cannot be perceived. This makes it clear that, if the essence of a perception were fully expressed in the sensory quality, the concept would be unable to add anything new. Thus, the sensory perception is incomplete and constitutes only one aspect — the one that can only be seen. Only through the concept do we understand what it is we are seeing.

Now we can formulate the significance of the *content* of what was developed *methodically* in the previous section. *What* something in the sensory world is appears only when we understand it conceptually. We cannot express the content of what we observe, because its entire content is given in *how* it appears, in the *form* of its appearance. Thus we find the *what,* the other content of what is given in the sense world, in the *concept.*

The world thus attains its full content only through concepts. But we have found that the concept points beyond the individual phenomenon to the interrelatedness of things. The separate and isolated appearances of sensory reality present themselves to the concept as a *unified whole.* Thus our scientific methodology itself leads to the ultimate goal of a *monistic natural science.* But this is not an abstract monism that presumes a unity and then simply includes the individual facts of *concrete* existence. Rather it is a concrete monism that shows, step by step, how the apparent multiplicity of sensory existence ultimately reveals itself as a unity in the realm of idea. Such a multiplicity is merely a form in which the unified essence of the world expresses itself. The senses adhere to the multiplicity, since they are unable to comprehend this unified content; they are inherently pluralists. Thinking, however, overcomes multiplicity and gradually works its way back to the unified world principle.

The particular *way* a concept (idea) manifests in the sensory world accounts for the differentiation of the natural kingdoms. When a sense-perceptible entity attains only an existence that is completely outside the concept — in other words, if the concept governs only as a *law* that determines its modifications — we call that entity *inorganic.* Everything that happens to such an entity can be traced back to the influences of another entity. And how the two interact can be explained by an external law. In this sphere we are dealing with phenomena and laws, which, if they are primal, may be called *archetypal phenomena.* The concept to be apprehended in this case lies outside the perceived multiplicity.

But a sense-perceptible unity may also point beyond itself and force us, when we try to understand it, to look for determining factors beyond what is perceptible. Then what we comprehend as concept appears as a sense-perceptible unity. These two — concept and percept — are not identical; but the concept appears as a principle *within* the sensory multiplicity instead of existing *outside* it as a law. We find the concept at the foundation of the phenomenon; it permeates the phenomenon but is no longer perceptible to the senses. This is what we call the *type*. We are now in the domain of *organic* science.

But here also, the concept still appears only as the *type* and not yet in its own form as concept. Where the type appears not just as such — as an inherent principle — but in its conceptual form, it appears as *consciousness*. What existed at lower levels only as being now finally reveals itself; the concept itself can now be perceived. This is the domain of the cognizing human being.

Natural law, type, and *concept* are the three forms of the idea. Natural law is an abstraction standing above the multiplicity; it governs inorganic science. Here, idea and sensory reality are completely separate. The type combines both into one being. Spirit becomes active being, but it is not yet active as such, nor is it present as such. To be observed in its actual existence, it must be perceived in its sense-perceptible form. This is what we find in organic nature. The concept is present in a form that can be perceived. In human consciousness, the concept itself is perceptible. Observation and idea coincide; we actually perceive the idea. This also allows us to see the inner principles of the lower levels of nature. Human consciousness allows us to perceive the fully manifested reality of what only exists — but does not appear — at lower levels.

4. The System of Goethe's Color Theory

Goethe lived at a time when there was a universal and powerful striving toward an absolute knowledge that finds its satisfaction in itself. It was a time when an ardent quest for deeper insight was again undertaken to explore every approach to knowledge and discover answers to the most significant questions. The age of Eastern theosophy, Plato and Aristotle, then that of Descartes and Spinoza, had been epochs of a similar inner deepening. Goethe is inconceivable without Kant, Fichte, Schelling, and Hegel. Whereas all those individuals shared a profound vision — their eyes raised to the heights — Goethe's own contemplation was focused on matters of immediate reality. But in his attentive gaze we find some of that depth. Goethe exercised this deeper sight in his observation of nature. The spirit of his time imbued his observations of nature with an inner life. And this is what gives power to his observation of details, which is always animated by a broader view. Goethe's science always focuses on questions of central significance.

We notice this especially in Goethe's theory of color. Besides his essay on the metamorphosis of plants, this is his only scientific work that has become a complete whole. And what a powerful self-contained system it is, conceived according to the nature of the subject itself!

Let us look at its internal structure.

There is a prerequisite to the appearance of anything rooted in the being of nature; there must be an enabling cause — an organ in which the thing can present itself. The eternal, immutable laws of nature would always remain in force, even if no human beings were present to picture them. But they could not manifest. They would be there in being but would not manifest. This is also true of light and color in the absence of a perceiving eye. We cannot, like Schopenhauer, assume that colors owe their existence to the eye. Nevertheless, we must find the possibility of perceiving colors in the eye. The eye does not determine color but causes it to appear.

This is where the theory of color comes in. It must examine the eye to discover its nature. This is why Goethe begins his work with a *physiological* theory of color. But his conception is very different from what is ordinarily understood in this area of optics. He does not try to understand the eye's function in terms of its physical structure, but observes the eye under various conditions to understand its characteristics and capacities. Goethe's process is always one of *observation*. For example, What is the effect of light and darkness on the eye? What happens when it encounters definite images? And so on. He does not begin by asking what processes occur within the eye when perception takes place; rather, he tries to get to the bottom of what actually happens in the eye in the *living* activity of seeing. For his purposes this is the only important question to start with. Strictly speaking, the other does not belong to a physiological theory of color but to the science of the human organism, or general physiology. Goethe is interested in the eye only to the extent that it sees, not in any explanation of sight derived from observing an eye that is dead.

From here, he proceeds to the objective processes through which color phenomena arise. Here we must remember that when Goethe thinks of objective processes he is not at all interested in hypothetical, imperceptible material processes or movements; he always limits himself to the perceptible world. His *physical theory of color,* which is the second part of his study, looks for the conditions related to color as it is produced independently of the eye. Nevertheless, he remains interested only in actual perceptions. Here he is looking at the way colors appear through a prism, a lens, and so on. For the time being, he is satisfied with following the colors as they occur, observing color as such as it arises, independent of objects.

Only in a separate chapter on the *chemical theory of color* does Goethe proceed to colors as they are fixed, or "attached" to an object. The *physiological* theory of color answers the question of how colors appear at all, and the *physical* theory of color deals with the external conditions of their manifestation. Now he answers the question of how the world of objects appears *colored.* Thus, Goethe advances from observing color as an attribute of the phenomenal world to a study of the phenomenal world itself as it appears with this attribute. In his chapter on the *sensory-moral effects of color* he then finally proceeds to the observation of the higher relationship between the colored physical world and the world of the human soul.

This is the rigorous, strict path of science — going from the subject as condition back to the subject as it finds its satisfaction in and with the world. The impulse of the age that led to the architecture of Hegel's whole system is obvious in this path moving from subject to object and back again.

In this sense, we must view the "Sketch of a Color Theory" as Goethe's main optical work. His two essays "Contribution to Optics" and "Elements of a Color Theory" may be seen as preliminary studies. "Exposing Newton's Theory" is only a polemical supplement to his work.

5. Goethe's Concept of Space

To fully understand Goethe's work in physics, we will need to develop his concept of *space*. Prerequisite for comprehending this concept are convictions inherent in the previous section: First, phenomena that appear in our experience as isolated events are inwardly interrelated. In fact, they are connected by a bond of unity that encompasses the whole world. *One* principle lives in all of them. Second, whenever we approach separate things and attempt to connect them by determining their interrelationships, the conceptual unity we create is not external to those objects but drawn from the very core of nature's being itself. As a process, human knowledge does not take place outside of things; it is not purely subjective and arbitrary; rather, what arises in our spirit as natural law, what comes to life in our soul, is the very heartbeat of the universe.

For our present purposes, we will examine the most external of all the connections that our spirit establishes among objects of experience. We will look at the simplest instance through which experience calls upon our spiritual activity. Imagine two simple elements of the phenomenal world. To make things as simple as possible, let us imagine two points of light. Disregard completely the fact that each of these points of light could represent a phenomenon of awesome complexity that would pose a great challenge to the mind. Also forget about their sensory qualities and consider only the simple fact of two separate elements — that is, separate as far as our senses tell us. There are two factors, each of which is affecting our senses; this is all we are predicating. We will also say that the existence of one of these factors does not exclude the existence of the other; they can both be perceived by *one* perceptual organ.

If we assumed that the *existence* of one of these elements depends in any way on the existence of the other, we would be confronted by a very different problem. If the existence of B is such that it excludes the existence of A and yet depends on it for its existence, this implies that they are connected in terms of *time*. For if the existence of B depends on A, and if the presence of B precludes that of A, then A must precede B. But that is another matter.

For our purposes, we will not imagine such a relationship. We are assuming that these two do not exclude each other but coexist. By disregarding all relationships demanded by their inner nature, only their relationship as two separate entities remains. I can go from one to the other, and there is no doubt about the kind of connection that exists between the two. If I can pass from one thing to the other, and each remains completely unchanged in the process, the only connection between them must be in terms of *space*. Any other relationship would involve their qualitative differences. But space is indifferent to everything except the fact that they are *separated*. If I say *A* is on top, and *B* is at the bottom, then it is a matter of indifference what *A* or *B* are. My only thought in connection with them is that they are two separate factors of the world presented to my senses.

When our mind approaches experience, it wants to overcome all separation; it wants to show that the power of the whole is visible in the particular. When we look at the world spatially, the only thing we seek to overcome is this separation itself. We strive to establish the *most universal connection*. This spatial relationship establishes that *A* and *B* are not each a world of their own, that they have something in common. This is what spatial juxtaposition means. If each thing existed only for itself, there could be no spatial juxtaposition. I would be unable to make any sort of connection between things.

Now, let us see where this establishing of external relationships between separate entities leads us. There is only *one* way I can think of two elements in such a relationship. I can think of *A* as *next to B*. I can do the same with two additional elements of the sensory world — *C* and *D*. I have thus determined a concrete relationship between *A* and *B* as well as between *C* and *D*. Now I can forget about the individual elements *A, B, C,* and *D*, and consider only the relationship between the two pairs. Clearly I can relate these particular entities to one another in the same way as I did *A* and *B*. I am merely relating concrete relationships. I can call these pairs *a* and *b*. Taking it another step, I can see the connection between *a* and *b*. But now I have lost track of all particularity. When I look at *a*, I no longer see *A* and *B* in relation to each other, and similarly with *b*. All I find in both cases, is the simple fact that relationships have been established. But the relationship is the same in both cases. What enabled me to distinguish *a* from *b* was that they referred to *A, B, C,* and *D*. If I abandon this vestige of particularity and relate only *a* and *b* — that is, the mere fact that they are relationships, not that specifics are related — I have again arrived quite generally at the spatial relationship from which I began. I can go no farther. I have achieved what I was striving for: an inner realization of *space*.

Herein lies the secret of three-dimensionality. In the first dimension I relate two concrete elements of the sensory world. In the second dimension, I establish a relationship between such spatial relationships: a relationship between relationships. The concrete phenomena have been eliminated, and all that remains are the concrete relationships. Now I bring these into spatial relationship, which means that I completely disregard the concrete nature of those relationships; I therefore find *exactly the same* thing in the one relationship that I found in the other. I establish relationships between like entities. Now the possibility of relating ceases, because all differences have disappeared.

What I began with as a point of view for my investigation — the completely external relationship — I have now come back to, but this time as a sensory picture. Having performed the process indicated above three times, I have gone from taking a spacial point of view to space itself, that is, to my point of departure. *This is why space must be three-dimensional.*

What I have shown here with regard to space is really only one particular example of our general method of observation. We observe concrete objects from a common point of view. In this way we gain concepts of particulars; we then observe these concepts themselves from the same perspective so that we have concepts of concepts; if we connect them again, they fuse as an ideal unity that may be seen only in relation to itself.

Let us take an example: I make the acquaintance of two people, *A* and *B*. I observe them from the perspective of friendship. In this case, I will have a very definite concept, *a*, of the friendship of these two individuals. Next I look at two other people, *C* and *D*, from the same viewpoint. I will have a different concept, *b*, of their friendship. Now I can proceed and place these two concepts of friendship side by side. What I am left with, when I abstract from my concrete observations, is the *general concept of friendship itself.* But this concept can also be achieved by observing the friendship of *E* and *F* from the same point of view and, later, that of *G* and *H*. In these cases as in countless others I can arrive at the concept of *friendship in general.* Essentially, all these concepts are identical, and when I look at them from the same viewpoint, I realize that I have found a unity. I am back where I started.

Space, then, is a way of viewing things, a way for our mind to unite what is separate. The three dimensions function as follows. The first dimension establishes a connection between two sensory perceptions (*sensations* in Kant's terms). It is a *concrete mental image.* The second dimension relates two concrete mental images to each other and enters the realm of *abstraction*. The third dimension only establishes the ideal *unity* of the two abstractions. Consequently, it is incorrect to think of the three dimensions of space as having the same significance. The nature of the first depends on the elements perceived. But the other two have a very specific and *different* meaning from the first. This was where Kant went wrong — thinking of space as a totality instead of as an entity that can in itself be conceptually defined.

Up to this point we have spoken of space as a relationship. We must now ask, Is there only this relationship of juxtaposition, or does each thing have an absolute position? These questions have not been touched on at all by our considerations so far. But let us try to see whether there is such a thing as "absolute location," or a specific "there." What do I actually mean by *there?* I only refer to a specific object in immediate proximity to the object under consideration. *There* means in proximity to a designated object. In this way absolute location is traced back to a *spatial relationship*, thus concluding our investigation.

Let us now put the question directly: What is space according to our inquiry? It is the necessity inherent in all things to overcome their separation in a completely external way, without reference to their essential nature, thus bringing them together in a unity, albeit an external one. Space is therefore a way of apprehending the world as a unity. *Space is an idea*, not a perception as Kant believed.

6. Goethe, Newton, and the Physicists

Originally, Goethe's interest in observing the essential nature of color was artistic. His intuitive genius soon recognized that the use of color in painting adhered to a deep lawfulness. He was unable to discover the nature of that lawfulness as long as he remained within the limits of theories of painting; nor were painters able to give him a satisfying answer. Painters knew in a practical way how to mix and use colors, but they were unable to conceptualize what they did. When Goethe went to Italy, he not only saw the most sublime examples of that art but also the most magnificent colors of nature, and a powerful desire awakened in him to understand the laws of color.

In his "History of Color Theory," Goethe gives a thorough account of historical aspects of the subject. Let us focus here on its psychological and factual aspects. Immediately after his return from Italy, Goethe began to study color. This intensified during 1790 and 1791 and remained a constant preoccupation of his until his death.

Let us consider the state of Goethe's worldview when he began to study color. He had already developed his grand thought of the meta-morphosis of organic entities. The discovery of the intermaxillary bone had already revealed the unity of all natural beings. The individual appeared to him as a particular modification of the idea. In his letters from Italy, he had expressed the notion that a plant is a plant because it carries within itself the "idea of the plant." To him, that idea is a concrete unity filled with spiritual content and active in each plant. It cannot be seen with physical eyes but can be apprehended with the eyes of the spirit. Those who see it, see it in *every* plant. This makes the entire plant kingdom — and, by further elaboration of this view, all of nature — a unity that can be comprehended by the mind.

But nobody can construct, from the idea alone, the multiplicity provided by our senses, The intuitive mind can know the idea, but the *particular forms* are accessible only when we direct our senses toward the outside, observing and contemplating. Why a modification of the idea takes one form and no other in the reality of our senses is a question whose answer cannot be found by intellectual speculations; we must *look* into the real world.

This is Goethe's particular way of viewing things, which can best be described as *empirical idealism*. We may summarize it this way; when observing the *multiplicity of things that arise for the senses*, to the extent that those things are similar, we can find a *spiritual unity* at their foundation, which is the source of all their similarities.

Thus Goethe came to ask, What is the spiritual unity behind the multiplicity of color perceptions? What do I perceive in *every* color? It quickly became clear to him that *light* was the necessary foundation of every color — no light, no color. Colors, however, are modifications of light. But now he had to find the element that modifies light and gives it specificity. He found that this element was lightless matter, or active darkness — in other words, that which opposes light. For him, therefore, each color was light modified by darkness.

It is incorrect to assume that when speaking of light Goethe meant concrete sunlight, or the usual "white light." The only real obstacle to an understanding of Goethe's color theory is the fact that people cannot let go of this notion, that they view sunlight with its complex composition as the representative of light as such. Light as Goethe sees it in its opposition to darkness, is a purely spiritual entity common to all color sensations. Although he never said so explicitly, his whole theory of color is presented in such a way that there is no other way to understand it. When he tested his theory by experimenting with sunlight, he did this only because sunlight, although the product of complex processes in the body of the Sun, nevertheless presents itself to us as a unity whose parts are suspended within it. What we obtain for the color theory by observing sunlight merely *approximates* the reality. We should not think that Goethe's theory implies that light and darkness as tangible realities are actually contained in each color. The reality of what meets our eye is only a particular shade of color. Only the mind can separate this sensory fact of color into two spiritual entities — light and nonlight.

The outer conditions and physical processes involved in this are not in the least affected by what has just been described. They are a completely different matter. There is no doubt that there is an oscillation in the ether when red appears to me. But, as has been shown (see pp. 172ff), the actual physical events involved in a perception have nothing to do with its *essential nature*.

One may argue that all sensations have been proven to be subjective and that, aside from occurrences in our brain, only the wave processes behind the sensations actually exist. This would render it impossible to speak of any *physical theory of perception*, but only of a theory of those underlying physical processes. This proof is not unlike the following argument: If someone located in *a* sends a telegram to me in *b*, the telegram I receive into my hands originated in *b*. The telegrapher is in *b*; he writes on a paper that never was in *a*, using ink that never was in *a*, and may not have any clue about where *a* actually is; in other words, it can be proven that what I have in front of my eyes did not originate in *a* at all. And yet all these things that originated in *b* are completely indifferent to the actual *content*, or essence, of the telegram; the thing that matters to me was simply mediated through *b*. If I wish to explain the meaning of the telegram, I must completely disregard what happened in *b*.

The same is true of the eye. Theory must encompass what is perceptible by the eye and look for interrelationships *within* this realm. Material processes in space and time may be very important for the *occurrence* of perceptions, but they have no relation to their essential nature.

This also applies to a question that is frequently asked today about whether the various natural phenomena of light, warmth, electricity, and so on are all caused by the same wave process in the ether. Heinrich Hertz (1857–1894) proved recently that electrical effects in space obey the same laws as the effects of light. One may infer from this that the waves that carry light also underlie electricity. It was already accepted that only *one* kind of vibration is active in the spectrum of sunlight, which produces warmth, light, or chemical effects depending on whether the reagents they contact are sensitive to heat, light, or chemical action.

All this goes without saying. If we investigate what happens in space while the entities under consideration are being mediated, we will find a *uniform* motion. In a medium where *only* motion is possible, any response to stimuli must be through motion. Any mediation that it carries out will be conducted in the form of motion. If I subsequently investigate the forms of this motion, I will not experience the nature of what is communicated, but only the way it is delivered to me. It is absurd to claim that warmth or light are motions. Motion is simply the response of matter capable of movement when it encounters light. Goethe himself lived to see the birth of the wave theory, and he saw nothing in it that did not agree with his own convictions about the nature of color.

We must let go of the idea that Goethe conceived of light and darkness as sense-perceptible realities and, instead, think of them *only* as principles, as spiritual entities. Then we will see his color theory in an entirely new light. If, like Newton, we see light as merely a mixture of all the colors, we lose any conception of "light" as a concrete entity. It evaporates into an empty generalization that has no correspondence to reality at all. Such abstract concepts were alien to Goethe. According to him, every concept had to have *concrete* content, but for him, *concrete* was not limited to the physical.

In reality, contemporary physics has no concept for light. It recognizes specific lights, or colors, that in certain combinations create the sensation "white." But this white cannot be considered the same as light. In fact, white is also a *mixed color*. Light in the Goethean sense is foreign to conventional physics, as is darkness. Goethe's theory of color moves in a realm untouched by the concepts of physicists, who know *nothing* of the fundamental concepts of Goethe's theory of color. It is therefore impossible for them to assess his theory, for Goethe begins where they end.

The constant talk about Goethe's relationship to Newton and to modern physics is based on a very superficial understanding of the issues that completely overlooks the fact that they are two entirely different things.

We are convinced that, if one correctly understands our discussion of the nature of sensations, one will also share the view of Goethe's color theory that has been presented here. But if one does not accept our fundamental theories, one will have to maintain the viewpoint of physical optics and reject Goethe's theory of color altogether.

Chapter 17

Goethe versus Atomism

1.

There is a great deal of talk these days about the progress of natural science in the nineteenth century. I believe that one can really only speak in this regard of significant scientific experience and how it has changed practical life. But when it comes to the fundamental conceptions through which modern science tries to *understand* the realm of experience, I must say that I consider them unhealthy and untenable when subjected to rigorous thinking [see pp. 76 and 166–67]. This view was expressed most recently by the well-known chemist Wilhelm Ostwald.[1] According to him,

> When asked, "How do you conceive of the inner makeup of the world?" every thoughtful scientist, from mathematicians to practicing physicians, will say that things are made up of moving *atoms*, and that those atoms and the *forces* acting between them are the ultimate realities; from these, individual phenomena appear. We have all heard it said hundreds of times that this is the only way to understand the physical world — that we must revert to the mechanics of atoms. Matter and motion seem to be the only concepts from which the whole multiplicity of natural phenomena can be derived. One might call this view *scientific materialism.*

1. Friedrich Wilhelm Ostwald (1853–1932), German physical chemist who helped to establish physical chemistry as a specific scientific discipline; he is credited with the law of dilution of an electrolyte (1888); researched the electrical conductivity of organic acids; developed a quantitative color theory; invented a process for preparing nitric acid by oxidizing ammonia. His lecture "Overcoming Scientific Materialism" was presented to the association of German scientists and doctors, Lübeck, September 20, 1895, shortly before this chapter was written. — ED.

I wrote in the previous chapter that the fundamental views of contemporary physicists are untenable. Ostwald concurs: *"This mechanistic view of the world does not serve the purpose for which it was designed.... It contradicts inarguable, well-known, and accepted truths."* This agreement continues. I say, *"The sense-perceptible world as it presents itself to us is an aggregate of metamorphosing perceptions without an underlying material substratum"* [p. 175]. And Ostwald says,

> When we realize that everything we know about a material relates to its properties, it becomes clear that *it is ridiculous to assert that a certain material is present, but without any of its properties.* The only utility of such a purely formal assumption is in creating an agreement between general facts of chemical processes, in particular the stochiometric laws of mass, and an *arbitrary concept of immutable matter.*

And in the present book, "These are the considerations that forced me to consider any theory of nature to be impossible that, on principle, goes *beyond* the realm of the perceived world, and that have led me to embrace *the sensory world as the only object of natural science*" [p. 165]. And Ostwald's lecture:

> What is our experience of the physical world? It is obviously no more than what our sensory organs give us.... The task of science is to gather *realities,* provable and measurable quantities, and to discover their interrelationships so that when one is given, the other will result. And this must be done not by postulating hypothetical models but by verifying the interdependent aspects of measurable quantities.

If we ignore the fact that Ostwald speaks from the perspective of contemporary science and, consequently, sees only the measurable aspects of the sensory world, his statement here coincides with mine: "Theory must encompass what is perceptible by the eye and *look for the interrelationships within this realm*" [p. 189].

In my discussion of Goethe's theory of color, I fight the same battle as Professor Ostwald's lecture against the intellectual foundations of conventional science. It is true that I focus on concepts that do not entirely agree with Ostwald's ideas, because (as I will show) he proceeds from the same superficial assumptions as the scientific materialists he opposes. I have also demonstrated that the faulty foundations of the modern view of nature are responsible for the unhealthy assessments of Goethe's color theory.

Let me proceed in greater detail with my discussion of the modern view of nature. To assess the soundness of this view, I will consider the *goal* it has set itself.

One finds in Descartes — not without justification — the basic formula that the modern view of nature has adopted to judge the perceptible world:

> When I consider physical things more closely, there is little in them that I can grasp *clearly* and *distinctly:* magnitude, or extension in length, breadth, and depth; form, which results from the termination of extension; the location of bodies of diverse forms with reference to one another; and motion, or the change of location; to which may be added substance, duration, and number. But light, colors, sounds, odors, tastes, heat, cold, and the other tactile qualities (smoothness, roughness), enter my mind with such *obscurity* and *confusion* that I am unable to determine whether they are true or false — in other words, whether or not the ideas I have of these qualities are in truth the ideas of real objects or only represent fantastic things that could never exist. (*Meditations*, Part 3)

This statement of Descartes represents what has become the habitual thinking of today's scientists — so much so that, to them, any other way of thinking is really not worth considering. They say, We perceive light as the result of a kinetic process that can be expressed mathematically. When a color appears, they trace it to a vibration and calculate the number of waves per second. They believe that the whole sensory world will be explained when we can trace every perception back to relationships that can be expressed mathematically. According to this view, a mind that could provide such explanations would have achieved the highest possible insight into the natural world. Du Bois-Reymond, a good example of such scientists, said of such a mind: "For it, the hairs on our heads would be numbered, and not a single sparrow would fall to the ground without its knowledge."[2] To

---

2. *Über die Grenzen des Naturerkennens* (On the Limits of Natural Science) Leipzig, 1882, p. 13. Du Bois-Reymond (1818–1896), German physiologist and professor in Berlin, best known for his research in animal electricity, physiology of muscles and nerves, and metabolic processes. — ED.

treat the world as a mathematical exercise is the ideal of conventional science.

Because there is no way for the parts of hypothetical matter to begin moving without the intervention of external forces, modern scientists make forces themselves into elements that can be used to explain the world. As Du Bois-Reymond puts it, "To know nature … means to trace changes *within* material bodies to the movements of atoms caused by their central forces that are independent of time, which means understanding natural processes in terms of *the mechanics of atoms*" (Ibid., p. 10). Through the introduction of the concept of force, mathematics becomes mechanics.

Today's philosophers are so deeply influenced by scientists that they have lost all courage to think independently. They do not hesitate to accept the views of scientists. Wilhelm Wundt, one of the most respected of German philosophers, says, "In keeping with and applying the principle that, given the qualitative immutability of matter, all natural processes ultimately consist of motion, the goal of physics is its translation into *applied mechanics*" (*Logic*, 1830–1833).[3]

Du Bois-Reymond finds it a matter of psychological experience that "achieving such a resolution (that is, reducing natural processes to the mechanics of atoms) always temporarily satisfies our need for causal explanation." This may well be a matter of experience for Du Bois-Reymond, but it must be said that there are others who are unsatisfied with such banal explanations of the physical world. One such person is Goethe. Anyone whose need for causal explanation is satisfied by reducing natural processes to the mechanics of atoms is incapable of understanding Goethe.

2.

Size, form, position, motion, force, and so on are just as much sensations as, for example, light, color, sound, smell, taste, cold, or heat. Any time we consider the size of a thing, isolated from its other characteristics, we are no longer dealing with the *actual* thing but with an intellectual abstraction. It makes no sense to attribute to an abstraction from sensory experience a higher degree of reality than to a

---

3. Wilhelm Wundt (1832–1920), physiologist, psychologist, and founder of experimental psychology. A student of Johannes Müller, he headed the first psychological laboratory. — ED.

sense-perceptible thing itself. The only advantage of employing spatial
and numerical relationships rather than other sensory perceptions lies
in their greater simplicity and the greater ease of surveying them at a
glance. Mathematical science gains its certainty from such simplicity
and surveyability. Modern science always reduces physical processes
to mathematical and mechanical terms, because of the ease and convenience with which they can be manipulated. Human thinking prefers
convenience. This comes to expression in Ostwald's lecture quoted
from above. This scientist wants to replace matter and force with
energy. Listen to him:

> What is the factor that determines when one of our senses be-
> comes active? No matter how we look at it, all we find is this: *the
> instruments of our senses react to energy differentials between
> themselves and their environment.* If we lived in a world where
> the temperature was always that of our body, we would never
> know anything about warmth, just as we have no experience
> of the constant atmospheric pressure under which we live. Only
> when the pressure changes do we become aware of it. . . . Just
> imagine someone hitting you with a stick! What is it that you
> feel — the stick or its energy? We must answer, its energy, be-
> cause the stick is the most harmless thing in the world as long
> as it is not being swung. But you will reply that we can bump
> into a resting stick. This is true. But what we experience is, as
> I said, an energy differential with our sensory apparatus, and
> from this perspective it makes no difference whether the stick
> strikes against us or we move into it. If they both moved at the
> same speed in the same direction, the stick would no longer exist
> from the point of view of our feeling sense, because it could not
> contact us and effect an exchange of energy.

Here Ostwald is isolating *energy* from the realm of perceptions —
that is, isolating it from everything that is not energy. He reduces
all perceptions to a single characteristic of the perceptible world —
the expression of energy — and thus to an abstraction. The extent to
which Ostwald is caught in current scientific habits is very obvious.
If we were to ask him, the only justification he could find for his approach is that it is a fact of psychological experience, that his need for
causal explanation is satisfied by reducing the processes of nature to
exchanges of energy. In fact, it makes no difference whether Du Bois-

Reymond resorts to the mechanics of atoms or Ostwald to exchanges of energy. In either case, the human need for mental convenience is satisfied.

Ostwald ends his lecture by saying,

> No matter how necessary and useful energy may be for understanding nature, is it *enough* to explain the physical world? Or are there phenomena that cannot be wholly represented by currently known laws of energy?...I feel a need to be as responsible in answering this question as I have been in the rest of my presentation today, and I must emphasize that the answer is *No!* Irrespective of the tremendous advantages of explaining the world in terms of energy (as opposed to materialistic or mechanistic explanations), in my opinion, there are already several cases that *cannot* be explained by the known laws of energy. These point to the existence of principles that go beyond them. Energetics will survive side by side with these new laws. But in the future it will not be, as we think of it now, the most comprehensive principle for the mastery of natural phenomena; rather, it will probably be seen as merely a special expression of more general relations *whose form we can barely imagine today.*

3.

If our scientists also read the writings of those who are not part of their club, Professor Ostwald could never have made such a remark. For as early as 1891, in my introduction to Goethe's color theory I wrote that we can very well imagine such "forms," and that science in the future will have the task of elaborating on Goethe's fundamental scientific ideas.

We can no more "reduce" physical processes to the mechanics of atoms than to states of energy. Such reductionism serves only to divert our attention from the content of the real sensory world, directing it instead toward abstractions whose impoverished qualities are nevertheless ultimately taken from that sensory world. We cannot explain one group of sensory qualities — light, color, sound, smell, taste, warmth and so on — by reducing them to another group of sensory qualities — size, form, location, number, energy, and so on. The task of natural science cannot be to "reduce" one category of qualities to another; rather, it must find the connections and relationships among the perceptible qualities of the world. When we do this, we discover particular conditions under which one sensory perception leads with necessity to another. We discover that particular phenomena are more intimately connected than others. We establish connections that are more than the haphazard results of random observation. We recognize that particular relationships are *necessary* and others are *coincidental*. Goethe calls necessary relationships between phenomena *archetypal phenomena*.

We know that we are dealing with an archetypal phenomenon when we can say that one sensory perception inevitably gives rise to another. This is what we call a *natural law*. For example, when we say that "objects expand when heated," we have expressed a lawful relationship between phenomena of the sensory world: warmth and expansion. We have identified an *archetypal phenomenon* and expressed it as a *natural law*. Archetypal phenomena correspond to what Ostwald was seeking — those forms that express the most universal relationships within inorganic nature.

The laws of mathematics and mechanics, like laws that formulate other sensory relationships, are also only expressions of archetypal phenomena. Kirchhoff is mistaken when he says that the task of mechanics is to describe natural motions in "the *simplest* and *most complete way*."[4] Mechanics not only describes natural motions in the simplest and most complete way, but also looks for certain *necessary* motions within the sum total of motions occurring in nature. It then formulates these necessary motions as *fundamental mechanical laws*. Only extreme thoughtlessness can account for the fact that this statement by Kirchhoff has been quoted repeatedly as tremendously significant, without the realization that the establishment of the simplest mechanical laws disproves it.

The archetypal phenomenon represents a lawful relationship between elements of the phenomenal world. One can hardly say anything more inappropriate than Helmholtz did in a speech to the Weimar Goethe Conference on June 11, 1892:

---

4. Gustav Robert Kirchhoff (1824–1887), German physicist and professor in Heidelberg and Berlin. "Kirchhoff's laws" allow for the circulation of currents, voltages, and resistances of electrical networks. He helped to discover a method of spectral analysis that led to the discovery of cesium (1860) and rubidium (1861); he also researched the Sun's composition. — ED.

It is a shame that Goethe was unaware of Huyghens' wave theory of light, which had already been established at the time. There he would have found a much more correct and concrete "archetypal phenomenon" than the hardly suitable and entangled process he selected for this purpose in the colors arising in turbid media.[5]

He claims that waves — which are imperceptible and constitute a *speculative addition* to the phenomenon of light — would have provided Goethe with a more correct and concrete *"archetypal phenomenon"* than does a process unfolding before our very eyes. This process is hardly complicated, consisting as it does of light seen through a cloudy medium as *yellow,* and darkness seen through a lighted medium as *blue.* The "reduction" of sense-perceptible processes to imperceptible mechanical movements has become such a habit for modern physicists that they seem unaware of having replaced reality with an abstraction.

Pronouncements like this by Helmholtz should be allowed only when statements of Goethe's like the one below have been refuted:

> The highest achievement would be to understand that everything factual is already theory. The blue of the sky reveals to us the fundamental law of color. *Do not look for anything behind the phenomena; they themselves are the theory. (Verses in Prose)*

Goethe remains *within* the realm of the phenomena; modern physicists gather a few bits and pieces of the world and place them *behind* the phenomena in order to derive the phenomena of actually perceived experience from these hypothetical realities.

4.

Certain young physicists claim that they do not make higher claims for the idea of material motion than for their sensory experience. One such individual is *Anton Lampa,* who has performed the remarkable feat of being both a mechanistic scientist and a follower of Indian

---

5. *Goethes Vorahnungen kommender wissenschaftlicher Ideen,* Berlin, 1892, p. 34. Herman Ludwig Ferdinand von Helmholtz (1821–1894), physicist, anatomist, and physiologist, was a founder of the principle of conservation of energy. He determined the velocity of nerve impulses, invented the ophthalmoscope, and investigated the mechanisms of sight and hearing. — ED.

mysticism.[6] He argues against Ostwald's statements by saying that his battle with scientific materialism

merely tilts at windmills. Where is the giant of scientific materialism? He does not even exist. Once upon a time there was the scientific materialism of Büchner, Voigt, and Moleschott. There still is, but not in the natural sciences, because it is not at home there. This was overlooked by Ostwald, otherwise he would have taken a stand only against the *mechanistic* view. Because of his misunderstanding, however, he does this only incidentally, and if it had not been for his misunderstanding, he probably would not have done so at all. Is it possible then that, following paths opened up by Kirchhoff, science can conceive of matter as materialism has done? Impossible; this is an obvious contradiction. The concept of matter, like that of force, takes on meaning only as precisely determined by the demand for the simplest possible description, or in Kantian terms, in an empirical sense. And if a scientist attaches further meaning to the word *matter*, he does so, not as a scientist but as a materialistic philosopher.[7]

Judging from these words, Lampa must be considered a typical scientist of our time. He uses the more convenient, mechanistic explanations, but he avoids thinking any further about the real nature of such explanations, because he fears becoming entangled in contradictions that he cannot resolve.

How is it possible for any clear-minded person to make sense of the concept of matter without going beyond the world of experience? In the experiential world, there are bodies of various sizes and positions; there are movements and forces; there are the phenomena of light, color, warmth, electricity, life, and so on. But experience does not tell us that size, warmth, color, and so on, are attached to "matter." Matter cannot be found in our experience. If we want to think matter, it must be thought up and *added* to our experience.

This intellectual addition of matter to the phenomenally experienced world is noticeable in the physical and physiological deliberations so common today in natural science as influenced by

---

6. See *Nights of the Seeker*, Braunschweig, 1893. Anton Lampa (1868–1938), Austrian educator and pioneer of high-frequency spectroscopy. — ED.

7. *Die Zeit*, Vienna, Nov. 30, 1895. — R. STEINER.

Kant and Johannes Müller.[8] They have led us to believe that the external events leading to sounds in the ear, light in the eye, or warmth in the organs sensitive to heat are in no way related to the *sensations* of sound, light, and warmth. These external events are simply supposed to be specific movements of matter. Scientists determine what sort of external motions cause sound, light, or color to arise in the human soul. They conclude that red, yellow, or blue exist nowhere outside of the human organism, but that there is a wavelike motion of a subtle, elastic matter, the ether, which is perceived as red, yellow, or blue when it is sensed through the eye. If there were no eye to sense this, there would be no color, only the movement of ether. They claim that ether is an objective fact and that color is subjective and created within the human body. Professor Wundt of Leipzig, who is acclaimed as one of the greatest philosophers in Germany today, says that matter is a substrate, "never observable directly but only through its effects." And he finds that "any explanation of the phenomena that does not contradict itself" must assume such a substrate (see *Logic*, vol. 2). Descartes' delusion about clear and confused mental pictures has become a fundamental way of representing matters in physics.

5.

Those whose capacity for forming a worldview has not been destroyed by Descartes, Locke, Kant, and modern physiology will never understand how it is possible to conceive of light, color sound, warmth, and so on as merely subjective states of the human organism, and at the same time claim that a completely objective world of processes exists outside the organism. If we claim that the human organism itself produces sound, color, and warmth, we must also say that it produces extension, magnitude, location, movement, forces, and so on. These mathematical and mechanical attributes are in fact inseparable from the rest of the perceptible world. Only abstract thinking separates the elements of space, number, motion, and the expressions of force from warmth, sound, color and other sensory qualities. Mathematical and mechanical laws refer to abstract entities and processes drawn from the world of experience, and as such they

---

8. In 1826, Johannes Müller (1801–1858), German psychologist and physiologist, proposed his theory of "specific nerve energies," which stated that different nerves (optical, auditive, etc.) carry a "code" that identifies their origin in the brain. — ED.

can therefore only be applied to the experienced world. But if we were to claim that mathematical and mechanical processes are also subjective, nothing would remain to serve as content for our concept of objective things and occurrences. And we cannot derive phenomena from empty concepts.

Modern scientists, and philosophers, their baggage carriers, cling to the idea that sensory perceptions are merely subjective states evoked by objective events. As long as this is so, healthy thinking must object that either they are playing with empty concepts or else they attribute to the objective world a content borrowed from that part of the world declared subjective. I have addressed this absurdity in several of my writings.[9]

I will not go into the question of whether wave processes and the forces that cause them (from which the most recent physics derives all natural phenomena) are to be ascribed to a different form of reality from that of sensory perceptions. I will simply ask, What is it that can be accomplished by mathematical and mechanistic views of nature? Anton Lampa's opinion is that

> mathematics as subject and mathematics as method are not the same, since mathematical methods can be applied without mathematics. Faraday, who could barely square a binomial, provides a classic example of this in his experimental investigations of electricity. Mathematics is simply a means of abbreviating logical processes, thus helping us with many complex matters that would prove too much for our usual modes of logical thinking. But mathematics does much more; to the extent that each formula expresses the process of its own becoming, it can build a living bridge to the elementary phenomena that served as the starting point of the investigation. Therefore a method that cannot use mathematics — which is the case whenever magnitudes are immeasurable — must not only adhere to strict logic if it is to use mathematical methodology, but it must also be very careful in following matters back to basic phenomena. Otherwise, it goes astray exactly where it lacks mathematical structure. When it achieves this, however, it may properly claim to be

---

9. *The Science of Knowing: Outline of an Epistemology Implicit in the Goethean Worldview*, 1886; *Truth and Science*, 1892; *Intuitive Thinking as a Spiritual Path: A Philosophy of Freedom* (formerly: *The Philosophy of Spiritual Activity*), 1894. — ED.

"mathematical" as a distinction of its precision. (*Nights of the Seeker,* p. 92)

I would not spend so much time with Lampa if he were not such a perfect example of the contemporary natural scientist. He satisfies his philosophical needs through Indian mysticism, which means that he does not muddle his mechanistic view of nature with all sorts of incidental philosophizing. The theory of nature he has in mind is, so to speak, the "pure" view of today's science. I find that Lampa has completely ignored an important characteristic of mathematics. True, every mathematical equation does "build a living bridge" to the elementary phenomena that served as the starting point for an investigation, but the elementary phenomena are essentially the same as the more complex factors from which the bridge is built.

Mathematicians trace the properties of complex spatial and numerical structures, as well as their mutual interrelationships, back to the properties and relationships of the most basic numerical and spatial structures. Mechanical engineers do the same in their field. They trace *composite* motions and forces back to simple, easily surveyable motions and forces. To do this, they employ mathematical laws to the extent that movements and the effects of forces can be expressed in geometric forms and numerical equations. In a mathematical equation that expresses a mechanical law, the individual elements, or equations, are no longer purely mathematical patterns but represent forces and motions. The relationships in which these formulae are embedded are not determined by purely mathematical lawfulness but by the actual properties of forces and movements. The minute we forget the specific meaning of these mechanical formulae, we are no longer dealing with mechanical lawfulness but only with mathematical lawfulness.

The relationship between mechanics and mathematics is paralleled by that between physics and mechanics. The task of physicists is to trace the complicated processes of color, sound, warmth, electricity, magnetism, and so on to simple occurrences *within the same sphere.* They must, for example, trace complicated color events to the simplest occurrences of color. In doing so, they must use mechanical and mathematical laws to the extent that color phenomena involve patterns that can be analyzed spatially and numerically. The mathematical method, when applied to physics, would mean investigating the connections among colors, sounds, and so on *within* those phenomena themselves — not tracing them back to forces and movements in matter devoid of color or sound.

Modern physics bypasses sound, color, and other qualities as such and examines only unchanging forces of attraction or repulsion and motions in space. Under the influence of this approach, physics has largely become a form of applied math and mechanics, and the other areas of science are headed in that direction as well.

It is impossible to build a "living bridge" between the fact that a particular movement of colorless matter exists at a given location in space and the fact that at another location someone sees red. Only motion can be derived from motion. Because there is a motion that affects the senses and consequently the brain, it follows — according to the mathematical and mechanical method — that the brain will be stimulated to respond with certain motions, but not that it will perceive actual colors, sounds, and so on. Du Bois-Reymond had already acknowledged this when he asked,

> What relationship can there be between the motion of particular atoms in my brain, on the one hand, and, on the other, the immediate, undefinable but undeniable fact that I experience pain, pleasure, sweetness, the smell of a rose, organ music, or red. . . . Motion can engender only motion.[10]

Du Bois-Reymond sees in this a limit to scientific knowledge. But the reason one cannot derive the experience of seeing red from a particular movement is, in my opinion, very easy to show. The quality "red" and a certain process of motion are in reality an indivisible unity. The separation of the two occurrences can only be an intellectual, conceptual one. The particular motion that corresponds to the quality of red has no independent reality; it is an abstraction. It is just as absurd to attempt to derive the experience of seeing red from a process of motion as it would be to try to derive the actual properties of a cube-shaped salt crystal from the mathematical formula for the cube. It is not a limitation of our knowledge that prevents us from deriving other sensory qualities from motions; attempting to do so simply makes no sense.

---

10. *On the Limits of Scientific Knowledge* (*Über die Grenzen des Naturerkennens*), pp. 35, 34. — R. Steiner.

6.

The desire to bypass colors, sounds, and warmth as such and deal only with the corresponding mechanical processes must arise from the notion that the simple laws of mathematics and mechanics are for some reason more easily understood than the characteristics and interrelationships of the other aspects of our perceptual world. But this is certainly not the case. We claim to have no difficulty in conceiving of the simplest properties and relationships in spatial and numerical configurations, because we can survey them easily and completely. All mathematical and mechanical understanding involves reducing matters to simple facts that can be understood as soon as we become aware of them. The statement that two values are equal to a third and, therefore, must also be equal to each other is understood immediately when we become aware of its content. Similarly, simple phenomena in the realm of sound, color, and other sensory perceptions are recognized through direct observation.

Physicists exclude the specific qualities of sound and color from the realm of phenomena and consider only their corresponding kinetic events, simply because their preconceptions lead them to believe that simple mathematical or mechanical facts are easier to understand than elementary perceptions of sound or color. And because they cannot conceive of motions without something that moves, they postulate a material devoid of all qualities as the carrier of motion. Only those who are imprisoned by this bias will fail to notice that kinetic states themselves are connected to sense-perceptible qualities. The contents of the oscillating motions that correspond to various sounds are the qualities of the sounds themselves. The same is true of all sensory qualities. Direct awareness, not the speculative addition of an abstract matter, allows us to recognize the content of the oscillating motions of the phenomenal world.

7.

I know that what I say here must sound impossible to the ears of contemporary physicists. But I cannot accept Wundt's view that the thinking habits of modern scientists are the binding norms of logic (*Logic,* vol. 2). The thoughtlessness of this assumption is particularly clear where he examines Ostwald's attempt to replace the idea of vibrating matter with the oscillating movement of energy. Wundt says,

> [The existence of] interference phenomena makes it necessary to assume a kind of oscillating motion. But since motion is unthinkable without a moving substrate, light phenomena must be traced back to some sort of mechanical process. However, Ostwald tried to elude this second assumption by defining "radiant energy" as energy in oscillating motion rather than as the vibrations of a material medium. In other words, we are looking at a two-sided concept that has a visible side and one that is wholly conceptual; the very presence of this ambiguity strikingly suggests that the concept of energy itself needs an analysis that leads back to observable elements. An actual motion can only be defined as a change of location of an actual substratum in space. The existence of that substratum can only be revealed either by the effects of the forces emanating from it or by the functions of those forces we assume to be sustained by it. But it seems impossible to me that these functions of force, which can themselves only be grasped as concepts, can be conceived of as moving unless we *postulate* some sort of substratum.

Ostwald's concept of energy is much closer to actual reality than Wundt's allegedly "real" substrate. The perceived phenomena of light, warmth, electricity, magnetism, and so on can all be brought under the general concept of force output, or energy. When light or warmth, for example, trigger a change in a body, an energy output is effected. When we describe light or warmth as "energy," we disregard their specific qualities in favor of one general, shared property. Such a property certainly does not exhaust all the aspects of reality, but it is a real property. On the other hand, the concept of the properties that physicists and their allies in philosophy have attributed to their hypothetical *matter* is inherently self-contradictory. These properties are borrowed from the sensory world, and yet they are supposed to apply to a substrate that is not a part of the sensory realm.

It is inconceivable how Wundt can maintain that the concept of "radiant energy" is impossible simply because it has two aspects — one *physically observable* and one that is *conceptual*. Wundt the philosopher fails to understand that all concepts related to sensory reality must contain both an observable and a purely conceptual

element. The concept "salt crystal cube" has the *perceptible* component of a salt crystal accessible to the senses and a *purely conceptual*
component established by solid geometry.

8.

The evolution of natural science in recent centuries has led to the
destruction of all conceptions that would allow science to participate
in a worldview that satisfies higher human needs. It has led "modern"
scientists to claim that it is absurd to say that *concepts* and *ideas*
belong to the real world in the same way as active forces and matter
occupying space. For such minds, concepts and ideas are products of
the human brain and nothing more. The Scholastics still understood
the nature of these matters, but modern science despises Scholasticism
without knowing what it is — especially which aspect of Scholasticism
was sound and which was not.

What was sound about Scholasticism was the feeling that concepts
and ideas are not merely fantasies invented by the human mind to
understand reality, but that they are connected in some way with
the things themselves, even more so than matter and force. This
healthy Scholastic sensibility was a legacy of the grand views of
Plato and Aristotle. What was unhealthy about Scholasticism, on
the other hand, was that this feeling became mixed with conceptions
that entered the medieval development of Christianity. This development claimed that an otherworldly, and therefore unknowable, God
was the source of all spiritual realities, including concepts and ideas.
It depended on faith in something that is not of this world.

A healthy human mind, on the other hand, adheres to this world
and has no need of any other. But it also imbues this world with spirit.
Such a mind attributes worldly reality to concepts and ideas just as
it does to the things and events of the sensory world. Greek philosophy flowed from this healthy thinking, and Scholasticism retained
an intimation of it. But Scholasticism tried to reinterpret it so that it
would correspond to an otherworldly Christian faith. Concepts and
ideas were no longer considered the most profound thing that human
beings could behold in the processes of this world; rather, it was God
and the other world. Once we apprehend the idea of something, we
have no need to look further for its "source," for we have found what
satisfies the human need for knowledge. But what did the Scholastics

care about such a need for knowledge? They wanted to preserve what they saw as the Christian view of God. They wanted to find the source of the world in an otherworldly God even though their search for the inner being of things led only to concepts and ideas.

9.

Over the centuries, Christian concepts became more powerful than the fading feeling handed down from Greek antiquity. People lost their intuitive sense for the reality of concepts and ideas. In the process, they lost their sense for spirit itself. People began to worship the purely material; Newton's era began in the natural sciences. There was no longer any talk of the unity that underlies the world's multiplicity. All unity was denied and degraded to a merely "human" notion. In nature, people saw only a multiplicity, an aggregate of particulars. It was this fundamental view that led Newton to see light not as a primal unity but as something composite. In his *Materials for a History of Color Theory*, Goethe described aspects of this historical development. It becomes clear that the conceptions of more recent science have led to unsound views in the realm of color theory. This science no longer understands light as one of nature's qualities. This is the reason science does not know why, under certain circumstances, light appears colored, or how color arises within the realm of light.

Chapter 18

Goethe's Worldview
in His *Verses in Prose*

We are not satisfied with what nature freely offers to the observing
mind. We feel that, to produce the vast variety of her creations, nature uses driving forces that she initially conceals from the observer.
Nature herself does not speak her final word. Our experience reveals
what nature can create but not how that creation takes place. The
means for unveiling the driving forces of nature exist in the human
mind itself. It is here that ideas arise that throw light on the way
nature brings forth her creations. What the phenomena of the external world conceal manifests within the human being. What we
think through as natural laws is not invented as an addition to nature; it is nature's own inner constitution. The mind is simply the
theater in which nature allows the secrets of her creativity to manifest. What we *observe* is only one aspect of things. The other is
what then wells up within our minds. The same things speak to
us from outside and from within us. We realize the complete reality only when we join the language of the outer world with that
of our inner being. True philosophers throughout time have desired
nothing but to proclaim the essential nature of things — what those
things themselves express when the mind is offered as their organ of
communication.

When we allow our inner being to speak about nature, we recognize that nature herself fails to fully achieve what her driving forces
could accomplish. Inwardly, we see in more complete form what experience contains. We discover that nature has not attained her goals
in her creations and feel a need to express her intentions in more perfect form. Thus we create forms that express what nature willed, but

209

could achieve only to a certain point. Such forms are works of art: human creations showing in more perfect form what nature manifests less perfectly.

Philosophers and artists have a common goal; they attempt to portray the perfection that their spirit sees when they allow nature to impress itself upon them. But they have different means available for achieving this goal. When philosophers are confronted with a natural process, a *thought,* or *idea* lights up within them. And this is what they express. In artists, on the other hand, a picture of the process arises that reveals it more completely than it could be observed in the external world. Philosophers and artists develop their observations differently. Artists do not need to know the driving forces of nature as they reveal themselves to the philosopher. When they perceive a thing or event, an image immediately arises in their mind in which the laws of nature are more completely expressed than in the corresponding things or events of the outer world. Laws in the form of thoughts do not need to enter their mind. Nevertheless, knowledge and art are related inwardly. They show the *potentials* of nature that have not been fully realized in the external world.

Now, if these driving forces come to expression in the mind of a true artist not only as perfect pictures of things, but also as thoughts, then the creative source common to both philosophy and art appears with special clarity before our eyes. Goethe is such an artist. He reveals the same mysteries to us in his works of art and in his thoughts. What takes on form in his poetry, he states as thoughts in his essays on science and art and in his *Verses in Prose.* These essays and verses offer such profound satisfaction because one sees in them the harmony of art and knowledge realized in a single individual. There is something uplifting in the feeling that arises in connection with each of Goethe's thoughts: someone is speaking here who can see as images what he expresses in ideas. This feeling strengthens the power of such a thought. All that originates from the highest striving of a *single* personality must be inwardly connected. Goethe's wisdom answers the question, What kind of philosophy corresponds with true art? I will now try to give a coherent sketch of this philosophy born of the spirit of a true artist.

•

The thought-content that arises within us when we confront the external world is truth. We cannot seek any knowledge other than the insight that we ourselves produce. Those who look behind things for something else that is supposed to explain them have not realized that all questions about the essential nature of things can arise only from our human need to permeate our perceptions with thinking. Things speak to us, and our inner nature speaks as we observe them. Both sides of this dialog arise from the same primal being, and we are called on to bring about their mutual understanding. This is what knowledge is all about. Those who understand inherent human needs seek this and nothing else. For those who lack such understanding, the things of the outer world remain alien. Such people do not hear the essential nature of things speaking out of their own inner being. Consequently, they presume that it is concealed behind the things. They believe in another external world behind the perceptible one. But things remain external only as long as we merely observe them. When we reflect on them, they are no longer outside us; we merge with their inner aspect. The contrast between objective, external percept and subjective, inner world of thought exists for us only as long as we fail to recognize that these worlds belong together. Our inner world is nature's inner being.

These thoughts are not refuted by the fact that different people view things differently. Nor are they refuted because people are organized differently so that we cannot know if a color is seen exactly the same way by different people. The question is not whether we form precisely the same judgment about something, but whether the language of our inner being is the language that expresses the essential nature of things. Individual judgments vary according to individual organization and the perspective of observation, but all judgments arise from the same element and lead to the essential nature of things. This may be expressed in various nuances of thinking, but it nevertheless remains the nature of things.

The human being is the vehicle through which nature unveils her secrets. The deepest essence of the world is manifested in the subjective personality.

When healthy human nature works as a whole; when we feel ourselves within the world as in a beautiful, worthy, and precious whole; when harmonious satisfaction grants us pure and free delight, then the universe, if it were self-aware, would rejoice at having attained its goal, and it would marvel at the pinnacle of its own becoming and being.[1]

The goal of the universe and the true nature of existence cannot be found in the products of the external world but in what lives within the human spirit and what arises from it. Thus, for Goethe, scientists make a mistake by attempting to penetrate the inner being of nature with instruments and objective experiments:

> Insofar as we make use of our healthy senses, we ourselves are the best and most exact scientific instruments possible. The greatest misfortune of modern physics is that its experiments have been set apart from the human being, as it were; physics refuses to recognize nature in anything not detected by artificial instruments, and even uses them to limit and to prove what nature can accomplish.... We human beings exist at such a high level so that what otherwise could not manifest itself does come to expression in us. What is a string and its various mechanical divisions compared to the ear of a musician? Indeed, we may ask, What are the elementary phenomena of nature herself compared to humankind, since we must first tame and transform them before we can assimilate them to a certain degree? (*Verses in Prose*)

As human beings, if we want to know the essential nature of things, we must allow them to speak through our own mind. All that we can say about their essential nature is taken from the spiritual experiences of our own inner being. Only out of ourselves can we form a conclusion about the world. We must think anthropomorphically. When we say something about the simplest phenomenon — when two bodies collide, for example — we anthropomorphize. Even to conclude that one body strikes another is anthropomorphic. If we want to go beyond mere observation of what happens, we must connect it to the experience of our own body when it sets another body in motion. All physical explanations are hidden anthropomorphisms. We humanize nature by explaining her; we project inner human experiences into her.

---

1. Quoted from Goethe's essay "Winckelmann." — R. STEINER.

But these subjective experiences are the essential inner nature of things. Thus, one cannot argue that we do not recognize objective truth, or the "things in themselves," because we can form only subjective representations of them.[2] There can be no question of any truth

---

2. Goethe's views contrast sharply with Kant's philosophy. Kant assumes that our inner world of mental images is governed by the laws of the human spirit, and that, consequently, everything brought into it from the outside can exist there only as a subjective reflection. According to this view, we do not perceive the things in themselves, but rather only the images that result from how those things affect us, and from how we connect those effects according to the laws of our intellect and reason. Kant and the Kantians have no inkling that the essential being of things speaks through our reason. Consequently, Kantian philosophy could never mean anything to Goethe. When he did acquire some of Kant's principles, he gave them a completely different meaning than they had in the teachings of their originator.

A note that came to light only with the opening of the Goethe archives in Weimar makes it clear that Goethe was very much aware of this antithesis between his own view and that of Kant. To Goethe, Kant's fundamental error was that he "regards the *subjective* cognitive capacity itself as an *object* and that he distinguishes the meeting point of the *subjective* and the *objective* sharply indeed but not without error." The subjective and the objective meet when we unite the expression of the outer world with what our inner being speaks and these become the unified being of things. Then the antithesis between subjective and objective disappears completely into this unified reality.

I indicated this in chapter 11 (beginning on p. 136). Now, in the first issue of *Kant Studies,* Karl Vorländer attacks what I wrote there. According to him, my view of the antithesis between Goethe and Kant is "strongly one-sided, at best, and contradicts Goethe's own clear statements, [and this because of a] complete misunderstanding [on my part] of Kant's transcendental methods." Vorländer has no idea of the worldview in which Goethe lived. There is no purpose in arguing with him, because we speak different languages. The fact that he fails to understand anything I have to say is an indication of how clear his thinking is. For example, I commented on this statement of Goethe:

> As soon as we become aware of surrounding objects, we regard them in reference to ourselves. And justifiably so, because our whole destiny depends on whether we like or dislike them, whether we are attracted or repelled, whether they are beneficial or harmful. This entirely natural way of viewing things and assessing them seems to be as easy as it is necessary.... We assume a far more difficult task when, in our active pursuit of knowledge, we seek to observe the objects of nature as they are *in themselves* and in their own mutual relationships; we then look for and investigate what exists, not what pleases. ("The Experiment as Mediator between Object and Subject")

I commented, "This shows how Goethe's worldview is the exact opposite of Kant's. According to Kant, there is absolutely no view of things as they are in themselves — only of how they *appear* in relation to us. Goethe sees this view as an inferior approach to things." And Vorländer responded,

> These words of Goethe are merely intended to express, in an introductory way, the trivial difference between what is pleasant and what is true. The researcher should look for "what *is* and not what *pleases*." It is advisable for those like Steiner (who dares to say that this second, indeed *very* inferior, way of relating to things is Kant's way) to first become clear about the basic concepts of Kant's doctrine — the difference between subjective and objective sensations, for example, which is described in passages such as section three of the *Critique of Judgment.*

Now, my statement makes it clear that I never said that this way of relating to things is Kant's way, but rather that, in Goethe's view, Kant's understanding of the relationship between subject and object does not correspond to the relationship we have with things when we want to know their intrinsic nature. Goethe's view is that the Kantian definition

other than subjective human truth. Truth is the projection of subjective experiences into the objective interrelationships of phenomena. These subjective experiences may even assume a completely individual character. Nevertheless, they express the inner nature of things. One can only put into things what one has experienced in oneself. Hence, in a certain sense, each person puts something different into things, depending on his or her individual experiences. My interpretation of certain events in nature is not quite comprehensible to someone who has not had the same inner experience. What is important is not that people all have the same thoughts about things, but that when we think about things, we all live in the element of truth. Therefore, we should not reflect on another's thoughts as such and accept or reject them, but we should view them as proclamations of that person's individuality. "Those who contradict and argue should occasionally reflect on the fact that not all languages can be understood by everyone" (*Verses in Prose*). A philosophy can never provide a universal truth, but it does describe the inner experiences through which the philosopher interpreted outer phenomena.

•

When something expresses its essential being through the agency of a human mind, complete reality manifests only through the confluence of outer objectivity and inner subjectivity. We come to cognize reality neither through one-sided observation nor through one-sided thinking. Reality does not exist as something ready-made in the objective world; it is brought about through the human spirit in its connection with things. Objective things are only an aspect of reality. Goethe answers those who extol only sensory experience: "Experience is only half of experience.... Everything factual is already theory" (*Verses in Prose*). In other words, an ideal element manifests in the human mind when it observes something factual.

This worldview — which recognizes the essential nature of things in ideas and conceives of knowledge as a living-into the being of things — is not *mysticism*. But it does have one trait in common with

---

does not correspond to human cognition but to our relationship with things when we regard them in terms of pleasure or displeasure. Those who are capable of misunderstanding a statement as does Vorländer would be better off learning how to read a sentence correctly before offering advice to others regarding their philosophical education. Anyone can look for Goethe quotes and order them historically, but to interpret them in the spirit of Goethe's worldview is something Vorländer certainly cannot do.

mysticism; it views objective truth not as something that exists in the outer world, but as something that can actually be grasped within the human being. The opposite worldview shifts the ground of things behind the phenomena into a realm beyond human experience. Such a view can either surrender itself to blind *faith* in that ground, received as religious revelation, or it can intellectually hypothesize and theorize about the character of that reality in a realm beyond.

Both mystics and adherents of Goethe's worldview reject belief in some "otherworld," just as they reject the hypotheses of such a realm; they maintain what is truly spiritual, which is expressed in the human being. Goethe wrote to Jacobi: "God has punished *you* with *metaphysics* and put an arrow in your flesh; but he has blessed *me* with *physics....* I hold more and more firmly to the atheist's [Spinoza's] worship of God... and leave to you all that you consider religion, as you must.... When you say one can only *believe* in God, then I say to you that I set a lot of store in *seeing*." What Goethe wanted to *see* was the essential being of things as it expressed itself in his world of ideas. Mystics also want to know the essential nature of things through sinking into their own inner being; but it is exactly the world of ideas — clear and transparent in itself — that they reject as unsuited for attaining higher knowledge. Mystics do not believe in developing their capacity for ideas to view the primal ground of existence, but concentrate on other inner forces of their being. Generally, mystics think they grasp the being of things in unclear sensations and feelings. But feelings and sensations are limited to subjective human nature and say nothing about things, which express themselves only in ideas.

As a worldview, mysticism is superficial, despite the fact that mystics take pride in their "depth" as compared to people of reason. They know nothing of the nature of feelings; otherwise they would not see them as expressions of the world's being. And they know nothing of the nature of ideas; otherwise they would not consider them shallow and rationalistic. They have no inkling of what people who actually have ideas experience in them. For many, however, ideas amount to no more than words. They are unable to get hold of their unlimited fullness. It is not surprising that they experience their own hollow words, devoid of ideas, as empty.

•

Those who look for the essential content of the objective world within their own being can also find the essence of the *moral world order* only in human nature itself. Those who believe in a transcendent reality behind that of human experience must also look there for the source of ethics. For the ethical, in the higher sense of the word, can come only from the essential nature of things. This is why those who believe in a transcendent world presume ethical commandments to which they must submit. Such commandments come to them either as revelations or they actually enter their consciousness, as is the case with Kant's categorical imperative. We hear nothing about how this enters our consciousness from the transcendent world of "things in themselves." It is simply there, and we must submit to it. A philosopher of experience, who holds to pure sensory observation, sees ethics as merely the effect of human drives and instincts. By studying these, we are supposed to arrive at norms that determine ethical conduct.

Goethe sees morality arising from the human world of ideas. Only ideas that are clear in themselves, through which we give ourselves our own direction, can guide moral conduct, not objective norms or mere impulses. We follow these not out of obligation, as we would have to follow objective norms of ethics, nor are we compelled as we might be by impulses and instincts. Rather, we serve them out of love. We love them as we love a child. We want to see them realized, and we intervene on their behalf because they are a part of our own being. The *idea* is the guideline for conduct, and *love* is the driving force in Goethean morality. For him duty means "to love what we have commanded ourselves to do" (*Verses in Prose*).

Action in the sense of Goethean ethics is *free* activity. We depend only on our own ideas and answer to no one but ourselves. In *Intuitive Thinking As a Spiritual Path: A Philosophy of Freedom,* I disproved the flimsy argument that a moral world order in which we each obey only ourselves can lead only to chaos and discord in human activity. Those who make this argument overlook the fact that human beings are essentially alike, and that we will never produce moral ideas that are different in essence and lead to discord.[3]

●

---

3. A story will show how little understanding is present in professional philosophers today, both for ethical views and for the ethic of inner freedom and individualism in general. In 1892, in an essay for *Zukunft*(issue 5), I spoke out for a strictly individualistic view

From Goethe's perspective, there could be no art if human beings did not have the capacity to create in ways that are in complete harmony with nature's works — creations that manifest nature's meaning more completely than nature herself. The products of art are the objects of nature at a higher level of perfection. Art is a continuation of nature. "Because human beings are at the pinnacle of nature, we in turn see ourselves as a completed nature, which must in itself likewise produce another pinnacle. Toward that end, we ascend by permeating ourselves thoroughly with perfections and virtues; we summon discernment, order, harmony, and meaning, and finally *we elevate ourselves to the production of a work of art*" (Goethe, "Winckelmann"). After seeing Grecian works of art in Italy, Goethe wrote, "These exalted works of art are at the same time the most sublime works of nature, brought forth by human beings according to true and natural laws" (*Italian Journey*, Sept. 6, 1787). As mere empirical and sensory reality, these works of art are beautiful likenesses; those who are able to look more deeply see them as "a manifestation of hidden laws of nature that would otherwise never reveal themselves" (*Verses In Prose*).

It is not the material the artist takes from nature that makes a work of art, but what the artist puts into it from within. The most elevated work of art causes us to forget that it is based on a content from nature and awakens our interest only through what the artist has made of it. The artist forms naturally but does not form as nature herself does.

These sentences seem to me to express Goethe's main thoughts on art as set forth in his *Verses in Prose*.

---

of ethics. Ferdinand Tönnies in Kiel responded in a brochure, " 'Ethical Culture' and its Retinue. Nietzsche Fools in the 'Future' and in the 'Present' " (Berlin, 1893). He offered nothing but the main principles of philistine morality in the form of philosophical formulas. He says of me, however, that I could have found "no worse Hermes on the path to Hades than Friedrich Nietzsche." It struck me as truly humorous that Tönnies, in order to condemn me, presented several of Goethe's *Verses in Prose*. He has no idea that if I did have a Hermes, it was not Nietzsche, but Goethe. I have already shown in chapter 10, section 5, of this book the connections between the ethics of inner freedom and Goethe's ethics. I would not have mentioned this worthless brochure if it was not symptomatic of the misunderstanding of Goethe's worldview that predominates in professional philosophical circles. — R. STEINER.

Participatory Science as the Basis for a Healing Culture

John Barnes

I
Participatory Science

> "Thoroughly exhilarating!"
> "A dazzling achievement! Triumphant!"
> "An emotional wake-up call!"
> "Howlingly funny!"
>
> —*New York Times,* Theater Section

It is true! As these "critical acclaims" indicate, there is *nothing* like the theater. Here our humanity seems to come alive. Here we experience it more vibrantly than anywhere else. Nowhere do we see so directly into the depths of human nature. Indeed, nowhere else, perhaps, do we come so close to the very heartbeat of what it means to be human. Although it is "only" theater, not "real life," we feel that here we are allowed breathtaking glimpses into deeper dimensions of reality that might otherwise have forever remained hidden from us. It is as though a curtain had been lifted and we were now able to see the true reality for the first time.

Who has not gone home deeply moved after a great play or film? Theater has the power to transform: to shake us to our foundations and to renew our humanity out of its pristine sources. *Catharsis* (purification), the ancient Greeks, the inventors of the drama, called it. Theater has the power to raise us out of our everyday vegetative indifference and petty self-centeredness. Through it we become

219

participants in the more essential struggle for truth, goodness, love. Inwardly renewed and rejuvenated, we return to our daily lives.

Though easily forgotten in the bustle of everyday existence, such moments of heightened inner participation testify with indisputable power to a reality unknown to contemporary science. Yet modern science can be rightfully regarded as the greatest achievement of the last five hundred years. Not only has it brought us immense empirical knowledge and incredible technological progress, but, perhaps even more important, its methods have given us an inner sense of certainty, of knowing what we know. Yet again and again, this sense of certainty has led scientists such as the prominent biologist E. O. Wilson to believe that "all tangible phenomena, from the birth of stars to the workings of social institutions, are based on material processes that are ultimately reducible, however long and tortuous the sequences, to the laws of physics."[1]

Despite such statements, the limitations of this reductionist methodology are becoming more and more apparent.

Modern science actually owes its strength to its limitations. Whenever possible, it limits our perception to what can be detected and measured by scientific instruments and restricts our understanding to what can be grasped as causal and quantitative relationships. By excluding the greatest part of our human experience from its domain, science is able to focus all the more accurately on the purely physical aspects of the world. Indeed, its extraordinary technological achievements demonstrate the ability of its methods to master the inanimate material world. But this powerful narrowing of focus has come at a price.

Our ecological and social crises can be seen not only as the result of human egotism and exploitation, but also as arising from our inability to understand the deeper lawfulness of living and human nature. This inability is not, as Wilson and many scientists argue, due to the fact that modern science has not yet progressed sufficiently to understand organic life. It is due, rather, to the inherent limitations of its quantitative, reductionist methods.

By focusing on the parts, and then on parts of parts *ad infinitum*, science has lost sight of the dynamic wholeness of living organisms and of their unique qualities. A complete biochemical analysis of an organism, in and of itself, can tell us nothing about the meaningful-

---

1. E. O. Wilson, *Consilience, the Unity of Knowledge*, p. 266.

ness of its form and behavior or about its intimate relationship to its environment.

The Swiss biologist Adolf Portmann was keenly aware of the limitations of the reductionist approach. Reductionist science, Portmann says, is like a person who seeks to understand a theatrical production by going behind the scenes to study how the effects are achieved.[2] Such a person will learn a great deal about staging techniques, about lighting equipment, the material makeup of the scenery, and so forth. From a technical point of view, this is a perfectly legitimate enterprise; but it can tell us nothing about the plot and meaning of the play. We can learn these only from in front of the stage, by taking the performance at its face value and immersing ourselves in its dramatic action. Indeed, the staging techniques become intelligible only in the light of the meaning of the play. In living nature, as in the theater, the material techniques are subordinate to higher laws that can be experienced and understood only through inner participation.

Steiner's introductions to Goethe's scientific writings lay the theoretical foundations for a participatory science — a science that enters into the dynamic processes of nature as intensively and rigorously as an actor enters into and rehearses a role in a play. Such an approach strives to enliven and deepen our understanding of nature, broadening the scope of science to encompass phenomena in their living wholeness and all their sense perceptible qualities.

Participation of this kind calls for the engagement of human faculties that modern science has hitherto attempted to eliminate from its domain — namely, sense perception, imagination, intuition, feeling, and ultimately even what we may call our deepest moral sensitivity. Just as logical, mathematical thinking and precision measurement techniques have gradually evolved into a highly sophisticated means of grasping the causal, quantitative aspects of the world, thus these other capacities must also be developed — transformed from faculties reflecting our own subjectivity into faculties of selfless participation and perception.

We all possess these capacities in varying degrees. We would, in fact, be utterly dysfunctional without them. Throughout our lives we depend upon our ability to distinguish the subtle qualities of colors,

---

2. A. Portmann, *An den Grenzen des Wissens — vom Beitrag der Biologie zu einem neuen Weltbild*, chapter 3: Lebensforschung heute, p. 29ff, Frankfurt: Fischer Taschenbuch Verlag: 1976.

shapes, and sounds. We are able to "read" the gestures, smiles, and frowns of our fellow human beings with an accuracy comparable to that of the finest scientific measurement. We rely daily upon our ability to grasp relationships and situations through direct intuition. Honed and deepened through life experience, this ability matures into powers of insight, judgment, and wisdom.

Creative artists have always employed these capacities in their penetrating depictions of human life. And so, perhaps because he was also a scientist at heart, Goethe realized that artists *experience* in themselves the deeper, creative laws of nature and that it is these laws they then strive to bring to fullest expression in their works. At the sight of the Greek sculpture he encountered on his Italian journey, Goethe therefore exclaimed: "These exalted works of art are at the same time the most sublime works of nature, brought forth by human beings according to true and natural laws" (*Italian Journey*, Sept. 6, 1787).

The laws of human nature that we experience in Greek sculpture or in a theatrical performance were not inferred from experiments or statistics nor were they derived from biochemical knowledge or from a mechanical model of human behavior. Rather, they were apprehended directly through imaginative participation and intuitive insight. And they reveal themselves to us directly through gesture, through actions and dramatic situations, and, in the case of drama, through the words of the characters themselves. It is as though the world itself were speaking to us directly, revealing its open secrets. And this we experience as beautiful. Thus Goethe wrote, "The beautiful is a manifestation of hidden laws of nature that would otherwise have forever remained concealed" (*Verses in Prose*).

But what are these hidden, yet manifesting laws of which Goethe speaks? Are they merely aesthetic laws pertaining only to our subjective human experience — or are they in fact *actual laws of nature* that can be known through rigorous scientific research? In order to answer this question, we need to penetrate to the very foundation of scientific knowledge. What does it mean to know scientifically? Goethe describes, for instance, how the inner lawfulness of plants manifests most fully in the culminating stage of their unfolding. He writes, "In the blossoms the vegetative law achieves its highest appearance" (*Verses in Prose*).

We certainly experience blossoms as beautiful, but we are not used to thinking of them as manifestations of a vegetative law. How then did Goethe apprehend such laws — laws that clearly elude the methods of modern science?

Goethe's scientific method may be characterized in a nutshell as *conscious inner participation*. By reenacting the life cycle of individual plants in his imagination, Goethe came to see their successive formations — their leaves, sepals, petals, stamens, fruit, and seeds — as the result of a continuous process of transformation, or metamorphosis. He observed how the unique quality of a particular plant expresses itself in the distinctive way this process takes place. He found that this quality, or lawfulness, can be discerned in the characteristic form of each of the plant's diverse organs, and that it comes to its fullest expression in its blossoms.

This insight, gained through exact imaginative recreation of the plant's unfolding, is as accurate and as immediate as any empirical observation. However, it is achieved through and relies on the inner cognitive capacities of the knower rather than external observation or measurement. In this sense, it achieves the inner clarity and lawfulness of mathematics.

Rather than thinking of the plant as a dynamic whole whose essential nature expresses itself in each of its parts, contemporary biology thinks of the plant as an aggregate of individual parts ultimately determined by random genetic mutation and natural selection — by physical causes. In other words, it seeks for explanations "behind the scenes."

Whereas reductionist science delves ever deeper into the material nature of the phenomena in its search for causes, Goethe allowed the phenomena themselves to speak, and probed no further. "Let us not seek something behind the phenomena," he wrote; "they themselves are the theory" (*Verses in Prose*).

This enigmatic sentence sets Goethe's approach apart from reductionism. For Goethe, the phenomena themselves reveal their own lawfulness. They are nature's open secrets. For Goethe, every manifest aspect of nature presents itself as an expression of its hidden lawfulness. But the phenomena are *only* manifestations. They do not reveal their secrets to our bodily senses. Simply staring at them leads us nowhere.

Where then are the laws of nature to be found if not in some hidden mechanism behind the phenomena?

This fundamental question, though hardly a topic of current scientific debate, may nevertheless, upon consideration, be seen as the most central question facing contemporary science. Throughout this book the attempt is made to point out that, contrary to commonly held, naive assumptions, the laws of the external world reveal themselves to us only through our own active inner participation. They are not conveyed to us through outer sense perception but *light up within us as intuitively perceived idea.* In the light of this idea, we see the phenomena differently. We see them in a new and deeper dimension — as revelations of their hidden lawfulness. The exhilarating power of this "Eureka!" experience indicates the depth and intensity of our inner involvement.

That the laws of nature reveal themselves to us in this way is an undeniable experience. At the same time, this experience presents us with an extraordinary paradox. How is it possible that the hidden lawfulness of the external world should reveal itself *in us?* Though never stated explicitly by Goethe, the answer to this question can be found lying implicitly at the heart of his worldview.

Goethe saw no break between humanity and nature. He saw the human being as nature's crowning achievement. For Goethe, the human being is to nature what the flower is to the plant: the quintessential form in which the hidden lawfulness, the unseen creative powers that work within, come to their highest expression. Within us, a portion of these powers awaken to consciousness as our own cognitive capacities. As they apprehend nature from without, they sense their kinship with her hidden lawfulness. There is no greater satisfaction for the forces of the human soul than to participate in, to discover, the creative principles at work in nature. For they are of the same origin.

Nature's laws *manifest* in the external physical world; but they *reveal* themselves to us only through our own inner capacities and individual efforts. As human beings, we are so constituted that reality presents itself to us from two sides: through sense perception on the one hand and through inner participation on the other. The former is given. The latter lies largely in the realm of our own freedom.

Once this fundamental truth has been recognized and *all* knowledge, including modern scientific theories, is seen to be participatory in nature, the development of participatory methods will appear as a logical and necessary next step in the evolution of science.

Strictly adhered to, reductionist science, in its physical analysis of phenomena, will never come upon what Goethe refers to as the laws of nature. Because such science seeks reality only in the external physical world, it can lead only to fragmented knowledge. It can never discover the lawfulness that shapes and animates a living whole. As Goethe has Mephistopheles say in his *Faust:*

> Who would study and describe the living, starts
> By driving the spirit out of its parts:
> In the palm of his hand he holds all the sections,
> Lacks nothing, except the spirit's connections.
>
> (lines 1936–39, translated by W. Kaufmann)

Goethe's scientific approach may be characterized initially as phenomenological, holistic, and participatory. Sensitively, and yet productively, it seeks to enter into and participate in the dynamic processes of nature in the same way that an actor enters into and rehearses a dramatic role. By inwardly recreating these processes, we come to experience them from the inside out as it were. We participate in their inner lawfulness. At this point, the "spirit's connections" are restored, and the parts are seen as expressions of the whole. The phenomena have become the theory: in heightened intuitive consciousness they are perceived, in all their qualities and particulars, as the expression of their own essential nature. When such insight is achieved, we not only experience, and experience deeply — we *know* with scientific certainty.

The ultimate goal of this science, which is still in its infancy, is to become as accurate in its qualitative, imaginative, intuitive grasp of living nature as mechanics is in its grasp of machinery.

It is no coincidence that the founder of this science was a poet and thinker who ranks with Shakespeare and Dante as one of the greatest figures in world literature but who, as a true contemporary of the scientific age, felt inwardly compelled to employ his prodigious powers of imagination in scientific research. At the turn of the eighteenth to the nineteenth century, Goethe laid the groundwork for a participatory science through his studies of plant and animal morphology and of color. His scientific approach was soon forgotten, however, as nineteenth-century science focused increasingly on the material aspects of nature.

It is also no coincidence that, one hundred years after Goethe developed his scientific method, it was rediscovered by Rudolf Steiner. Perhaps more than any other individual in modern times, Rudolf Steiner achieved direct insight into the deeper dimensions of reality that remain hidden to our everyday consciousness and to the methods of contemporary mainstream science. Steiner found in Goethe's scientific method a bridge between this hidden world of generative forces and the manifest world of sense experience. In his introductions to Goethe's scientific works, which comprise the central content of this book, the young Steiner explores the structure of this methodological bridge and uncovers the epistemological pillars that support it. After completing his study of Goethe, Steiner went on to further develop Goethe's participatory method in his own spiritual scientific research. Like Goethe, he knew that all knowledge is achieved through direct experience and the inner activity and life that we bring to it. And he described how, by strengthening and disciplining this inner life, we become able to participate, methodically and scientifically, in the generative activity of hidden dimensions of reality.

Steiner himself developed his research to the point where he was able to apply it in the practical fields of education, medicine, agriculture, and social life. The success of these endeavors demonstrates that it is in fact possible to participate in and work with the creative laws of living and human nature. Through this extraordinary achievement, which has been called "the best kept secret of the twentieth century," Steiner laid the foundations for a new, healing culture.

The reader may be surprised to find Michael Polanyi featured prominently in this essay. Again, this is not a coincidence, for Polanyi stands out in the twentieth century as a champion of participatory science, who, because he came to his insights independently of Goethe and Steiner, can help to put their work in perspective.

Before we begin our exploration of participatory science, let us first seek to deepen our understanding of the predicament in which we find ourselves today. we will then be able to assess the actual implications of participatory science for the future.

II
The Crisis of Objectivism

> In this — your nothingness — I hope to find the all.
> — GOETHE, *Faust* (Faust to Mephistopheles)

Whether millionaire or homeless, black or white, male or female, something hidden deep within each of us unites us all and may, in the end, prove more powerful than all our differences. From this our common humanity comes the dream of unity in diversity, of a society of free human beings whose dignity is protected by equal rights and who live and work together in a country whose "good," as an early anthem sings, is crowned "with brotherhood, from sea to shining sea."

During the twentieth century, we have twice defended this ideal on the world stage: once against the racist totalitarianism of National Socialism, and more recently against the leftist totalitarianism of Communism. Then, with the sudden disintegration of the communist regimes in Eastern Europe and the final fall of the Iron Curtain in 1989, the ideal of a free society was declared victorious.

This is not to say, however, that all is well in the free countries of the West. Telltale symptoms abound. The income gap between the rich and the poor is increasing; violence, crime, and drug abuse have become endemic. Our children are at risk. The conclusion of a presidential commission on the state of American public education in 1983 acquires new, ominous overtones with each passing year: "If an unfriendly power had attempted to impose on America the mediocre educational performance that exists today, we might well have viewed it as an act of war. As it stands, we have allowed this to happen to ourselves." In other words, the ideals that we successfully defended abroad are now being seriously threatened at home by our own institutions and our own way of life.

Vaclav Havel, dramatist, dissident, and more recently, president of the Czech Republic, a keen observer of developments in both East and West, points out that Communism was in fact the product of a type of thinking that, originating with modern science, has become the dominant feature of Western culture.[3] Havel believes both the demise of Communism and the crisis of Western civilization stem from the inability of this mechanistic thinking to grasp life in its fullness and in its deeper dimensions. He sees the fall of Communism as a sign that an age dominated by objectivist thinking has come to an end. "Communism was not defeated by military force but by life, by the human spirit, by conscience, by the resistance of Being and of humanity to manipulation." He speaks of "the end of the modern era . . . an era when there was a cult of depersonalized objectivity, an era when ob-

---

3. All passages quoted are from Havel's speech at the World Economic Forum in Davos, Switzerland, on February 4, 1992, quoted in the *New York Times*, March 1, 1992.

jective knowledge was amassed and technologically exploited, an era of belief in automatic progress brokered by the scientific method."

After listing the crises to which this era has led, Havel makes a startling observation: "The extraordinary paradox at the moment is that... traditional science, with its usual coolness, can describe the different ways we might destroy ourselves, but it cannot offer us truly effective and practicable instructions on how to avert them." Nevertheless, he says, we continue to look for objective scientific solutions to our problems, "for an objective way out of the crisis of objectivism."

The problem goes deeper still however. Not only are we unable to solve our ecological, social and human problems, but we have neglected, even denied, the very source of our dignity, cultural creativity, and inner freedom. This was the primary concern of Michael Polanyi (1891–1976), a central European like Havel, and, like him, an uncompromising and perceptive seeker for the truth. Polanyi's search led him from Hungary through Germany to England and the United States, and through careers as a medical doctor, physical chemist, and sociologist to a final grappling with fundamental philosophical questions.

As he followed events in Hitler's Germany and Stalin's Soviet Union, Polanyi saw that objectivist science had failed in these instances to provide any theoretical foundations for human freedom and dignity. And yet, as he looked about him in the Western home to which he had fled, he realized that here too these foundations were being systematically undermined:

> We in the Anglo-American sphere have so far escaped the totalitarian nightmares of the right and the left. But we are far from home safe. For we have done little, in our free intellectual endeavors, to uphold thought as an independent, self-governing force.... [Even before World War I] positivism had set out to eliminate all metaphysical claims to knowledge. Behaviorism had started on the course that was to lead on to cybernetics, which claims to represent human thought as the working of a machine. Sigmund Freud's revolution had started, too, reducing man's moral principles to mere rationalizations of desires. Sociology had developed a program for explaining human affairs without making distinctions between good and evil. *Our*

true convictions were being left without theoretical foundations.
(*Meaning*, p. 22, emphasis added)

Polanyi recognized that objectivism led to reductionism which, for him, lay at the very heart of the crisis of Western civilization. He saw it as "the cause of our corruption of the conception of man, reducing him either to an insentient automaton or to a bundle of appetites" (ibid., p 23). As a member of the free scientific community, Polanyi experienced the tragedy that "we also have been busily engaged in laying the groundwork for nihilism" (ibid., p 22f.).

By reducing all aspects of life to lower levels of reality, modern reductionist science, in its pursuit of objectivity, has created a world-view in which there is no room for our human ideals, for our religious inclinations, indeed, for all that we love most deeply. We have, in fact, developed a science in which we ourselves, along with our entire human experience, have no place. Outwardly, we have overcome fascism and communism, but spiritually we are still living with the same basic scientific assumptions, with the same materialistic worldview, upon which they were based.

Nevertheless, our dream has grown stronger. The civil rights movement, the humanitarian efforts to overcome hunger and injustice, and the environmental movement are unprecedented in human history. These movements are inspired by the same invincible forces that led to the fall of Communism, characterized by Havel as "life, the human spirit, conscience, the resistance of Being and man to manipulation." Havel hopes to lead these forces onward to victory over scientific objectivism, which he sees as the main obstacle to true human progress. In the speech quoted above he states his profound conviction that, if we wish to forge a future for our world community, we must "release from the sphere of private whim such forces as a natural, unique, and unrepeatable experience of the world.... *We must seek to get to the heart of reality through personal experience.*" He makes an interesting qualification for the postmodern politician: "*Above all,*" he says, "*he must have trust in his own subjectivity as his principal link with the subjectivity of the world*" (emphasis added).

As a dramatist, Havel knows that only by activating the creative forces in the depths of our own soul can we connect with the deeper, moral forces that live in the hearts of other human beings. The dramatist, like the actor, knows that our own subjectivity is our only organ for apprehending the subjectivity of others. Havel suggests that it is also our only organ for apprehending the essential nature of the world.

Havel's exhortations clearly defy the ideal of "objective" knowledge. They only highlight what remains a deep, seemingly insoluble and still largely unconscious contradiction in our culture, which manifests in the fact that we passionately believe in ideals that have no place in our scientific worldview. It is therefore no wonder that, in spite of our best efforts, we are unable to realize them in practice.

Science, the objective pillar of progressive Western culture, appears to have become, at best, indifferent toward its other, subjective, pillar: the ideal of human freedom and dignity. A symptomatic expression of this dilemma was described by C. P. Snow in his famous essay "The Two Cultures." Snow, a contemporary of Polanyi in England, realized that in that country the polarization of the sciences and the humanities was leading to the formation of mutually exclusive cultures. "I believe the intellectual life of the whole of Western society is increasingly being split into polar groups... literary intellectuals at one pole — at the other, scientists, and as the most representative, physical scientists. Between the two a gulf a mutual incomprehension" (*The Two Cultures*, pp. 11–12). These two groups reflect a polarity that is inherent in human nature and that can, in fact, be found in each of us. Whereas the physical scientists devote themselves to the *outer* world, seeking to discover the "objective" laws of nature, the literary intellectuals are at home in the "subjective" *inner* life of humanity as it expresses itself in history, art, literature, philosophy, and religion. Thus the "Two Cultures" reflect the fundamental polarity of self and world, of spirit as we experience it in our ideals and impulses, in our thinking and feeling, and physical reality as we experience it in the external world. The resolution of this duality has, of course, been the perennial quest of philosophy, and indeed, ultimately, the goal of all human striving. The recent reflection of this duality in the seemingly irreconcilable polarization of human culture is rapidly undermining the health of our civilization and gives new urgency to this quest. Objectivist science, with its abstract, reductive thinking, has clearly lost its relationship with the subjective pole of human life and has created a shallow, mechanistic worldview that is entirely divorced from the rich experience of the human soul. Our inner life, unable to relate to the objective world of science, has been cut adrift as it were in a sea of subjectivity. Meanwhile we allow much of our practical life to be directed by a science that is foreign to our own humanity.

Is science, then, to be blamed for our predicament? Should we — can we — abandon this great, central achievement of our Western culture?

Snow speaks with great satisfaction of the progress that science and technology have brought us. He cannot countenance the arrogance of literary intellectuals in their moral condemnation of this progress, upon which even they themselves depend for their daily convenience. In fact, he seems to have more sympathy for the scientists, whose down-to-earth, can-do spirit conveys "an optimism that the rest of us badly need" (ibid., p 14). Of the scientists, he says, "If I were to risk a piece of shorthand, I should say that naturally they had the future in their bones" (ibid., p 16). Whereas much of our literary intellectual culture is based on past tradition, science is a new development, the product of newly evolved human capacities.

It would seem, then, that what we need is not a repudiation of science but a carrying forward of the future-bearing, objective spirit of science into the realms of qualitative experience, of life, soul, and spirit, which have been hitherto inaccessible to scientific investigation and have therefore been stigmatized as subjective.

This would require a radical renewal of science: the conscious incorporation of sense experience, participatory imagination, and intuitive insight into the scientific method. Imagination, hitherto the province of poets, the vessel of high visions and powerful passions, the vehicle that has traditionally transported us beyond the immediate here and now, would have to descend into the world of natural phenomena, subject itself to the sobering rigors of systematic observation and become the selfless servant of scientific truth. Sense perception, understood today as a subjective response to external stimuli, would have to be carefully cultivated as a qualitative revelation of essential realities.

The requirement that scientific knowledge must be "objective" appears, however, to preclude such a possibility — especially if "objective" means *fully independent of our human experience.*

This question of objectivity became the central issue for Michael Polanyi. Havel's call for the validation of personal experience will, perhaps, be brushed aside as a literary, humanistic, even anti-scientific outburst. Polanyi, however, was a scientist, both by background —

he was a member of the Royal Society and highly acclaimed as a chemist—and by inner disposition. It is surprising, therefore, to find him in fundamental agreement with Havel.

By penetrating the process of scientific discovery itself, Polanyi came to see the fallacy of objectivism. He pointed out that such natural forces as gravity, for example, were not discovered through "objective" empirical observation. Newton, it is said, discovered gravity by observing the fall of an apple. Obviously, observing falling fruit does not, in itself, constitute a scientific discovery. For millennia people had experienced gravity in the lifting of stones, or simply in the heaviness of their own bodies when they were ill or exhausted. They realized that the weight of a body is related to its inclination to fall. It was Newton who saw in this inclination the same hidden universal force that also holds the Moon and the planets in their orbits. Newton brought coherence and meaning to all these various phenomena by grasping the invisible reality that governs them.

As Polanyi puts it, universal gravity was discovered through an "act of the imagination" (*Meaning*, p. 57). Newton "saw" more than people before him had seen. With the eyes of the imagination, he saw not only the apple, but all the bodies in the entire solar system gravitating toward their common centers. In that moment of genius, he participated in the reality of universal, cosmic forces. His "own subjectivity" became his "principal link with the subjectivity (the hidden lawfulness) of the world." Scientific discovery, Polanyi explains, "while using the experience of our senses as clues, transcends this experience by embracing the vision of a reality beyond the impressions of our senses, a vision that speaks for itself in guiding us to an ever deeper understanding of reality" (*Personal Knowledge*, pp. 5–6). Reality, therefore, is not something objectively given. It is only through our imaginative and intuitive vision that we begin to grasp it. Once we have thus conceived of the force of gravity, however, we can measure and quantify its effects. We can then place this mathematical abstraction into a formula for calculating the path of a projectile. But when the thinking involved in this type of operation becomes mechanical, it ceases to participate in the reality that it represents. Only in this fully abstracted form is our knowledge independent of our human experience.

In other words, we engage in "the art of knowing," as Polanyi called it, through our own personal, "subjective" experience: through our senses, our immediate feeling, and our intuitive and imaginative thinking. Through personal experience we can thus participate in the essential reality of *all* the hidden forces that work within and determine the outer, sense-perceptible world. Through such participation we can come to see the growth of a plant as the manifestation of forces opposed to gravity, which bring cohesiveness to the plant just as gravity brings cohesiveness to the Earth. The fury of a lion can be seen as the expression of yet more dynamic powers. The decisive action of a human being reveals an inner force of a completely different, higher nature. Are these not also, like the falling apple, the manifestations of hidden realities? And can we not experience the power of these realities as strongly as we feel the force of gravity? Are not the life of a plant, the soul of an animal, and the human spirit as real as the forces of inanimate nature? Polanyi claimed that minds are *more* real than cobblestones (*Tacit Dimension*, p. 33). For minds not only conceive of cobblestones, they create civilizations. Minds contain the seeds of the future of our planet, whereas cobblestones are end-products of a past creation. If the exact, participatory imagination can grasp the invisible force of gravity, why should it not be able to work its way up to a grasp of the more dynamic forces of life, soul, and spirit? It is not science itself that is to blame for its restriction to physical laws, but rather a false view of science that does not perceive its participatory nature and its inherent potential to apprehend the lawfulness of higher levels of reality as well.

By recognizing that imaginative and intuitive participation are involved in all knowing, Polanyi released them "from the sphere of private whim." He showed how, by engaging these creative cognitive capacities, scientific knowledge can rise to participation in higher, generative levels of reality. Whereas contemporary mainstream science focuses on the horizontal expansion of knowledge through the discovery of new empirical facts, Polanyi points the way toward a vertical extension of science that penetrates the external facts to the hidden, generative realities that underlie them. Such a vertically extended science by no means contradicts the legitimate findings of empirical science; on the contrary, it reveals their deeper significance.

Discovering the hidden lawfulness that manifests through the empirical facts has often been likened to reading. As we decipher the printed text, we *know* — through the inner cohesiveness of the unfolding story—that we are discovering the actual, hidden reality that underlies it. Through active imaginative participation, we enter ever more deeply into this reality of which the visible characters on the page are only the external hieroglyphs. A Polanyian science begins to read the "book of nature." What seems to the objectivist to be nothing but a vast conglomeration of chemical elements governed by physical laws, reveals itself to the participating scientist as a living drama of unspeakable profundity and beauty.

Readers see the same external signs as nonreaders; yet they see infinitely more. As we begin to read nature's dynamic script, the curtain starts to rise. We begin to awaken to the hidden forces at work within a living world that has thus far eluded our blind efforts to predict and control it. As true actors on the world stage, working not only with the forces of gravity and inanimate nature, but also with the higher, generative forces of life, soul, and spirit, we can begin to build the healing culture that we so urgently need today.

III
From Monism to Dualism

> It is the story of all life that is holy and is good to tell, and of us two-leggeds sharing in it with the four-leggeds and the wings of the air and all green things; for these are children of one mother and their father is one Spirit.   —BLACK ELK

Thus Black Elk, holy man of the Oglala Sioux, begins the story of his life and people.[4] We may sense, shimmering up through our easily embarrassed or sentimental response to these words, an intimation like a golden memory of a paradise lost. The life of primordial cultures sprang from a feeling of kinship with all of nature. Nature was not then the objective world it is for us today but was the living expression of creative spiritual forces whose working and weaving united all things. Life, though outwardly primitive, consisted in ritual dialogue with these divine powers as they manifested in the animals, the stars, or in a particular place, and as they played into all aspects and practical details of everyday existence. This deep sense of

---

4. John G. Neihardt, *Black Elk Speaks*, Lincoln: University of Nebraska Press, 1961, p. 1.

connectedness sprang from the primal participation of a dreamlike consciousness. It was a living *with*, and within, nature. The human being had not yet separated out from nature or from the ritualistic forms of tribal community life. Life was deeply embedded within a greater whole, held spellbound as it were by the mystery, wisdom, humor, and majesty of it all. There was no change, no outer progress, no science or technology — only a profound sense of sharing in "all life that is holy and is good to tell."

How and when did the monistic worlds of the early cultures disintegrate? In his book *Goethe's World View*, Rudolf Steiner traces modern dualism back to Plato. Like Native Americans, the early Greeks of whom Homer sang still saw divine forces at work *in* nature. Plato, however, compellingly described the dualism of a transitory physical world and an eternal ideal world. In his allegory of the cave he depicted the outer sense world as a mere shadow of the radiant world of the archetypes. The highest of these, the spiritual counterpart of the Sun, is "the Form of the Good," from which all goodness and life emanate into the world. For Plato, physical appearances are but imperfect, shadowy projections, devoid of spiritual life. As naive human beings imprisoned within the cave of earthly existence, we take this realm to be the sole reality. Only philosophers are able to free themselves from this illusion by turning their vision away from the sense world and directing it toward the creative realm of the spirit where they behold the ideal beauty of the archetypes.

The Greeks originally experienced their thinking as *seeing*. Our word "idea" comes from the Greek verb *idein*, to see. With Plato, the monistic seeing of reality as a physical-spiritual whole has become differentiated into two separate faculties: outer sense perception on the one hand, and inner, spiritual perception, or thinking, on the other. For Plato, the faculty of thinking revealed an infinitely more substantial and potent reality than the dim and ephemeral world of the senses. By emphasizing the distance between the two realms and demonstrating their sheer incompatibility, Plato set the stage for subsequent dualistic worldviews.

This dualistic tendency was countered by Plato's great pupil Aristotle. In contrast to Plato, who saw the idea in a realm above and separate from outer nature, Aristotle saw nature as a unified being, of which the idea is the inner aspect, and external appearance the outer. Only by studying this outer appearance, according to Aristo-

tle, could human thinking come to grasp its hidden inner nature, or being, as idea.

In Raphael's famous painting *The School of Athens*, Plato is depicted pointing upward toward the lofty realm of the archetypes, whereas Aristotle's hand gestures forward and slightly downward toward the earthly world in which he saw the ideas at work.

With the awakening of human thinking in Greek philosophy, the dreamlike experience of the divine in nature ended. The translucent veil of the sense world became an impenetrable curtain. Significantly, it was in this context that theater was born. As human consciousness became more centered in itself, the *otherness,* the object-nature of the external world increased. A deeper understanding of this world now had to be attained through individual effort. Thus, the first foundations of natural science were laid in ancient Greece. At the same time, the new, emerging sense of selfhood also led to the birth of democracy.

Medieval Christianity still bore the stamp of Plato's dualism. The Earth was looked upon as a place of temptation, error, trial, and suffering. Monastic orders cultivated their inner religious life in isolation from the outer world. Altogether, medieval European culture was characterized by its inwardness and religiosity.

With the Renaissance, the modern age was ushered in and human attention began to shift from the eternal to the temporal, from the inner world to the outer. The Age of Exploration began. Painters learned to give objects new plasticity and "reality" and to place them into the newly discovered world of space. Scientists began to disregard the wisdom of the ancients and to investigate the laws of this world for themselves. This was also the time of the Reformation, when Luther and others stood up as individuals against the immense authority of the Church.

As scientists struggled for certainty of knowledge, Platonic dualism emerged again, in a different form. There were those who sought security in the certainty of their own inner cognitive activity. For Descartes (1596–1650) this was the pivotal experience, expressed in his famous statement, "I think, therefore I am." He felt most secure in mathematical thinking, built entirely upon the transparent clarity of its own lawfulness, unswayed by personal feeling and untainted by the opaque and foreign element of sense experience. Unlike platonic thinking, this was no longer a beholding of eternal archetypes. Descartes experienced his thinking as the self-determining, transparent activity of his own being. Like Plato, however, Descartes had little confidence in what his senses conveyed to him. The only aspects of the physical world that he felt he could grasp exactly and objectively were the so-called "primary qualities," such as extension and position in space, motion, and weight, all of which can be abstracted through measurement, quantified, set into mathematical relationship, and thus objectified. Qualitative perceptions such as color, tone, warmth, smell, touch, or taste seemed to him to evade objective distinction. They were subsequently designated as the subjective "secondary qualities" and, as such, were eliminated from the world of the exact sciences. Descartes explained them as the effects upon our senses of a hidden objective world of measurable material particles whose movements and interactions could be understood in mechanical terms.

Meanwhile, in England, Francis Bacon (1561–1626) was formulating the empirical method of modern science, which seeks certainty in outer experience. According to Bacon, scientific knowledge is to be pursued inductively, by making experiments and drawing conclusions to be tested in further experiments, for "The nature of things betrays itself more readily under the vexations of art [mechanical devices] than in its natural freedom" (*The Great Instauration, The Plan of the Work*). Bacon no longer conceived of science as seeking to discover the divine intentions of the creator. "The real and legitimate goal of the sciences," he wrote, "is the endowment of human life with new inventions and riches" (*Novum Organum*, Book I, CXXXI). As John Davy has pointed out, Baconian science is the origin of today's utilitarian, technological science, which creates models of reality whose validity is tested by their ability to predict and control the phenomena (*Hope, Evolution, and Change*, pp. 36–46). Bacon further proclaimed that religion belongs to a realm apart from the purely objective world of scientific facts.[5] Bacon's outer, empirical objectivism combined with Descartes' inner, mathematical objectivism to form the basis of modern science.

Since the beginning of the modern age this science has continued its apparently unstoppable exploration of the external physical world. Mathematical thinking grasps the quantitative aspects of this world, but it does not participate in its essential reality. Therefore this reality is sought in the given *outer* world. Science is thus drawn ever more deeply into the material world in its search for causal explanations. Breaking through the barrier of the sense perceptible, it has penetrated to a subsensory realm of subatomic forces that can be grasped only indirectly through highly sophisticated technical experiments and abstract mathematical thinking. This is the ultimate reality of reductionist science. There can be no other. In view of this reality, our entire human experience — indeed, the entire world as we perceive it — is seen to be a subjective illusion caused by the blind interplay of complex subsensible forces.

---

5. This point is stressed by Al Gore in his book *Earth in the Balance*. Gore's interpretation of the development of Western thought (pp. 248–252) is strikingly similar to that given by Steiner 95 years earlier.

As modern human beings we live in what appear to be two mutually exclusive worlds. When we think about it, we have to admit that the "normal" condition of a culture that bases itself upon scientific objectivism on the one hand and the integrity of our human experience on the other is dangerously close to a kind of schizophrenia.

Though Western philosophy may be "a footnote to Plato," as Whitehead put it, our modern dualism bears little resemblance to his. Whereas Plato saw phenomena as projections of supersensory archetypes, modern reductionist science sees them as the projections of subsensory forces. It has no use for archetypes. The only element of the ideal world that it cannot dispense with is mathematics. Morality, soul, and the creative spirit are relegated to the "private" world of the humanities.

Whereas in the Platonic worldview the spiritual was the primal cause and the material only its imperfect projection, in our reductionist worldview the material has become the primal cause and the spiritual is seen as its shadowy epiphenomenon. Modern science has stood Platonism on its head. If Raphael had included a modern scientist in his painting, he would have depicted him or her pointing downward toward a subsensory realm.

Since Snow published his essay in 1956, the polarization of Western and, with it, world culture has taken on new and more extreme forms. On the "objective" side, Francis Bacon's completely detached empirical science has finally caught up with the human being and produced behavioral science. Rejecting the existence of soul or spirit as a hypothesis lacking any foundation in outer, empirical experience, B. F. Skinner subjected human beings to experiments as one would a chemical compound or an amoeba. He concluded that human behavior was determined by previous outer conditioning and that it could be further determined, or engineered, through systematic positive and negative reinforcement. In his book *Beyond Freedom and Dignity,* Skinner wrote:

> What is being abolished is autonomous man — the inner man, ...the man defended by the literatures of freedom and dignity. His abolition has long been overdue. Autonomous man is a device used to explain what we cannot explain in any other way. He has been constructed from our ignorance, and as our understanding increases, the very stuff of which he is composed vanishes. (p. 200)

Soon after Skinner wrote this in 1971, behaviorism became the prevalent psychology in American education, and it is still being applied in more subtle ways in schools throughout the United States. It is hard to believe that this could happen in a country founded upon the ideals of human freedom and dignity. As the commission on education said in 1983, however, *"We have allowed this to happen to ourselves."* The devastating effects of this educational psychology, although all too obvious, are fortunately mitigated by teachers who still love and respect their students and strive to awaken and strengthen the autonomous human being within them.

But there is method in Skinner's madness, and he is correct on one point. We will never find the "stuff" of human freedom through purely empirical investigation, for this "stuff" is self-directed spiritual activity, and, as such, is inaccessible to external observation.

Recent rapid progress in molecular biology and particularly in genetic research can only be welcomed as a positive advance in scientific knowledge. The empirical findings will, however, be placed into the conceptual framework of a reductionist worldview. Within this framework, organisms will be viewed as complex mechanisms that can be manipulated for utilitarian purposes. The inner integrity of nature is at stake. Even if "subjective" factors such as religious faith, moral outrage, or considerations of human rights should limit human biotechnology, the view of the human being as a purely physical entity determined by its genetic makeup and its environment would have — and is already having — far-reaching consequences. For when one lacks certainty of one's autonomous individuality, of one's inner freedom and dignity, then one lacks the very source of one's inner health and creativity as well as the ability to recognize and respect the autonomous inner being in others. A culture without this certainty is doomed to degeneracy.

On the "subjective" side there are increasing numbers of religious fundamentalists who have taken an inflexible stand against the inroads of materialistic science and of the cultural relativism so prevalent in our open, pluralistic society. Seeking a secure foundation for their moral and religious inclinations, they stand dogmatically on a literal interpretation of their holy scriptures. While fundamentalists have been digging in, so to speak, others have been trying to break out. In the 1960s the hippies staged a romantic, emotional rebellion against the meaninglessness and inner emptiness of materialistic civilization. Since that time the interest in Eastern mysticism has grown tremendously. The New Age movement has attempted to combine Eastern spirituality with Western technology. Despite all efforts to suppress it, the consumption of consciousness-altering drugs has taken on epidemic proportions. Here we see a tragic manifestation of dualism as a human reality: an inner life that is searching for stimulation, satisfaction, and fulfillment in a material world that cannot provide them, except in the form of subjective illusions.

More and more, in fact, we are witnessing one-sided developments of human nature through which the balance that constitutes our humanity is lost. What is being lost is what we have come to see as the positive fruit of Western culture: the power of creative, independent selfhood with its potential to participate in the deeper dimensions of reality and thereby to reunite itself with the world.

Ultimately, I believe, our future will depend upon whether or not we can find a firm scientific foundation for what we *feel* to be the inviolable integrity of nature and of the human being. In the long run, the idealism of the warm human heart cannot coexist with a mechanistic worldview — the product of a cold, detached intellect. Everything will therefore depend upon whether we are able to transform our abstract, intellectual thinking into one that, while maintaining its discerning clarity, participates with warmth and interest in the creative processes of life. Such thinking cannot become the blind tool of exploitative egotism. Nor can it lose itself in self-indulgent subjective fantasies. This is a thinking which allies itself fully with the human heart, which, like selfless love, pours itself out into its object and comes to know it, as it were, from within.

IV
Michael Polanyi's Personal Knowledge

We now see that not only do the scientific and the humanistic both involve personal participation; we see that both also involve an active use of the imagination.

— Michael Polanyi, *Meaning*

In 1958, two years after Snow published "The Two Cultures," Michael Polanyi completed his major work, *Personal Knowledge.* It was the culmination of his investigation of the ideal of scientific objectivism and contained a careful, detailed presentation of what he had been long developing as a new understanding of human knowledge.

Polanyi combined the down-to-earth, sober clarity of the physical scientist with a passionate love of nature and humanity. As few others of his time, he saw how reductionist science undermined the foundations of human culture, and he set out to break the powerful spell of a worldview that seemed to him not only to reject our deepest convictions but to fly in the face of actual scientific experience.

Personal Knowledge requires a great deal of inner activity to read, but when truly read it is immensely rewarding. Through it, we participate in an original, deeply perceptive thinking that penetrates to the fundamental principles of scientific inquiry. In fact, the reading of Polanyi's work calls upon and exercises the very kind of thinking that we need to overcome the crisis of objectivism.

Objectivism rests upon the assumption of Baconian empiricism that all objective knowledge comes from outside — through the senses or, more accurately, through the measurements of objective scientific instruments. Such empiricism is based on the conviction that nothing from within, from the subjective side, mathematics excepted, may enter into the process of objective, scientific knowing. For the empiricists, Polanyi writes, "scientific theory is merely a convenient summary of experience . . . the most economical adaptation of thought to facts, and just as external to the facts as a map, a timetable, or a telephone directory" (*Personal Knowledge*, p. 9).

Polanyi's own experience as a scientist strongly contradicted these assumptions, and he soon realized that they were also refuted by the findings of Gestalt psychology.[6]

Most of us have had experiences like the following. As a guest sleeping in an unfamiliar room, we awaken to find our gaze resting upon something that we cannot make out. Various shades of light and dark, perhaps also blotches of color, appear in our field of vision. We are baffled as it were, unable to establish any meaningful structure in this apparition. Yet our attention is held, even entertained,

---

6. Here we may note that Polanyi accepted the observations of Gestalt psychology but not its conclusions. Gestalt psychologists claim that *Gestalten* (perceived wholes) are formed by the spontaneous equilibration of their elements caused by a corresponding purely physical process in the brain. Polanyi protested that Gestalt psychology lacks the essential element of active participation on the part of the knower. (Compare *Personal Knowledge*, pp. 57, 97–8, 340–2.)

though in an animated, dreamlike state of limbo, as if peeking for the first time into an unknown universe. Finally we sit up in bed and look about. Having oriented ourselves in the room, we may discover that our eyes had opened on a section of window casement and curtain upon which the morning sun was playing. What we had been unable to comprehend in isolation now appears as meaningful three-dimensional form in the conceptual context of a greater whole. Moviemakers, who consciously control our sense perceptions, like to begin a scene with audible and visual apparitions of this kind, holding us spellbound until an illuminating concept brings order and meaning into what had been pure, incoherent yet fascinating perception.

Gestalt psychology has confirmed what these experiences reveal, namely, that the world initially appears to our senses as pure apparition, gaining coherence and meaning only through what we bring to it in the way of concepts. What is given to our sense of sight is nothing more than a juxtaposition of color, dark and light, a flatland completely lacking in three-dimensional depth, without any indication of objects or their spatial interrelatedness. Polanyi realized that we are only beginning to assess the full significance of this fundamental insight. These discoveries of Gestalt psychology are also confirmed by the experience of people who were born blind or who became blind in early childhood and whose physical ability to see was restored through surgery. Only after the most arduous struggle, if at all, are such people able to integrate the elements of the visual tapestry they perceive into recognizable objects.

Thus, what we in our naive, everyday consciousness take to be the outer reality simply given to our senses already contains the thought content and structure with which we grasp it in the act of recognition. The window casement and curtain that we "see" include not only our sense perceptions but the concepts that we bring to them and through which they gain their coherent Gestalt, or form.

Our senses analyze the world into all manner of unconnected sense perceptions. Our ears hear cascades of sounds; our eyes see a kaleidoscope of colors. By connecting them with their conceptual counterparts, our thinking actively integrates them into meaningful wholes. The reality of the window casement is grasped as the unity of its perceptual and conceptual content. Object recognition synthesizes the manifold elements that come through our senses from without *and* the unifying concepts that come from within through our thinking. The more thoroughly we penetrate our sense experience with our thinking, the closer we come to the full reality of what we are perceiving. Reality, then, is not given to us but rather can be attained only through what we bring to our sense perceptions through our own cognitive activity.

In this sense, the world presents itself to us as an enigma, as an open secret that only we can solve. Let us look for a moment at a riddle such as children love:

> Many crooked miles it goes
> Within the smallest space.
> The farther it travels, the shorter it grows,
> But you can always find its trace.
>
> The wisest men can lead it well
> Along its path so narrow
> And silently great secrets tell
> To those able to follow.

A riddle presents us with clues, with mysterious and seemingly unrelated particulars. We ourselves have to find what it is that brings coherence to them all. This can be an arduous search of which our intellect, impatient for an answer, quickly tires. In a sense, the process of solving a riddle is similar to that of object recognition, which, as Polanyi points out, is akin to scientific discovery. It requires "laborious efforts of the imagination"; the solution, however, comes as a spontaneous and effortless "concluding intuition" (*Meaning*, pp. 56, 96). Such an integration of particulars into a meaningful whole involves a "sensory quality," a seeing, "which is intentional throughout and as such, can be carried out *only by a conscious act of the mind.*" Whereas logical, operational thinking can be carried out by a computer, "*such integration cannot be replaced by any explicit mechanical procedure.... It can only be lived, can only be dwelt in*" (*Meaning*, p. 41, emphasis partly added).

Once we have found the hidden solution to the riddle, everything falls into place. What we at first glimpsed only from the outside, so to speak, piecemeal, we can now experience as it were from within, as a unified and meaningful whole. We have added something that was not given but that is the essential element without which the riddle would remain foreign and confusing. Solving a riddle, like solving any problem, requires effort but affords the deepest satisfaction. Children take great joy in the experience of being on the "inside" of the riddle. For those who are "in on the secret," it is obvious. They delight in the clumsy efforts of those who remain on the "outside" and simply don't get it.

This secret, the essential element that we bring to our experience, the golden thread that holds it all together and illuminates it, is what Polanyi calls "personal knowledge." It is personal in that it comes from within as a result of our own effort and is not given through outer experience. It is personal in that, like a secret, it is a hidden knowledge that nevertheless is the key to outer events. In spite of its personal nature, however, it is not anything subjective that we ourselves make up and project into our sense experience. Polanyi observes that "personal knowledge in science is not made but *discovered* and as such it claims to establish contact with reality beyond the clues on which it relies" (*Personal Knowledge*, p. 64). "Such knowing is indeed *objective* in the sense of establishing contact with a hidden reality" (ibid., p. vii).[7]

Polanyi points out that our discovery of a unifying concept changes our perception of the outer particulars to which it pertains. This change is instantaneous and irreversible. Before we hit upon the solution to a riddle, we see its clues as isolated pictures that have no apparent bearing upon one another. Then, in a flash, what was incongruous nonsense becomes a unified Gestalt of transparent clarity. Similarly, by recognizing the window casement as a whole, our awareness of its parts is irreversibly changed. What, in isolation, we might have seen as a board, we now perceive as a window sill. Thus conceptual integrations literally change our worldview.

Polanyi distinguishes between two elements in this process: our *focal awareness* of the whole and our *subsidiary awareness* of its parts.[8] When we view an object as a whole, its perceptual elements play a subordinate or subsidiary role, and we see them in this role and not as objects in themselves. The familiar figure below can clarify the distinction between focal and subsidiary awareness.

---

7. It is interesting to compare Polanyi's conception of personal knowledge with Steiner's description of thinking as the key to the central idea-content of the world, pp. 103–105.

8. Focal awareness corresponds to the capacity of *reason* as defined by R. Steiner on pp. 110ff. By focusing on the material parts, the *intellect* isolates them from the whole.

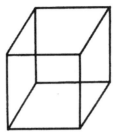

The famous Gestalt cube can be "seen" either from above right or from below left. Through our focal activity we connect the twelve subsidiary lines that make up the figure with our concept of a cube and "see" them as an integrated, three-dimensional whole. Because of the arrangement of the sense-perceptible lines on the page, we can focus on the cube either as it appears from the upper right, or as viewed from the lower left. As we shift from one perspective to the other, the lines, or subsidiaries, appear to jump forward or backward. How we perceive them is therefore clearly subordinate to our conceptual focus. Our ability to see the two-dimensional figure as a three-dimensional cube and the considerable effort required to maintain our focus or to change our view at will demonstrate the formative or integrative activity of our focal awareness.

Thus a closer examination of the process of object recognition reveals the degree to which we actually participate in our perception of reality.

Naive empirical objectivism rests upon the mistaken assumption that reality presents itself to us from the outside only and that as knowers we must remain detached and play a passive role, merely recording what comes to us through our senses. When adhered to strictly, this objectivism precludes the possibility of any knowledge; for, as we have seen, what comes to us through our senses is, in itself, without coherence or meaning. In practice, objectivists do of course see objects as integrated wholes, but they do not realize that these wholes already contain an *essential, constitutive* element that is *not* to be found in their parts.

As a scientist with an intimate experience of the process of scientific discovery, Polanyi knew that significant discoveries did not in fact result from Bacon's inductive method of subjecting nature to the experimental "vexations" of mechanical devices. The well-known anecdote of Galileo and the altar lamp, like that of Newton and the apple, demonstrates clearly how most scientific discoveries actually occur.

For generations the pious people of Pisa had seen the slow, swinging motion of the altar lamp that hung from the high ceiling of their cathedral. Galileo, however, watched it with fascination, sensing that this phenomenon harbored some hidden, tantalizingly tangible but as yet unconceived lawfulness. There was something inexorable about its motion. Galileo "saw" that its ponderous slowness was linked to the length of its chain. When the lamp swung in a wide arc, however, its speed was greater; as it gradually came to rest, its speed diminished with its arc. As he followed its slowly decreasing oscillations, he noted that its rhythm nevertheless kept time with his own heartbeat and breathing. Regardless of the speed and width of its sweep, the lamp seemed to swing with imperturbable regularity. Galileo was beginning to "see" more and more in the phenomenon. Like Archimedes in his bath, Galileo at Mass must also have found it hard, in his excitement, to sit still.

Only after this initial engagement did experimentation begin. Later, Galileo's insight into the regular periodicity of the pendulum led to its application in clocks, greatly increasing their accuracy. But Galileo must have "seen" more in the pendulum's swinging. Why did it swing? Was it not falling? And was not its fall arrested by its chain? And, in arresting its fall, did not the chain convert its downward motion into a rising one, so that at the end of its swing it could fall again? Did Galileo conceive of kinetic and potential energy? Did he entertain the thought that, if friction could be overcome, the dynamic motion of the pendulum would perpetuate itself? And how about the relationship between the length of the pendulum and the frequency of its oscillations?

Such examples led Polanyi to realize that the process of scientific discovery is similar to that of object recognition. Just as the perceptual elements of an object take on meaning in the conceptual context of the object as a whole, thus the motion of a pendulum becomes meaningful in the light of the laws that we grasp through our thinking. In both cognitive processes we can distinguish between given subsidiary elements of a perceptual, outer nature, and focal components of a conceptual nature that we must discover through our own activity. By comprehending outer phenomena as manifestations of an inner lawfulness, we come to see them as immanently meaningful, as transparent manifestations of this lawfulness. And the law, seen as that which expresses itself through the phenomena, is experienced concretely, not as an abstraction. Thus Polanyi's distinction between focal awareness of the conceptual-lawful component of cognition and subsidiary awareness of its outer, perceptual elements leads into a holistic and living experience of scientific knowledge.[9]

The phenomenon of the pendulum had been known for centuries. Galileo's achievement lay not in the empirical discovery of a new phenomenon but in observing it in a new way, with a new interest in it as the revelation of hidden principles.

The implications of Polanyi's personal knowledge become more profound as we move from inorganic science to the study of organic nature.

Polanyi approaches the study of organic nature having established that all knowing involves "two levels of awareness: the lower one for the clues, the parts, or other subsidiary elements, and the higher one for the focally apprehended, comprehensive entity to which these elements point" (*Knowing and Being*, p. 214). The lower level is given through sense perception; the higher is apprehended through our own cognitive activity.

Now, Polanyi asserts that the "two levels of personal knowledge, that of a comprehensive entity and that of its particulars . . . *represent two distinct levels of reality.*" He observes "that there obtains between such levels *a peculiar logical relationship* derived from the distinction between subsidiary and focal awareness." This peculiar logical relationship consists in the fact that the higher level is the *law, or organizational principle* that governs, or shapes the lower level. This provides Polanyi with a key to understanding organic nature. He continues:

> Once I have established this relationship for the example of two comparatively low levels of reality, I shall proceed to erect on top of these *a consecutively rising set of levels, right up to that of responsible human personhood.* Within this framework it will appear possible for the human being to exercise a responsible choice, even though we admittedly remain rooted in lower forms

9. Compare with R. Steiner's discussion of scientific discovery on p. 77; also with his discussion of Goethe's discovery of the intermaxillary bone and how it was received by other scientists: "Their way of observing was not through ideas but by external comparison, for which the intermaxillary in fact did not exist in the human being" (p. 32; see also p. 37).

of existence in which there is no room for such choices. (*Study of Man*, p. 46., emphasis added)

The "peculiar logical relationship" of which Polanyi speaks can be seen in the relationship between living organisms and inanimate nature. Plants assimilate and organize inorganic substances. As we shall see in connection with Goethe's morphology, the generative principles of plant growth and metamorphosis comprise a higher lawfulness of their own that is irreducible to the laws of the inanimate world. Polanyi speaks of these organizational principles as "morphological," or "vegetative," principles, or as "morphogenetic fields." Because they are subject to their own morphological principles, Polanyi writes, it is a "fact that biotic achievements cannot — *logically cannot* — be ever represented in terms of physics and chemistry" (*Personal Knowledge*, p. 399). On the subsidiary level of organic life, he says, biochemical laws hold sway. However, they do so under boundary conditions set by higher formative principles. Thus, nowhere in an organism will we find the laws of chemistry violated; yet we find the chemical processes so finely sublimated and orchestrated that they become the vehicles for life processes, which are determined by principles of a higher order. A plant, then, is an expression of a higher level of reality as it manifests through its organization of inorganic substances.

Reductionists will protest that biochemistry is well on its way toward explaining organic growth and morphological development in chemical terms. Clearly, the structure of the genes and the various highly complex proteins involved in the differentiation of all growth are necessary conditions for morphological development. But what "informs" those substances to bring forth the metamorphosis of plants? How does one fertilized human egg cell evolve into the highly differentiated harmony of the human organism? What orchestrates the timing and incredibly complex three-dimensional sculpting of embryonic development? The more one participates with one's thinking in these processes, the more one comes to realize that any attempt to explain them as resulting only from the organism's DNA molecules is equivalent to explaining the performance of a Beethoven sonata as resulting from the keyboard of the piano upon which it is played.

How then do morphological principles orchestrate biochemical processes? The highly complex protein molecules involved in regulating the formation of the organism are far from the inert equilibrium of inorganic matter. Here, "the deterministic view of chemistry fails" (Ilya Prigogine, *Order out of Chaos*, p. 177). Such proteins are always close to an indeterminate state of chaos, which allows for chemically unpredictable developments. It is here that principles of a higher order can enter into the formation of the organism. The subtle but important difference between Polanyi's view and that of systems theory or chaos theory is that the latter do not see biochemical processes as subsidiary to higher organizational principles but rather as *self-organizing*. They do not recognize the existence of higher levels of reality that manifest on the biochemical level.

At this point we inevitably encounter the question of vitalism. This question can be resolved only by realizing that what comes to us through our senses is only a part of the full reality. The living morphological principles that form a plant are hidden to our physical senses. We can come to know them only through the direct intuition gained by inner participation. Polanyi writes, "We may conclude that the *insights* by which we recognize life in individual plants and animals... reveal a reality *to which we have access by no other channels*" (*Personal Knowledge*, p. 359, emphasis added). Life can only be apprehended focally, for it is itself a focal force that organizes its physical subsidiaries. Vitalism becomes untenable as soon as it claims life to be a field of physical force like magnetism. Recent research shows that morphological activity, like thinking activity in the brain, is accompanied by subtle electromagnetic phenomena (see R. O. Becker, *Cross Currents*, Tarcher, 1990). However, the laws of electromagnetism, like the laws of chemistry, can account neither for thinking nor for the formation of organisms.

Beyond the vegetative level of life and organic growth, Polanyi recognizes a further, active-perceptive level characterized by sentience. This level appears in animals, whose bodily form and physiological functions are subsidiary to their instinctual inner life. Just as organic growth is subject to laws of its own and is irreducible to chemical terms, so the appetitive-perceptive consciousness of animals has its own dynamic lawfulness that cannot be explained as resulting from the lower levels of reality in which it is rooted. Polanyi explains:

> Just as arithmetic is not logically rich enough for us to deduce a calculus from it, and words are not rich enough for us to deduce a grammar from them, so the laws of physics and chemistry

would now be understood to be not rich enough for us to deduce the characteristics of sentience from them, and we would cease trying to do so. We would instead simply derive the principles of sentience, and those of still higher states of consciousness, resting for their existence upon sentience, directly from a study of the operation of these states themselves, in a manner unembarrassed and unencumbered by an ideological necessity to reduce them all to levels of being lower than themselves. (*Meaning*, p. 178)

The highest level in the hierarchy of living beings is the human, a level characterized by the search for truth, the exercise of responsibility, and the ability to rise to deeds of freedom and selfless love. Just as the vegetative principle transforms, organizes, and enlivens the physical substances it incorporates, so the human being transforms and humanizes the sentient level and, through it, the lower levels insofar as they are integrated components of the human organism.

In this way, Polanyi changes the scientific worldview from one that reduces all forms of life to their lowest, biochemical level to a hierarchical view of nature in which biochemistry is seen as subsidiary to organic life and in which the level of the responsible human individual is fully recognized as a generative reality.[10]

The term *hierarchy*, which is commonly understood to imply "higher" and "lower" levels of reality, is misleading here. It would be more accurate to speak of "deeper" and "shallower" dimensions of reality, for the worldview we are exploring places the "higher" dimensions of living beings *within* them, not above them. These dimensions are "higher" only in the sense that they are more essential in that they determine the "lower" levels of their being.

But how does the "higher" level of human selfhood determine the "lower" levels incorporated into its being? This is something that we *do* unconsciously throughout our waking hours. When I rise from my chair and cross the room to fetch a book from the shelf, my focus is on what I am looking for in the book. This intent galvanizes my bodily movements. My body responds to my intentions, not because I am conscious of it as an object and consciously control its movements,

---

10. The four consecutive levels of reality described by Polanyi — the inorganic, the vegetative, the sentient, and responsible human personhood — correspond to those depicted by R. Steiner in his book *Theosophy* and elsewhere as the physical, the etheric, the astral, and the "I."

but because I *dwell* within it, because it is an extension of my self, my instrument.

Polanyi points out the inherent structure of practical, physical activity through the example of hammering in a nail. As my attention focuses on the nail, every voluntary muscle in my body is coordinated in the concerted effort to hit it. While my focal awareness is on the nail, I am subsidiarily aware of my body. My focal awareness organizes my bodily movements into the meaningful whole of my action.

One of Polanyi's central insights, the implications of which are profoundly significant, is his realization that *the fundamental structure of skillful bodily activity is the same as that of cognitive activity.* Common to both is the integration of outer, subsidiary elements through an inner focusing activity. In a nutshell, "The arts of doing and knowing ... are ... only different aspects of the act of extending our person into the subsidiary awareness of particulars that compose a whole" (*Personal Knowledge*, p. 65). While we are more or less awake in our cognitive scientific thinking, we remain for the most part entirely unconscious of how we coordinate our bodily movements.

Intermediate between bodily activity and thinking is the activity of speaking, which involves not only the integration of particulars through thinking, but also the formulation of words into sentences and the coordination of complex bodily movements as we form sounds and shape them into words. When we speak, our awareness of our language and our bodily speech formation is subsidiary while we focus on the meaning we are striving to convey. If our formulation is particularly apt and to the point and captures the full force of our meaning, we rightfully find that we have "hit the nail on the head." Thus we dwell within and master language in the same way that we dwell within and master our body, and our awareness of both is subsidiary while we focus on "what we are trying to get at."

When I hammer in a nail, my idea, or purpose, is the center of action that determines all my external movements. My action is determined from the inside out. The process of knowing proceeds from the outside in. It begins with the perception of an external event and seeks to discover the inner principle out of which the event arose. My understanding of the event is complete when I am able to inwardly *recreate* the event out of its determining principle. Let us take the example of observing a pendulum. I participate in its movement with my imagination until I grasp the principle that determines its movement and am able to reenact its movement from the inside out, as it were, as I dwell, cognitively, in all of its particulars — its length, the amplitude of its arc, the dynamics of its motion — while grasping their interrelationship. Thus, in full, heightened consciousness I dwell within and master the movement of the pendulum, just as I unconsciously dwell within and master the movements of my body when performing a skillful action. Polanyi calls this "knowledge through indwelling" (*Meaning*, p. 37). Through indwelling, I come to know the object from the inside out, as actors know the characters they are portraying. Indwelling in other words is a kind of heightened intuitive knowledge in which the dualism of subject and object is overcome.[11]

When we grasp an idea through intuitive thinking, we actually dwell within its generative potential. Polanyi writes: "We actually make existential changes in ourselves when we modify our judgments. For we literally dwell in different principles from the ones we have been at home in, and we thus change the character of our lives" (*Meaning*, p. 62).[12] Such a principle becomes a motivating force within our lives, a source of inspiration from which creativity and strength can flow into our actions.

We are now ready to approach the question of how we gain knowledge of the higher levels of reality that manifest in living beings. A key to all scientific discovery, according to Polanyi, is to "*look at the known data, but not in themselves, rather as clues to the unknown, as pointers to it and parts of it*" (*Personal Knowledge*, pp. 127–28). Applying this principle to living nature, Polanyi writes:

> We therefore recognize and study the coherence of living things by integrating their motions — and any other normal changes occurring in their parts — into our comprehension of their functions. *We integrate mentally what living beings integrate practically* — just as chess players rehearse a master's game to discover what he had in mind. We share the purpose of a mind by dwelling in its actions. And so, generally, we also share the purposes and functions of any living matter by dwelling in its motions in our efforts to understand their meaning. (*Meaning*, p. 45, emphasis added.)

---

11. We find this same point addressed by Steiner on pp. 104–105.

12. Steiner formulated the same principle at the end of the first section of his book *How to Know Higher Worlds*: "Every idea that becomes an ideal for you creates forces of life within you." He also deals with the relationship between ideas and human action in chapter 10, section 5 of this book ("Ethical and Historical Sciences").

Through what Polanyi calls *"participation through indwelling"* (*Meaning*, p. 44) we begin to see the formation or behavior of a living being as a revelation of hidden principles. Polanyi speaks of this as a "reading" of the outer, subsidiary phenomena as the expression of these principles:

> The meaning of an animal's actions can be understood only by *reading* the particulars of its actions (or by reading its mind in terms of these actions) and not by observing the actions [in] themselves as we may observe inanimate processes.... Only by being aware of these particulars subsidiarily, in relation to a focal awareness of the animal as an individual, can we know what the animal is doing and knowing. (*Personal Knowledge*, p. 364)

In chapter 4, Steiner goes to great lengths to point out the essential difference between inorganic and organic nature. Events in the inorganic realm, he writes, are determined by factors that lie within the sense-perceptible world. Therefore, as Polanyi puts it in the paragraph quoted above, we understand inanimate events by observing their external particulars *in themselves*. It is the length of the pendulum that determines its frequency and the weight of the bob that sets it in motion. Though the law of the pendulum can only be grasped in intuitive thought, it is nothing more than a summary formulation of causal relationships between discrete sense-perceptible factors. Living organisms, on the other hand, are not primarily determined by sense-perceptible causes. On the contrary, a "center of action" as Polanyi calls it, which is hidden to our senses, determines the physical events. This generative principle — unlike the law of the pendulum — is a living reality in its own right that brings forth or moves its sense-perceptible parts out of itself.[13] This view corresponds with our naive, heartfelt relationship with other living beings. We do not treat them as we would inanimate objects but with a respect for the integrity of what expresses itself through them. Why is it that we have also come to view nature through the reductive eyes of modern science?

In his discussion of skillful human activity, Polanyi emphasizes that it is our own inner focus that integrates our subsidiary actions. When hammering in a nail, for example, it is our focal awareness on hitting the nail that integrates our bodily movements, of which we are

---

13. Compare with Steiner's descriptions on pp. 44ff. and pp. 121–22.

subsidiarily aware. As soon as we shift the focus of our attention away from the nail, our original focus is immediately lost, and we will have to reestablish it before we can resume our work. A pianist who becomes focally aware of his or her fingers during a performance will lose the focus on the flow of the piece and have to stop. Like the proverbial centipede, when engaged in a skillful activity we must avoid thinking about how we coordinate our limbs and keep our minds focused on our goal while letting our limbs follow under the supervision of a subsidiary awareness. In this way our activity remains an organic whole whose parts are integrated through an inner focus.

Polanyi repeatedly pointed out the similar structure of our practical and cognitive activity. Let us now again briefly turn to the latter. When I read a sentence, I am caught up in its meaning. I hardly notice the individual words and am only subliminally aware of the individual letters on the page. All of these outer particulars become transparent as I focus on their joint meaning. As soon as I shift my focus to the printed figures on the page, however, they lose their transparency and face me in their "raw bodily nature" (*Meaning*, p. 39). Polanyi points out that "anything serving as a subsidiary [or manifestation] ceases to do so when focal attention is directed on it. It turns into a different kind of thing, deprived of the meaning it had while serving as a subsidiary" (*Meaning*, p. 39).

Just as pianists "fall out" of the dynamic flow of the music when they focus on their hands, I lose the connection with what expresses itself through a text when I focus attention on one isolated part. Polanyi emphasizes that this is due not to a shift from awareness to unawareness, but to a shift between two kinds of awareness. A good pianist will combine focal awareness of the music as a dynamic gestalt with strong subsidiary awareness of his or her hands. But because this attention to detail is subsidiary, it only leads to a more expressive articulation of the whole.

Similarly, a strong subsidiary awareness of particular features of an organism can serve only to enhance and clarify one's focal perception of what speaks through the whole. A true organic science will see every organ and detail of the physical body, right down into its chemical composition, as a clue to the nature of the whole. It will exercise what Polanyi calls a "from-to" thinking (*Meaning*, pp. 34–5), which can seesaw back and forth between the investigation of the outer clues and its grasp of the whole as that which is revealed through those clues, and thus gain an ever more living grasp of the organism in its full, distinctive reality (*Knowing and Being*, pp. 129–30).

In the absence of this active bridging thinking, we lose the connection between the whole and its parts, and a gap opens up between the idea or inner aspect of the organism and its raw bodily nature. We therefore *focus* on the latter, analyze it, and seek causal explanations. We fall back into a mechanistic thinking that is incapable of grasping the organism as a meaningful whole. We find ourselves living with a dualistic worldview in which we are unable to relate our inner "subjective" experience of living beings, humanity, and morality to our "objective" experience of the outer material world. With a brevity born of deep insight, Polanyi explains that "dualism occurs when one shifts one's attention from the direction on which subsidiaries bear and focuses instead on the subsidiaries themselves" (*Meaning*, p. 49).[14]

By establishing the legitimacy of "from-to" knowledge, a knowledge that sees the working of hidden principles in the outer phenomena, Polanyi paved the way for overcoming dualism. Polanyi's fundamental insight into the focal-subsidiary structure of human cognition and action opens the way for us to reconnect the parts with the whole, the visible with the invisible, the "objective" with the "subjective." It establishes a firm foundation upon which a participatory science can be built that recognizes the primacy of the creative spirit in all of living nature.

V
Goethe's Scientific Approach

If in fact we seek in the moral sphere, through faith in God, virtue and immortality, to raise ourselves up into a higher realm and approach the Primal Being, then may we not also, in the intellectual sphere, through contemplation of an ever creating nature, make ourselves worthy of spiritual participation in her productions?   — GOETHE, "Judgment through Intuitive Perception"

Johann Wolfgang von Goethe (1749–1832) is recognized as perhaps the greatest of those individuals who brought German culture to its

---

14. Compare with Steiner's distinction between the task of the intellect and that of reason pp. 110–111. Whereas the intellect focuses on the particulars, isolates them, and analyses them, reason apprehends them as manifestations of a unifying principle.

flowering around the year 1800.[15] Though it is his extraordinary human stature, depth, and universality of being that bring him this distinction, he is acknowledged primarily as a great poet. Goethe himself, however, considered his scientific insights as his most significant achievement.[16] And yet, ever since the objectivist, reductionist tendency prevailed in the second half of the nineteenth century, Goethe's scientific work has been either ignored or rejected by the scientific establishment.

This is now beginning to change. Since the 1960s, there has been a resurgence of "Goethean" science in German-speaking countries, and there is now a significant new interest in his approach in the English-speaking world as well. The physicist-philosopher David Bohm and F. David Peat have given Goethe's science serious consideration in their book *Science, Order, and Creativity* (1987).[17] In a more recent major work, *The Wholeness of Nature: Goethe's Way toward a Science of Conscious Participation in Nature* (1996), Henri Bortoft has succeeded splendidly in articulating Goethe's scientific method in its distinction from, but compatibility with, analytic science.

Generations have drawn deeply from the power and wisdom of Goethe's poetic works, finding in them insights into the deeper dimensions of human nature. Is it possible for this same imaginative power to participate in "objective" things such as the study of color, geology, botany, or zoology? Can creative imagination be subject to the rigor and discipline of scientific research? And if so, where does such an imaginative science lead?

Goethe was helped by the fact that he was a great observer. In all his scientific studies, he began by setting out to gain as comprehensive and detailed a view of his subject matter as possible and to order this knowledge in a manner consistent with its own nature. His home in Weimar was filled with numerous specimens from his work in geology, botany, and zoology, as well as many instruments for experiments in electricity and optics.

In botany, Goethe found that Linné's systematic classification of plants provided a solid basis for what he himself would develop as a further methodological step. An accurate classification of plant

---

15. The period includes Fichte, Hegel, Schelling, Schiller, Novalis, Hölderlin, Kleist, and Beethoven.
16. Goethe to Eckermann, February 19, 1829
17. See pp. 162–4.

species or of the organs of individual plants requires ever more refined distinctions into ever more numerous categories. And Goethe
soon noticed that the inner mobility and adaptability of the plant de-
fied rigid definition. Thus, it was in response to Linné's analytical,
defining tendency that Goethe's great contribution to organic science
began. For he realized that Linné's approach was unable to grasp
the plant's essential nature, which he found lay in its inner flexibility, in its ability to bring forth ever changing shapes out of one basic
form. Grasping the formative activity of the plant in this way, Goethe
brought his exact imagination into play. He sometimes called the resulting participatory approach his "genetic" method, using this term
in its original sense to denote the genesis, or coming about, of the
phenomena. In his notes on the physiology of plants, he writes:

> When I see before me something that has come about, inquire
> into how it has arisen, and follow the course of its development
> as far back as I can, I become aware of a series of steps that
> I cannot perceive simultaneously but must recall as a kind of
> ideal whole.
>
> First, I am inclined to think of discrete steps; but since nature
> makes no leaps, I am finally compelled to view the successive
> results of an uninterrupted activity as a whole by suspending
> the particulars without destroying their impression.
>
> Division into overarching stages; attempt at a finer division;
> attempt at still more intermediary points.
>
> When we imagine the results of these attempts, we see that
> empirical observation must finally cease, giving way to the intu-
> itive perception of an entity in the state of becoming, and that, in
> the end, the idea must be formulated. ("Studies for a Physiology
> of Plants," Suhrkamp, p. 75)

The "genetic" method, then, is the reenaction of nature's creative processes through imaginative participation. Polanyi formulated
it succinctly in the words already quoted: "We integrate mentally
what living beings integrate practically" (*Meaning*, p. 45). By actively
participating in nature's processes, we come to see them as the expressions of her hidden principles. We grasp these creative laws, nature's
open secrets, through what Goethe called "the *idea:* that which always manifests and thus presents itself to us as the lawfulness in all
manifestations" (*Verses in Prose*).

The application of Goethe's method to plant morphology leads directly to the imaginative perception of metamorphosis. Since metamorphosis can be grasped only through an act of personal knowledge, by "participation through indwelling," the reader is invited to enter actively into the metamorphosis of specific plants.

For example, let us take the common buttercup found in fields and meadows, where it blossoms in early summer. Like most flowering plants, the buttercup derives its name from its blossom, whose shiny, buttery yellow seems to reflect the warm sun of early June. Few people would be able to identify it by its leaves. These appear with the first green of spring. Like the plantain or dandelion, the buttercup forms a basal rosette. Its leaves, however, do not remain clustered as closely around their center as those of these other plants but rise up on slender stalks, stretching their elaborate, starlike forms out into the surroundings. This first spring phase of the buttercup's unfolding gives us an intimation of what is to follow: as the sun grows stronger, a central stem springs up, sending a single leaf from each node as it lifts and branches upward.

At first glance, we may notice the contrast between the rounder, fuller leaves of the rosette and the more segmented, lanceolate leaves higher up on the stem, from whose peculiar shape the *crowfoot* family receives its name. Through closer observation, however, we come to see an orderly sequence of leaves beginning with the first, outermost leaf in the rosette and ending in the last little spike just below the blossom. The first leaf is relatively small and undifferentiated. Its rounded shapes are swelling and full. The next leaves grow successively larger and more differentiated. There is more concavity in their contours, and they are more sharply pointed. Their stalks lift them ever further into the periphery. As the central stem of the plant rises up, its leaves become more lanceolate, and their stalks grow shorter. They soon contract into ever smaller, simpler, stalkless forms (see Figure 1). In following the succession of leaves from first to last, we begin to enter into the consistent movement underlying their progression. We begin to participate in a continuous dynamic process in which the leaves are only specific intermediate steps: gradual expansion, extension, and elaboration in the rosette, followed by a more rapid contraction and simplification as the leaves proceed up the stem. In order to grasp their metamorphosis fully, we have to dwell within its movement with all the forces of our concentration. In this exercise, our thinking is transformed into a dynamic, formative activity.

We have seen how, toward the top of the stem, the green, vegetative leaves diminish. Now, finally, the growth of the plant comes to an end in the flower bud. The completion of the growth process, however, allows for the beginning of something altogether new. The bud is to the vegetative plant what the cocoon is to the caterpillar. Closed off and protected from the outer world, the organism goes through complete and radical metamorphosis. Succulent metabolic life is transformed into ephemeral beauty. In the shiny gold petals we see leaves that have undergone what we might call a process of transubstantiation. They are no longer vessels of photosynthesis and vegetative life processes but appear as the purest revelation of a yet higher level of reality. The petals open in an expansive gesture. Then, in the stamens, the leaf reaches its most delicate and contracted form.

Whereas the green plant had developed through a succession of metamorphosing leaves, unfolding, step by step in time, the blossom is a *simultaneous display of many transformed leaves*. The five petals forming the cup are all identical, as are the numerous stamens within it. What was a whole sequence of gradually expanding and contracting leaves in the growing plant now appears in the polarity of outer and inner forms. In the radial symmetry of the blossom's shiny golden cup there is an inner dynamic of a qualitatively different nature from that of the green plant. Whereas the latter invited us to participate, with a kind of muscular, imaginative thinking, in a sculptural time-process, the blossom appears all at once as a complete picture and calls forth a spontaneous feeling response. It is through participatory feeling that we form the intimate inner relationship with flowering plants that prompts us to cultivate them in our gardens and display them in our homes. And it is primarily in our feeling relationship with the blossoms that we sense an inner expressiveness not so apparent in the purely vegetative process. In its blossom, the culminating phase of its unfolding, the plant reveals its innermost nature in a way that it cannot in its green, vegetative stage.

After the ephemeral blossom has fallen away, the small cluster of fruits begins to swell. Here, in the fruiting stage, the vegetative principle turns inward so to speak and reverts back into itself. The buttercup, however, maintains its character even in the formation of its fruit. Unlike the fruit of most other plants, the buttercup's seedpods orient themselves outward and, when fully ripened, give themselves over to their surroundings as they separate and fall away. Within each tiny pod lies a seed in which the buttercup achieves its ultimate con-traction as it separates itself from the withering mother plant. In the dry, hardened seeds, life processes almost cease; the plant withdraws from the living, metamorphosing stream of time and attains a state of pure potentiality.

By participating imaginatively in the unfolding of the buttercup, we come to distinguish three consecutive stages of expansion and contraction in leaf, blossom, and fruit. As each preceding stage comes to an end in a phase of contraction, a new principle is able to enter the plant. The principle of vegetative, leafy growth ends in the formation of the bud. At this point the blossoming impulse takes over — which comes to its completion in the fertilization of the ovary. Now the fruiting process begins, resulting, finally, in the formation of the seeds. Each point of contraction is an end and a critical new beginning. The conditions must be right before the new impulse can unfold. Wet, overcast weather or continuous shade will retard or even prevent blossoming. Most plants bear no fruit without fertilization. Seeds can lie dormant for years in dry, desert conditions until a rainfall brings the moisture they need for germination.

As Goethe recreated the plant in exact imagination, he observed it as the continuous transformation of one basic organ: the leaf. Goethe called the leaf the true Proteus of the plant kingdom. (Proteus was the Greek god who was so difficult to recognize because he was forever concealing himself by taking on different forms.) In his treatise *The Metamorphosis of Plants* Goethe takes great pains to demonstrate that all the various organs of the plant arise out of the metamorphosis of the leaf.

The plant's inner plasticity can also be seen in the fact that seeds from the same plant develop differently under different environmental conditions. And, when we look at a plant family as a whole, we can see how a certain family type manifests itself in various species as it responds to different conditions.

In the early, wet spring woods, before the trees unfold their leaves and cast their shade on the forest floor, we find the buttercup type fully transformed. Here, amid freshets, and most luxuriantly at the forest's edge, we find the marsh marigold, or cowslip, drawn forth by the warm spring sun. Its large, gold-yellow blossoms stand upon thick, hollow, succulent stems. The glossy, dark green leaves are rub-bery to the touch. Their form remains strongly rounded (see Figure 3).

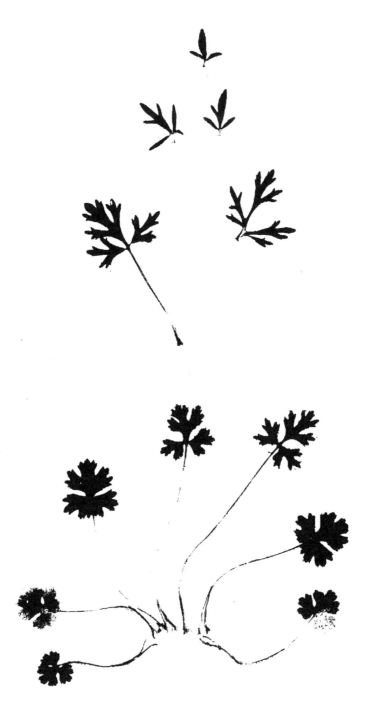

Fig. 1. *Leaves of Common Buttercup.*

Fig. 2. Leaves of Kidneyleaf Buttercup.

Fig. 3. Marsh Marigold.

There is no leaf metamorphosis, no transformation of the watery suc-
culence of the vegetative plant. Upon opening, the green bud-leaves,
or sepals, are transformed directly into large gold petals. As in the
tulip, the sun itself brings forth the transformation of the green, vegetative bud into the colored blossom. The overall impression of the
marsh marigold with its lush, rounded leaves and large gold-yellow
blossoms is somewhat reminiscent of the floating yellow water lily.

Also appearing in the damp woods of early spring, the inconspicuous kidneyleaf buttercup (*ranunculus abortivus*) reflects the world
of the forest interior, an environment that is not only less watery, but
also less fertile, and less sunny than that of the marsh marigold. These
conditions account for its diminutive size. Its small basal rosette is like
a miniature marsh marigold and manifests the moisture of the forest
floor. Whereas the marsh marigold blossoms immediately in the full
May sun, the kidneyleaf buttercup seems to lack the light and the vitality to do so. Hence, perhaps, its name *abortivus*. Instead, it begins a
new, radically different stage of growth that seems to reflect the dryer
conditions of midsummer: It stretches its central stem upward toward
the light that filters down through the forest canopy. The round leaves
of the rosette undergo rapid and dramatic metamorphosis as they pass
through the intermediate crowfoot stage. Like the upper leaves of the

common buttercup, the leaves that now appear close to its slender stem grow ever simpler in their lanceolate forms (see Figure 2). Soon fully shaded by the forest canopy, the kidneyleaf, like many forest flowers, produces only the most stunted, tiny blossoms. Nevertheless, as in the common buttercup, the metamorphosis from the vegetative leaves to the blossom is complete with sepals. As it adapts to the forest interior, this inconspicuous plant seems to be caught halfway between the marsh marigold and the common buttercup.

In this way one can begin to experience the extraordinary plasticity of a plant family that loves the growing power of the sun and the moist conditions and freshness of the spring. But what is it that unites the members of this family? Is membership in a plant family determined only by certain outer traits, or is there a specific quality or inner gesture that speaks through all its members?

E. M. Kranich has done pioneering work exploring the specific qualities of various plant family types. I owe most of what follows to his observations of the buttercup.

We learn from Kranich that, in order to grasp the qualitative character of a phenomenon, we must participate in it not only with our thinking but also with our feelings. When we practice this with heightened sensitivity, it becomes clear that our feelings are not only a personal response but can also reveal the inner nature of the observed phenomenon to the extent that we succeed in participating in its qualities. We all know how to interpret the physiognomic expressions of our friends. But can we interpret the qualitative gestures of plants? Clearly there is no inner person in a plant. A plant, rather, can be seen as a more permanent expression of a particular inner mood of nature.

We have already begun to characterize the qualitative gesture of the common buttercup. The gesture of its leaves is one of reaching out and opening up to the surrounding world. In this sense it can be characterized as radiant. We find this same gesture in the blossoms, most markedly in the shining gold-yellow of the cuplike petals and in the abundance of golden stamens; and we find it again in the fruit.

When we participate in the quality of this inner gesture, we find it to be the same gesture that we make inwardly when we experience joy. Kranich describes how the power of sympathy opens itself to the world in the feeling of joy. It turns, strives toward everything beautiful and noble that approaches it from without. In doing so, it frees itself from everything narrow and heavy; it becomes light and unites itself in inner devotion with the beautiful and noble, feeling itself enriched and fulfilled through what it experiences. And it feels the urge to give the world something in return. Thus in joy there lives, besides devotion and the feeling of being united with the world, also a selfless tendency.

> When we feel joy, our soul lives in these inner movements and gestures. The same inner gestures and movements appear to us in the unfolding development of the buttercup. (Kranich, *Pflanzen als Bilder der Seelenwelt*, p. 164)

Once we have grasped the essential inner gesture of the buttercup type, we can take it into a sunny meadow in early summer, and it becomes a common buttercup; we can take it to the fertile edge of a wet spring forest, and it becomes a marsh marigold; and if we take it further into the forest, where it can hardly come to full manifestation, it becomes *ranunculus abortivus*. Each family member appears as a different manifestation of the same type as it expresses itself under different environmental conditions. Thus Kranich was able to take Goethe's botanical insights a significant step further by following the method that Goethe formulated when he wrote:

> I . . . found that my whole method rests upon derivation; I persist until I find a pregnant point from which much can be derived, or rather which voluntarily brings forth much out of itself and carries it toward me, since in putting forth effort and in receiving I am careful and approach my work faithfully. ("Significant Furtherance through a Single Ingenious Word")

If we then go farther and compare one plant family with another, we come to see each as a dynamic manifestation of a particular inner gesture. Just as the human physiognomy can express an infinite variety of inner feelings, thus the plant kingdom reveals in more permanent forms not only the life but what we can come to experience concretely as the manifold intimate feelings of the earth as they express themselves in various environments, climates, and seasons.

Goethe's interest lay primarily in grasping the formative aspect of the plant world. The infinite variety of specific plant forms can be seen as arising through metamorphosis out of the formative potential of what Goethe called the *archetypal plant*. Just as the various organs of the individual plant arise through the metamorphosis of the protean leaf, thus the extraordinarily diverse plant forms comprising the plant kingdom can be seen in exact imagination as arising out of the archetypal plant. This creative, sensory-supersensory form principle is the "pregnant point" from which all plant forms can be derived. It is not an abstraction. The living idea of the archetypal plant can only be grasped when an intimate knowledge of the plant kingdom is penetrated by the most rigorous and lively imaginative activity. Within this activity we can become subsidiarily aware of any individual plant form within its environment as a unique manifestation of the archetypal plant.

When we rise, through imaginative participation, from the observation of plants as they appear to our senses to a grasp of the generative principles of which they are the outer manifestation, we enter a new dimension of scientific research. In connection with his botanical studies, Goethe distinguished four levels of scientific inquiry characterized by the kind of questions asked by their practitioners, whom he designated as *users, knowers, beholders,* and *encompassers:*

1. The users, who seek and demand use from their knowledge, are the first to stake out the field of science as it were and to seize upon the practical. Consciousness gained through experience gives them sureness; needs lead to a certain breadth of knowledge.

2. Those with an appetite for knowledge require a dispassionate, unselfish gaze, a restlessness born of curiosity, and a clear intellect. They always stand in relationship to the first group; they also work, in a scientific sense, only with what is given.

3. The beholders already take on a productive attitude, and knowledge, as it intensifies its activity, inadvertently demands imaginative seeing and merges into it. And, as vehemently as the knowers may reject imagination, before they know it, they are nevertheless compelled to call upon the aid of productive imaginative powers.

4. The encompassers, whom one could, in a prouder sense, call "the creators," become productive in the highest degree; for, by proceeding from ideas, they already express the unity of the

whole, and it is then, so to speak, up to nature to comply with this idea. ("Studies for a Physiology of Plants," Suhrkamp, p. 74)

Our current technologically oriented, purely empirical science is clearly the work of the first two groups. The research of the "knowers" is often conducted with an eye toward its application by the "users."

The "knowers" strive for a systematic and comprehensive knowledge of their field. Linné was representative of this group. But whereas their strength lies in their detailed factual knowledge, they are not yet able to free themselves from the limitations of what is given externally. They are therefore unable to grasp the dynamic interrelatedness and deeper significance of the facts.

The step from the second to the third level of scientific inquiry involves the transformation of abstract logical thought into what Goethe here calls *productive imagination*. As this capacity is central to Goethe's contribution to scientific inquiry, we will explore it in some depth before continuing. Calling it "reason" (*Vernunft*), the eighty-year-old Goethe characterized this transformed thinking in its relationship to the creative forces in nature and contrasted it with abstract logic, which he called the "intellect" (*Verstand*).

> The divine, however, works in the living, not in what is dead; we find it in all that is in a process of becoming and transformation, but not in what is finished or frozen. Therefore reason, with its tendency toward the divine, engages only in what is alive and in the process of becoming, and the intellect only in what is finished and rigid, in order to put it to use. (Goethe to Eckermann, February 13, 1829; compare pp. 54–55 and 110–11 of this volume)

When Steiner distinguishes between inorganic and organic nature (in chapter 4 of this volume), he also describes the different cognitive capacities involved in grasping these two different levels of reality. The thinking involved in grasping an event in inorganic nature understands this event as the result of discrete sense-perceptible factors. Goethe calls it the intellect; Kant refers to it as "discursive thinking." Living beings, on the other hand, bear their own generative principle, or entelechy, within them. They are not the result of external factors only; on the contrary, their external characteristics are generated by their own inner principle. This active, supersensible principle cannot be grasped by the intellect. It can only be grasped by what Goethe here calls "reason," what Polanyi refers to as "from-to" thinking, and Steiner speaks of as "intuitive" knowledge. In other contexts Goethe calls this capacity "exact, sensory imagination" (*exakte, sinnliche Fantasie*), or "judgment through intuitive perception" (*anschauende Urteilskraft*).

Whereas the intellect defines outer particulars as separate entities and grasps their causal relations, reason participates in organic processes as they bring forth their external particulars and comes to grasp them as manifestations of an inner principle. Its understanding proceeds, through its grasp of this principle, from the whole to the parts, whereas the intellect, in understanding an inorganic event as the result of external factors, proceeds from the parts to the whole.

Goethe was naturally gifted with a productive, imaginative thinking. As a poet, artist, and scientist, he had developed it to a high degree. Yet, until the middle of his life, it remained a largely unconscious capacity that he naively experienced simply as "seeing." This changed, however, as a result of his famous meeting, in 1794, with the more philosophically inclined poet Schiller. In this conversation of these diametrically opposed personalities, Goethe's ability to "see" the dynamic principles working in the outer phenomena was strongly in evidence.

Goethe was trying to acquaint Schiller with the metamorphosis of plants and finally, to make his point, drew a characteristic sketch of an unfolding plant. When he had finished, Schiller shook his head and said, "That is not an observation from experience, that is an idea." Goethe's deep-seated aversion to abstract philosophical ideas rose up within him. As he had feared, Schiller's sharp philosophical mind had fully misunderstood him. Swallowing his frustration, Goethe replied: "Then I may rejoice that I have ideas without knowing it and can even see them with my own eyes" (*Fortunate Encounter*, Suhrkamp, p. 20).

Schiller's discerning clarity had awakened Goethe, however. As he began to reflect on the act of cognition, he realized that

> when artists speak of nature, they always intuit the idea without being clearly conscious of doing so. It is the same with all those who exclusively extol experience; they do not realize that experience is only half of experience. (*Verses in Prose*)

Polanyi would have pointed out that they remain unconscious of the fact that while they are subsidiarily aware of the outer, sense-perceptible particulars, they are focally aware of the idea through which the particulars appear as an integrated, meaningful whole. Two years after this pivotal conversation with Schiller, Goethe wrote:

> An idea about objects of experience is, in a manner of speaking, an organ that I use in order to grasp them, in order to make them my own. (Letter to Sömmerring, August 28, 1796)

Goethe had come to realize that

> there is a difference between seeing and seeing, that the eyes of the spirit have to work in continuous living conjunction with the eyes of the body, for one otherwise falls into the danger of overlooking what one sees. (*History of my Botanical Studies*, section on "K. F. Wolff: A Few Comments")

The art of knowing, according to Polanyi, involves "the pouring of ourselves into the subsidiary awareness of particulars" (*Personal Knowledge*, p. 64). All cognitive perception, then, may be seen as consisting of two concurrent movements. The one proceeds from the outside world and enters "the eyes of the body," bringing us the given perceptual elements of which we are subsidiarily aware. The other proceeds from within through "the eyes of the spirit" that apprehend the unifying conceptual element of which we are focally aware. While we remain passive recipients of the former, we are active and productive in the latter.

The deeper, generative dimensions of living nature are revealed only to "the eyes of the spirit"; to the eyes of the body, which perceive only the outer world of the senses, nature remains a riddle. Reductionist science, with its physical instruments, will never be able to torture nature's secrets from her. As Goethe says in his *Faust*:

> Mysterious in the light of day,
> Nature will not allow you to unveil her;
> What to your spirit she will not betray
> You cannot force from her with thumbscrews, rack or lever.
>
> (lines 672–5)

Shortly after encountering Schiller, Goethe realized that "if he took to be an idea what I formulated as the experience of my senses, then there must be something mediating and relating between the two" (*Fortunate Encounter*, Suhrkamp, p. 20). When he "saw" the plant with all its sensory particulars as the expression of an idea, the mediator between the two was his exact sensory imagination: the working together of the eyes of the body and the eyes of the spirit, the capacity to participate in the becoming of the plant, in the manifestation of the idea in time and under various environmental conditions.

Rudolf Steiner repeatedly points to the transformation of knowledge itself that occurs when "idea and experience, in full interpenetration, mutually enliven one another and become one whole" (see p. 5). Steiner speaks of the concept of metamorphosis as a *living concept*, as a revelation of the forces of becoming, which remain hidden to our outer senses. By thinking such concepts, we bring these forces to life within ourselves. In one of his later lectures Steiner says that we need an elixir, "not to perfect our physical body, but something that enlivens our thoughts, that demummifies them" (September 30, 1922). This elixir, he said, we find in living concepts, which have the power to revitalize our whole being right down into our physical body and our outer actions.

In his essay "Significant Furtherance through a Single Ingenious Word," Goethe writes that the psychologist Heinroth had characterized his thinking as "objective" (*gegenständlich* — compare footnote 1, p. 88), by which he means that

> my thinking does not separate itself from the objects; that the elements of the objects, the perceptions, enter into my thinking and are most intimately permeated by it; that my perceiving is itself a thinking, my thinking a perceiving.

This helps to explain Goethe's aversion to abstract ideas. For him, ideas were the perceptions of the eyes of the spirit. Polanyi, likewise, to avoid empty abstractions, shied away from the words *idea, concept*, or even *thinking* and favored the more perceptual connotation of *focal awareness* of what speaks through the outer subsidiaries. Steiner described how Goethe's thinking

> immerses itself in what it is observing and unites itself intimately with it, that it slips out of its subjectivity, as it were, and into the object, that the objects of his perception are completely pen-

etrated by his concepts, and that his concepts, in turn, enter fully into his perceptions. (lecture of August 30, 1921)

In this way Goethe was able to grasp the object in the fullness of its being. "To grasp this inner being," Steiner wrote, "productivity of spirit is necessary" ("The Rightness of Goethe's Science" ["Goethes Recht in der Naturwissenschaft"], an essay published in 1884). For only the momentary outer appearance is given through sense perception. The being itself, its becoming and its working, is only revealed through our own spiritual activity. Only a productive, living thinking can bring inner life and wholeness to the outer clues of sense perception.

The third level of scientific inquiry described by Goethe, that of the "beholders," includes an approach to the phenomena that we have already taken in our attempt to determine the type of the buttercup, but that we have not yet sufficiently distinguished from participation in the metamorphosis of the plant. Whereas through the latter we come to experience the formative principles of organic development over time, this *physiognomic* approach views the phenomena as the direct expression of inner qualities of being. This approach to nature, which at the time of Goethe's youth was prevalent in the study of human character and animal types, immediately appealed to his artistic nature and sparked his interest in zoology. Steiner describes in chapter 3, however, how Goethe's sculptural bent eventually led him away from the physiognomic approach to a consideration of form in its own right and to the exploration of the laws of metamorphosis.

The physiognomic grasp of reality begins on the level of object recognition. Polanyi draws attention to the large tacit, or unspecifiable, component in this knowledge: "We know a person's face, and can recognize it among a thousand, indeed among a million. Yet we usually cannot tell how we recognize a face we know" (*Tacit Dimension*, p 4).

Just as we recognize the inner identity or momentary feelings of people through their facial expressions, we can also learn to see the specific characteristics — of a plant, a chemical element, or a particular landscape — as the manifestations of specific inner qualities or forces. This kind of knowing, however, generally remains largely tacit and unspecified, as it is based primarily on our feeling for things. It is therefore considered to be of a more or less subjective nature and to lie outside the boundaries of the exact sciences.

It is a task of Goethean science to objectify physiognomic knowing by raising it into full consciousness. This can only be done by learning to "read" the subsidiary outer appearances as the manifestations of inner qualities, by learning not just to react to them out of our own personal sympathy or antipathy but — methodically yet sensitively — to live our way into their language. "In observing nature on a scale large or small," Goethe wrote, "I have always asked, Who speaks here, the object or you" (*Verses in Prose*).

Physiognomic perception is always intimately connected with the grasp of metamorphosis. For the physiognomy of an organism expresses itself through the metamorphosis of a basic, archetypal form. We have seen how the buttercup family type expresses itself differently in the common buttercup, the marsh marigold, and the kidneyleaf buttercup, and how each of these species comes about through the metamorphosis of their common type. In the animal kingdom this becomes far more dramatic when we come to see, for example, how the lion, the elephant, and the mouse appear as metamorphoses of their common mammalian type. Metamorphosis is the means whereby nature has the inner plasticity and mobility to manifest in so many unique and highly specific ways.

Goethe's study of color lies beyond the scope of this essay, but it should be noted that its significance for the inorganic sciences is comparable to the importance of his study of metamorphosis for the organic sciences. Let it suffice in our present framework to draw attention to one section of this work, entitled "The Sensory-Moral Effects of Colors." This section deals with what we might call the physiognomies of the colors. Each color has its characteristic inner quality, which we sense not only through the eye but through our feelings to the extent that we succeed in participating in its inner dynamic. It was in this sense that Goethe spoke of the "moral" qualities of color. For just as the term "sensory" implies the infinite richness of our sensory experience of color and is not limited to black and white, the term "moral" as used here implies the entire spectrum of our qualitative inner experience and is not limited to what falls within the narrow concepts of traditional morality.

In this sense, the deepening of all physiognomic perception leads to sensory-moral perception. This requires the introduction into science of what we consider our most subjective inner capacities: feeling and moral sensitivity. Just as a grasp of metamorphosis requires a transformed, revitalized thinking, an "objective" thinking in the sense that it unites itself with its object and dwells fully within it, thus physiognomic perception requires a transformed, purified capacity of feeling, which becomes "objective" in the sense that it makes itself fully identical with the inner nature of its object. "There is a delicate empiricism," Goethe wrote, "which identifies itself intimately with the object and, in doing so, becomes the actual theory. This heightening of our spiritual capacity belongs, however, to a highly cultivated age" (*Verses in Prose*). The caution that Goethe expresses through this qualification is not to be taken lightly, for at this level of scientific research our most intimate inner experience becomes our instrument. This requires a high degree of inner objectification and the overcoming of anything in our emotional life that could mar its selfless perceptiveness. Furthermore, if it is to rise from a largely unconscious, tacit knowing to an actual science, the physiognomic approach requires the penetration of our perceptions and feelings with rigorous and fully conscious thinking. We have seen an example of such conscious penetration in Kranich's physiognomic research into the nature of the buttercup.

Sense perceptions such as color, tone, warmth, smell, and taste lose their indeterminate, subjective quality when we perceive them as clues to a deeper reality that we can grasp only through the feelings and concepts they awaken in us. The fact is that the essential qualities of the world become manifest only through our own participatory inner experience. We are reminded of Havel's call to "release from the sphere of private whim such forces as a natural, unique, and unrepeatable experience of the world . . . to seek to get to the heart of reality through personal experience," to trust in our "own subjectivity" as our "principal link with the subjectivity of the world." Through a deepened physiognomic perception a color, a tone, a face, an animal, or a plant reveals the hidden reality of which it is the outer manifestation. In one of his lectures Steiner said, "The outer world is, in the end, only the physiognomy of a spiritual world" (November 21, 1910). By transforming our faculty of feeling into an objective organ of perception, we establish the basis for a qualitative, physiognomic science that will become a much-needed complement to our purely quantitative science.

A full and balanced view of the world is essential, according to Goethe, not only in life in general but also in the sciences. The human being has access to a rich spectrum of experience, much of which is eliminated from science through the use of "objective" instruments:

> Insofar as we make use of our healthy senses, we ourselves are the best and most exact scientific instruments possible. The greatest misfortune of modern physics is that its experiments have been set apart from the human being, as it were; physics refuses to recognize nature in anything not detected by artificial instruments, and even uses them to limit and to prove what nature can accomplish. (*Verses in Prose*)

Based as it is on the measurements of artificial instruments and logical thinking, objectivist science is best suited to a technical grasp of the inorganic realm. Its success in this area has been and continues to be overwhelming. On the other hand, its inability to grasp the deeper, more essential dimensions of reality as they manifest in living nature is becoming increasingly clear. Two hundred years ago Goethe had already realized the fallacy of objectivism and sought to expand the instrument of science to include all healthy human perceptive and productive faculties. Thus Goethe laid the foundations for an expanded science that begins to encompass reality in its fullness.

In his notes on the four levels of science, Goethe indicated that his own work usually moved back and forth between the second level of the "knowers" and the third level of the "beholders." He saw the fourth level of the "encompassers" as the highest goal of all scientific striving. It is attained as a culmination of the preceding stages when the subsidiary, sensory clues are no longer needed as cognitional crutches, and the knower dwells fully within the creative principles of the idea. Having gained a full grasp of the archetypal plant as a key to the plant world, one could, as Goethe once suggested, "invent" a new species that would have the same inner integrity as any existing one. It is in this sense that Goethe characterized those who have attained this level as "creators."[18]

Through genetic technology the idea of the biologist as creator has taken on new meaning. When Goethe suggested that it might be possible to invent new organisms, he meant the conceiving of new organisms out of a deeper understanding of their inherent prin-

---

18. Goethe uses the German word *die Erschaffenden*, which means "those who create"; he does not use the word *Schöpfer*, or "creator" in the traditional religious sense.

ciples. The external manipulation of organisms without such an understanding could have disastrous effects.

Goethe's relationship to nature was anything but technocratic. The deeper his insights into the workings of nature became, the deeper grew his awe for her wisdom. This is evidenced by the wonder he felt while observing the simplest natural phenomena and his profound reverence for what he experienced as the divine in nature. When his friend Jacobi wrote, "Nature conceals God!" Goethe added: "But not from everyone!" (*Verses in Prose*).

On August 23, 1794, shortly after their encounter over plant metamorphosis, Schiller wrote Goethe a letter in which he characterized Goethe's central striving as he observed it. In this deeply perceptive letter Schiller speaks of how Goethe's Greek spirit, thrown into a northern land and into modern times, had to create a Greece from within. Schiller had in mind not only the land of Greece but the age of ancient Greece when the divine was still tangible in nature. He saw Goethe's great striving as the attempt to "give birth to a Greece from within, as it were, and on a rational path." Goethe himself once stated that "the nature with which *we* must work is no longer nature — it is an entity quite different from that dealt with by the Greeks" (*Verses in Prose*).

In the broad context of the evolution of human consciousness, Goethe takes his place as a pioneer of a scientific method that leads from the empirical observation of nature to a new grasp of the creative spiritual principles that work within it. In contrast to ancient times, however, this new perception of the divine in nature is no longer given as a kind of dreamlike vision but can only be realized through the free and fully conscious inner activity of each individual. Goethe's scientific method is a "rational path" upon which this can be achieved.

VI
Art and Science

Those to whom nature begins to reveal her open secret feel an irresistible longing for her worthiest interpreter — art.

— GOETHE, *Verses in Prose*

In 1886, Steiner gave a lecture entitled "Goethe as the Father of a New Aesthetics." The thoughts expressed in that lecture and in chapter 8 of this book, "From Art to Science," are based on Goethe's fundamental insight already referred to at the beginning of this essay:

> The beautiful is a manifestation of hidden laws of nature that would otherwise have forever remained concealed.... The law that manifests with the greatest freedom, on its own most individual terms, evokes the beautiful in its objective form, which then, to be sure, must find worthy subjects to perceive it. (*Verses in Prose*)

Artists, whose gift it is to dwell deeply in their experience, sensing the inner principles at work within it, allow these principles to come to their fullest expression in a work of art. For this reason, we experience a work of art as beautiful. True art, for Goethe, has nothing to do with arbitrary fancy or subjective whim. Both art and science, as Goethe conceives them, involve an exact, participatory imagination.

What, then, is the difference between art and science? Both the artist and the scientist may begin with an initial intuition of an as yet unspecified but strongly sensed lawfulness underlying their experience. But then their ways part. The scientist embarks on the methodical exploration and testing of the initial insight and finally achieves its formulation as a general law. The inner principle is thus extracted from the outer experience in which it was discovered. It is thereby removed from its immediate connectedness with this experience; it loses its vivid sensory-supersensory life, and it finally dries up and is filed away as a dead concept. Meanwhile the outer appearance from which it was extracted remains untransformed in its raw bodily nature. The scientist is unable to hold the two aspects of reality together except in brief moments of intuition.

The artist, on the other hand, never separates the insight from the outer matrix of experience. The outer and inner aspects of reality remain united in imaginative, intuitive perception. In this sensory-supersensory experience of the artist, the inner principles maintain their creative potential. They are not lifted out of experience as concepts but allowed to work on within it as dynamic forces. In the "real world" of every day, these forces are only able to manifest in a very limited way. Their expression is stunted, and they therefore remain at least partially hidden. We are often painfully aware of the gap between "what is" and "what might be." We therefore receive the greatest satisfaction from works of art because here, and only here, can we experience inner forces playing themselves out to their fullest.

Polanyi became particularly interested in the role of the arts. His thinking on this subject led him to the following considerations: Whereas the scientist tends to see the phenomena only as clues leading to the discovery of a general law, the artist sees them as motifs whose inner potential life calls for artistic development. In the act of knowing, the subsidiaries (phenomena) become transparent as we focus through them on their meaning (their lawfulness). Here they are merely indicators and are of no intrinsic interest. In the act of artistic creation, however, the outer subsidiaries are so organized and transformed as to reveal their inner meaning more fully. They themselves take on a heightened life and significance. They are neither transparent nor do they appear in their opaque, raw bodily nature: they take on a wonderful translucency, as it were, a beauty that gives us the greatest pleasure to behold. The subsidiary sensory appearance becomes the focus of our attention. But instead of seeing it in its raw bodily nature, we see it as the revelation of the deeper reality that lies enchanted within it. Polanyi writes that in art "it is the subsidiary clues that are of intrinsic interest to us, and they enter into meanings in such a way that we are carried away by these meanings" (*Meaning*, p. 71).

To illustrate the approach of the knower, Polanyi relates a personal experience:

> My correspondence arrives at my breakfast table in various languages, but my son understands only English. Having just finished reading a letter I may wish to pass it on to him, but must check myself and look again to see in what language it was written. I am vividly aware of the meaning conveyed by the letter, yet know nothing whatever of its words. I have attended to them closely but only for what they mean and not for what they are as objects. (*Personal Knowledge*, p. 57)

This changes in poetry, however, where the dynamics of the language with its sounds, pictorial qualities, and rhythms takes on an expressive life of its own within the framework of the poem. Take, for example, these lines of Gerard Manly Hopkins, in which he depicts the flight of "The Windhover":

> ... then off, off, forth on swing,
> As a skate's heel sweeps smooth on a bow-bend:
> the hurl and gliding
> Rebuffed the big wind ...

We become completely caught up in the language itself. The words and images, which normally function as mere signs, have been composed in such a way that their own qualitative richness and dynamic movement come into play. Each sound now conveys something of the life of the whole. As we begin to dwell within them more and more fully, participating in their every nuance with a heightened consciousness, we are transported into an exhilarating realm of experience in which inner life and outer expression are one.

Just as in poetry words come into their own and begin to "sing," colors, in painting, are liberated and allowed to reveal something of their own dynamic nature. Naturalism in art relegates its medium to the purely subsidiary role it plays in nature. Its focus is on the subject matter, the "what." Goethe reminded us that the "what" is important, but that even more important is the "how," the way in which the medium, the subsidiaries, are formed (*Faust*, line 6992). As we have seen in this brief sample of Hopkins' poetry, the medium itself is beginning to play a more and more important role in modern art. In one of his lectures on the arts, Steiner said:

> We can see a time coming ... when the *medium* of artistic creation will be experienced far more intensively by the human soul ... when the human soul will have the moral and spiritual capacity to live with color and tone in a far more intimate way.... It will attend not only to the outer impression of color, tone, or form, but also to what one can experience behind the tone, behind the color, behind the forms ... what reveals itself in color, tone, or form. (lecture of January 1, 1915, emphasis added)

This latter is the supersensory, moral quality that lies hidden within the sensory and that can be brought to expression through art. The intensification and deepening of sense perception in the arts will go hand in hand with the development of a physiognomic science that will be able to recognize and assess the qualitative aspects of the phenomena just as we today subject them to quantitative analysis.

Each word has its place within the composition of a poem, and each color relates to the other colors in a painting. Similarly, in a good novel, each descriptive detail, each event has a significance of its own that is, at the same time, an elaboration of a greater, meaningful whole. Thus each work of art has the integrity of a living organism, with its own distinctive Gestalt and physiognomy.

It may now be understood that only in art do we experience life in its wholeness. Only in art does the outer manifestation give full expression to the inner reality, thus overcoming the discrepancy between the inner experience and the outer world. And only in artistic experience is our entire being — sensory, psychological, and spiritual — fully and harmoniously engaged. We therefore cannot overestimate the potential of art for *healing*.

In his book *The Turning Point*, Fritjof Capra points to the connection between the words *health* and *whole*:

> Both these words, as well as "hale," "heal," and "holy," derive from the Old English root word *hal*, which means sound, whole, and healthy. Indeed, our experience of feeling healthy involves the feeling of physical, psychological, and spiritual integrity, of a sense of balance among the various components of the organism and between the organism and the environment. (p. 234)

Participation in creative artistic experience is *wholesome* because it allows spiritual forces to stream into and transform the soul and to penetrate right down into the manifest, physical realm. Thus artistic activity permeates the lower levels of reality with the healing power of the creative spirit.

In our modern age the spirit has been relegated to the realm of religion. For Goethe, however, scientific research led to the grasp of creative spiritual principles; and in his art he strove to give the sense perceptible a form that reveals these deeper principles. As the Goethean scientist Wolfgang Schad points out, "Science, art, and religion had been equally led by Goethe back to their sources, where no partitions exist between them" ("The Historical Basis for Anthroposophy in the Modern Era," *Zivilisation der Zukunft*, p. 25).

Steiner spoke of this common source as "Goethe's perception of the idea." He said that it was characteristic of Goethe not to speak of the idea of *truth*, of the idea of *beauty*, of the idea of *goodness*, since Goethe believed that the idea is one and all, that it manifests sometimes as human goodness, then as beauty, and at other times as truth. In this view, however, Goethe saw something far more alive and spiritual than the abstraction that many people today think of as "idea." He perceived the idea as ensouling nature herself in a living way, and as what human beings also find within themselves when descending deeply enough into the depths of their own being. (lecture of October 19, 1919)[19]

Inherent in Goethe's worldview is the gradual reconvergence of art, science, and religion. In early cultures these three basic relationships to the world were still united through a dreamlike perception of the divine in all things. By modern times, however, they had each become an independent realm of human endeavor. Steiner saw their separation as necessary for the evolution of human consciousness:

Humanity could only progress in its development through the separation of knowledge, artistic creativity, and religious experience. The life of the soul became richer through this separation. The streams of forces that make up life had to present themselves separately to the inquiry of thought, to artistic feeling, and to the deep experience of religion.

Humanity has now reached the age when these three streams want to come together. Further separation would deprive human soul life of its health. (lecture of September 26, 1920)

Steiner viewed Goethe as the forerunner of a culture in which a living, experiential grasp of the creative spirit becomes the source of the revitalization of art and science, a revitalization that leads to a deepened religious relationship to the world. Art will play an important role in bringing this culture about. Art is, as Goethe called it, "the true mediator" between the world of the senses and the world of the creative spirit.

---

19. Compare p. 211: "The human being is the vehicle through which nature unveils her secrets. The deepest essence of the world is manifested in the subjective personality."

VII
From Goetheanism to Anthroposophy

> Anthroposophy is a path of knowledge that seeks to lead the
> spirit in the human being to the spirit in the world.
> — RUDOLF STEINER, *Anthroposophical Leading Thoughts*

Both Goethe and Polanyi developed worldviews that lead to the perception of higher levels of reality as they manifest in the phenomena of
nature. Neither, however, was able to extend his grasp of reality from
these intuitive "sensory-supersensory" perceptions to a perception of
the actual spiritual entities that work within them. While both point
to higher levels of existence as the creative sources of life, neither is
able to directly describe them.

At the very beginning of the second part of his *Faust*, Goethe brings
what can be seen as a poetic picture of his worldview. The first part
of the drama ends in one of the most gripping scenes ever written: the
heartrending tragedy of Gretchen. Faust, guilty, is inwardly crushed
and devastated. When the curtain rises on Part II of the drama, we
find Faust asleep in a beautiful landscape, tended by nature's nurtur-
ing spirits. As he awakens, the Sun rises over the mountains. Faust,
refreshed, rises to greet it. Unable to bear the brightness of the direct
sunlight, Faust turns his gaze toward a waterfall in the west. There,
glowing in veils of mist above the torrent, the most glorious sight
appears: "The rainbow's shimmering presence, ever changing." In its
ephemeral play of color, Faust (Goethe) sees a symbol for all the earthly
manifestations of a creative life that we cannot apprehend directly.

Like the prisoners in Plato's cave, Faust is unable to look directly
into the radiant sources of existence. But, unlike them, he is able to
apprehend the creative working of these sources in their manifestations. These are not grey shadows as in Plato's cave; they are vibrant
appearances with an intrinsic value of their own. They do not obscure
the deeper dimensions of reality; they reveal them.

In our times Rudolf Steiner succeeded on the path of those who
leave the cave of Plato's analogy to explore the realm of light outside
it and who then return as initiates. Through his highly developed
faculties of spiritual perception, he was able to explore the hidden,
generative sources of reality and to reveal them in a conceptual form
fully accessible to intellectual understanding.

Yet Steiner clearly saw his spiritual-scientific research, which he later called anthroposophy, as a further development of Goetheanism. Speaking in 1916, he said that in Goethe's worldview there lies "really something like a seed...out of which spiritual science can be developed" — but only, however, when one becomes more than an observer of Goethe and begins to participate in his deeper impulses. He describes how Goethe

> wanted initially to see the weaving and working of the spirit, which remained unconscious to him, in its manifold, colorful reflections in the outer material world — and he could then only perceive it in living matter through his metamorphosis. When Goethe's way of thinking is extended to body, soul, and spirit, a true science of body, soul, and spirit will actually appear. (lecture of April 15, 1916)

In 1917 Steiner said that he would have liked to call his spiritual-scientific worldview "Goetheanism." Applying Goethe's method to the phenomena of the human soul, he continued:

> What we usually call "will" is not just placed next to feeling and thinking, but feeling has arisen simply as a transformed will, or as developed from willing, just as petals are transformations of the green leaves; and thinking, likewise, develops out of feeling....What we recognize as willing is, fundamentally, a young, still childlike being, which transforms into thinking when it grows older. (lecture of October 18, 1917)

As we rise to higher levels of knowledge, capacities lying ever deeper within us are awakened to conscious participation in the cognitive process. We have seen how even the most elementary knowledge arises only when our own cognitive activity comes to meet our sense perceptions. Polanyi pointed out that, in recognizing an object, we pour ourselves out into its particulars and dwell within them just as we dwell within our own body. Thus already on this most elementary and *unconscious* level, our entire inner being is subtly engaged in the cognitive process. After recognition occurs, however, this living inner activity fades, and what remains in our consciousness, besides a mental picture or memory of the object, is a dead, abstract concept, or mere label.

We have also seen how, on the level of Goethean science, this initial inner activity is raised into consciousness and becomes stronger and more differentiated: In order to participate in the process of metamorphosis, our ability to grasp objects as wholes has to develop into a *sculptural thinking*. In order to participate in the inner gestures and qualities of nature's beings, we have to awaken our inner life of *feeling*. The most mysterious and central aspect of all knowing, however, is the sudden inner lighting-up of the concept, the "concluding intuition" through which — as in a flash — the formative and physiognomic aspects of the object are seen as manifestations of a heretofore hidden lawfulness, or being. This most essential, intuitive aspect of cognition arises when we no longer experience the object from the outside but from its very center — that is, from the inside out. Intuitive knowing occurs when our deepest capacity enters into the object and is raised up into full consciousness: it is cognitive *will*. On this intermediate level of cognition, the inner activity of the knower is still guided by outer sense perception. It can therefore be called *the sensory-supersensory level*.

Steiner described how the yet higher level of *supersensory* cognition is attained through a further rigorous transformation of our soul capacities. The capacities of thinking, feeling, and willing have their physiological bases in the threefold nature of the physical human organism. Thinking has its basis in the nerve-sense system, which is centered in the head; feeling is connected with the rhythmical respiratory-circulatory system centered in the chest; volition has its basis in the metabolic-limb system. Toward the spiritual side, however, they are also rooted in modes of spiritual experience that are inaccessible to normal, everyday consciousness. By enlivening and strengthening our soul capacities, Steiner says, we can come to participate consciously in the modes of spiritual experience that underlie our thinking, feeling, and willing. The capacity of *Imagination* is the mode of experience of which our *thinking* is but a pale reflection. To it, metamorphosing creative forces are revealed, as in for example the metamorphosis of plants or the transformation of will into feeling and thinking. *Inspiration* is the mode of experience that is reflected in our *feelings*. Through it we penetrate to a perception of the inner nature of spiritual beings and come to see them in their inner relationships. Finally, through *Intuition* we attain a conscious grasp of the forces that work within our *will*. Through these forces we come to know spiritual beings by fully uniting ourselves with them. Thus Intuition is a fully conscious indwelling of the highest order.[20]

The three stages of supersensory knowledge referred to here must be clearly distinguished from what we generally mean by imagination, inspiration, and intuition. There is, however, a relationship between this highest level of spiritual cognition and the intermediate level that is still dependent on sense perception. There is a certain correspondence between Imagination and thinking in metamorphoses, between Inspiration and physiognomic perception, and between Intuition and intuition. Nevertheless, the fact that the former are modes of *direct* spiritual perception means that a whole realm of powerful experience is accessible to them that remains hidden to knowledge on the intermediate level. Steiner says, however, that Goethe's capacity to grasp the metamorphosis of plants in concrete, living concepts came very close to Imagination.[21] The intermediate level, therefore, the level of Goethean science proper, can be seen as a bridge connecting the sense-perceptible with the spiritual world.

After the Flood, the Book of Genesis tells, God set his rainbow in the clouds as a token of his new covenant with humanity and the Earth. After the Gretchen tragedy, Faust turns his gaze toward the rainbow. As the symbol of the manifestation of divine powers in the sense world, it is a bridge between the earthly and the divine.

When engaged in research on the level of Imagination, Steiner participated in the metamorphosis of spiritual phenomena in a way similar to Goethe's participation in the metamorphosis of plants. Through Inspiration, the perceptions gained through Imagination become transparent as it were, and their hidden meaning is revealed. In this sense, Imagination presents a riddle that is solved through Inspiration. Thus Steiner calls Inspiration a "reading of the hidden script." Whereas Imagination can be compared with sight, which perceives only the outer surface of things, Inspiration can be likened to a hearing that perceives their hidden inner nature. Intuition, finally, is a knowing from the inside out. The innermost center of the human being, the human entelechy, or I, can be grasped only through Intuition.

Just as Goethe had traced the metamorphosis of plants through successive stages of expansion and contraction, Steiner was able to

---

20. Rudolf Steiner, *Riddles of the Soul*, postscript 6, "The physical and spiritual dependencies of the human being."
21. Lectures of Mar. 22, 1921; Apr. 6, 1921; July 28, 1922; Sept. 30, 1922.

follow the metamorphosis of the human entelechy as it passes through successive stages of earthly life and spiritual existence. He gave concrete descriptions of how, at death, the soul goes through a transformation that can be compared to that of the vegetative plant into the blossoming plant or the metamorphosis of the caterpillar into the butterfly. He describes how, at death, the soul expands into the spiritual cosmos, where it is fertilized, as it were, by higher spiritual beings, and where it gathers forces for its next incarnation. Like a seed, the entelechy now contains the fruits of its past life. Drawing its forces together, it builds momentum toward a new incarnation. The earthly life that now ensues can be seen as a lawful metamorphosis of the previous life. Whereas the cycles of plant or animal life repeat themselves with little variation, the human entelechy, with its capacity for freedom, bears within it the potential of ongoing evolution.

Steiner called Goethe the Copernicus and Kepler of the organic world. He himself, however, became the Copernicus and Kepler of human life. By placing the striving human individuality into the context of repeated earthly lives governed by laws of destiny, Steiner shed new light on the meaning of human existence. It is therefore fitting that he called his spiritual science *anthroposophy*, or "wisdom of the human being."

The extension of Goetheanism through anthroposophy opens up a comprehensive worldview in which all life and evolution are seen as resulting from the creative impulses of exalted beings that evolve through rhythmical processes of externalization and internalization. This worldview corresponds with that taught by initiates throughout the ages. Spiritual science rises to a majestic overview of Earth evolution, which opens up a new understanding of the great religious revelations of the past.[22] At this point, spiritual science attains a perspective that, because of its elevated nature, can be called *theosophy*, or wisdom of the gods. This term, as used here, refers neither to the teachings of the Theosophical Society nor to Rudolf Steiner's book *Theosophy*, but to the highest cosmological views of spiritual science.

How do the various levels of knowledge that we have thus far considered relate to one another? Their relationship can be depicted through an analogy that, though necessarily limited by its static picto-

---

22. See Steiner's lecture cycles, *Occult Significance of the Bhagavad Gita* and *Genesis*.

rial quality, is nevertheless helpful.[23] In this mountain analogy, *natural science* can be compared to an explorer who wanders back and forth over a plain, investigating every tree, plant, stone, and bush. In doing so, he compiles a tremendous wealth of detailed knowledge. *Theosophy*, on the other hand, is like an explorer who climbs to the top of a mountain where he gains a breathtaking overview of the land but loses sight of its manifold detail. *Anthroposophy*, or spiritual science, is like one who takes a position between the two, rising to a foothill from where the details are still visible but can now be seen in their relationships, through which they begin to form a meaningful whole.

Goethean science can be added to this picture as a mediator between natural science and spiritual science. It can be compared to an explorer who is at home on the plain but is constantly ascending a slope in order to gain perspective. Whereas Goethean science always proceeds from the sense perceptible and rises through inner participation to a grasp of the supersensory forces that work within it, natural science, in its search for explanation, tends to descend into ever greater analytical detail until, tunneling beneath the plain as it were, it comes upon sub-sensible forces.

Together, these different levels of knowledge comprise a unified view of reality in its hierarchical structure. In this hierarchy, Goethean science is the all-important linchpin between natural science and spiritual science, between the sense-perceptible and the creative, spiritual worlds.

VIII
Applied Goetheanism

I think one could call science the knowledge of general laws, abstracted knowledge. Art, on the other hand, would be science applied in action. Science would be reason and art its mechanism, wherefore one could also call it practical science. And finally, therefore, science would be the theorem, art the problem.

— GOETHE, *Verses in Prose*

A friend and connoisseur of Goethe's poetic works once said to me, "Goethe's science is all very interesting and very beautiful, but

---

23. Rudolf Steiner uses a similar analogy in the first chapter of his *Anthroposophy (A Fragment)*.

what use is it?" He was implying that the technical applications of the physical sciences are legion, but where are the practical applications of Goethean science? I was stumped. The fact is that even the further development of Goethean science through anthroposophy has only produced very few of the useful technical conveniences that we associate with applied science. Why is this?

The traditional physical sciences investigate the fully abstractable, quantifiable laws of cause and effect that govern the inanimate, physical world. These can be applied in machines and contrivances that comprise a technological world that functions independently of nature's living process and of human participation. Goethean science, however, because it is a participatory science that investigates the deeper, generative dimensions of reality, can never lead to applications that separate themselves from human participation and from the creative workings of nature. Whereas the traditional physical sciences operate on the levels that Goethe characterized as those of the "users" and the "knowers," Goethean science begins at the level of the "beholders," whose knowledge becomes productive imaginative activity.

There is a correlation between the traditional physical sciences and their application in technology on the one hand, and spiritual science and its artistic applications on the other. Just as abstract mechanical or electrical laws are employed in technology, the dynamic principles of life, soul, and spirit can only be grasped and worked with out of artistic experience. Of the highest form of art, which he called "style," Goethe said:

> Style rests on the deepest foundations of knowledge, on the essential being of things to the extent that it is given to us to know it in visible and graspable forms. ("Simple Imitation, Mannerism, Style")

Art on this level, then, is the appropriate tool for working with the principles of living nature. As we learn to grasp the essential being of things in its external manifestations, the emphasis of our civilization on technology will be complemented by a new emphasis on artistic techniques that will be employed to cultivate all realms of life and to heal them from the destructive effects of the human and environmental crises of our time.

The distinction between technical and artistic application notwithstanding, I have found, upon further consideration, that my friend was quite right to question the practical applicability of Goethe's science. For to the extent to which Goethe himself developed it, his science had not yet reached the stage where it could find practical application. Only when developed further through Rudolf Steiner did it reach the point where it could bear fruit in practical life.

Rudolf Steiner devoted the first phase of his life's work in anthroposophy to laying its spiritual-scientific foundations. The second phase brought an enlivening of this knowledge through the arts. In the last phase of his life, beginning after the First World War, the emphasis of his work lay on its practical applications.

In 1919 Steiner began the Waldorf school in Stuttgart, Germany. Today Waldorf education is the most widespread application of spiritual science and has become the largest non-parochial, independent educational movement in the world.

Waldorf education proceeds from an intimate, multidimensional, participatory knowledge of the human being and of child development, and its methods and curricula are designed to allow this development to take place in a healthy way. Though Waldorf education imparts the knowledge and skills required today, in doing so it works *with* the dynamic processes of child development to help the children fully develop and strengthen their essential human capacities.

Conscious inner participation in the unfolding development of children reveals dramatic changes which occur with a dynamic lawfulness and rhythm of their own. Steiner distinguished three major phases of child development. The first phase begins at birth and ends with the change of teeth at about age seven. The body of a newborn child is soft and pliable; its "voluntary" movements are entirely uncoordinated. Steiner compared the child's brain at birth with a sculptor's clay before he begins his work. This view of the brain is corroborated by recent neurological research. In *Endangered Minds* Jane Healy writes, "You might envision the newborn brain as a large mass of clay that has been formed in a rough template of a final product. On it, the environment acts as a sculptor."[24] We would have to add that it is the extraordinarily intensive inner participation of the child in its perceptions of its environment that actually does the sculpting. Rudolf Steiner describes the very young child as "wholly a

---

24. Jane Healy, *Endangered Minds*, New York: Touchstone/Simon and Schuster, 1990.

sense organ" (Aug. 10, 1923) The sense perceptions of the newborn child must be pure perceptions devoid of concepts, similar to those we adults experience only in exceptional situations, such as upon awakening.

We may now begin to appreciate the extraordinary engagement of the infant in the game of peekaboo: the depth and joyous intensity of its involvement in the recognition of a beloved *other* in the unstructured world revealed to its sense of sight.

The challenge of learning to coordinate voluntary bodily movements in infancy is equally daunting. Only after a year of arduously living into its body is the child ready to raise itself into the vertical position. The radiant, triumphant smile on the face of the child as it stands or walks for the first time reveals its deep joy in attaining a new, infinitely more satisfactory relationship to the world. Practice leads to mastery of the bodily instrument, and later on, through skipping, jumping rope, ice skating, swimming, and all manner of games, the child continues to gain ever greater virtuosity.

But let us return to the one-year-old. After learning to walk, the child enters more actively into the world of language. Those who, in later life, have had to learn a foreign language piece by piece, word by word, and through the conscious understanding of its complex grammatical structure can appreciate the capacity of the small child to slip into its mother tongue as into a whole garment.

By the age of seven the child has actively lived itself into its native language, into the sense-perceptible world of its environment, and into its own body. The sense-perceptible world has become a meaningful outer home; the body has been transformed from a soft, unstructured model into a more individualized vehicle for the child's own entelechy. Just as the sculptural forces of the plant transform the seed leaves into the more differentiated leaves of the new plant organism, thus sculptural forces mold the child's inherited body into a responsive instrument. At the end of the first phase of childhood this sculpting process is brought to a certain completion when the far more individualized adult teeth replace the baby teeth.

The achievements of the small child are unparalleled in later life. How then does the child accomplish them?

It is well known that infants fail to develop if they are deprived of contact with caring adults. They do not learn to stand, walk, or speak unless they are surrounded by people who do these things.

Observation of a four- or five-year-old reveals outer behavior that also appears extraordinary to us as adults: the child is constantly imitating those around it. It is either simultaneously engaged in the same activity — for example, washing dishes *with* its mother — or engaged in such activities hours or even days after it has observed them. What is going on here?

Polanyi's concept of indwelling would seem to be a significant clue; an observing child can give itself over to the observation of an adult so entirely that it literally *dwells* in the adult's activity. Only this intense indwelling can account for its ability to imitate the activity right down into the adult's particular nuances of gesture. However, it is also obvious that the child has no intellectual understanding of what it is imitating, that its activity is without utilitarian purpose. Imitation is pure, uninhibited will activity. This same phenomenal capacity to participate in the world around it also accounts for the child's ability to enter into and grasp the sense-perceptible world and the world of language. Thus the question arises, Where does this capacity come from?

Rudolf Steiner describes the life of the eternal individuality before birth as being, in a sense, the reverse of our incarnated earthly consciousness. Whereas the latter is strongly centered in itself, the former, he says, actually dwells in the periphery: that is, it is given over to the spiritual beings that surround it. After birth, children continue this same fundamental relationship with their environment. Through their senses, they now participate in what lives and reveals itself in their earthly surroundings. Children dwell deeply — one might say religiously — in the inner nuance of every sound and gesture of the people who surround them (Aug. 9, 1919). This instinctive ability of children to dwell within the beings who surround them is nothing other, Steiner says, than the unconscious working of the power of *Intuition* (Sept. 24, 1919, and Aug. 16, 1922). Intuition, the highest form of human knowledge, is the capacity of the awakened, cognitive will to become one with another being. Instead of being raised into consciousness and ending up as a dead concept, the will-participation of the child remains vitally alive and works directly into every fiber of its physical organism, coordinating, molding, and structuring it; it becomes unconscious organic will activity.

Because its development occurs through imitation, the small child depends strongly on the surrounding people. The whole question of bonding in its broadest sense — how the child inwardly connects itself with earthly life — depends on how deeply and strongly it can enter into and unite itself with what it finds in its human surroundings. It is not just the physical contact with its mother but her love, the inner mood of being with which she conducts her activity, and the quality of the whole environment that allow the child to feel fully at home and encourage it to say a wholehearted "Yes!" to earthly life.

Thus spiritual-scientific research into life before birth provides us with the solution to the riddle of early childhood development. But Steiner's research also revealed a relationship between this early age and later life, namely that imitation in early childhood leads to the capacity for freedom in adult life (Aug. 9, 1919).

This appears to be a contradiction in terms. Is not imitation incompatible with the concept of freedom? An essential aspect of the capacity for true inner freedom, Steiner said, is the ability to liberate oneself from the fetters of one's own physiological and characterological predisposition, of one's social conditioning, and of one's own particular point of view.[25] Only when one can transcend one's own instinctual drives, one's egotism, and all that has been "programmed" into one in the past will one be able to enter selflessly into a given situation, to experience and understand it deeply, to dwell within it. One will then be able to act freely — unbiased by one's own egotistical desires, one's background and past experience — out of direct insight into what the situation calls for. It was this capacity, for example, that enabled Galileo to participate in the lawfulness of the swinging altar lamp. Whereas in Galileo this inner participation led to the discovery of its hidden lawfulness, a small child might have found some way of imitating the motion.

Though imitative action is itself unfree, the fact that it springs from intuitive participation and not from an inherited predisposition or from bodily cravings prepares the ground for freedom in later life. Through playing house, cooking, or caring for their dolls, children mold their bodies into responsive instruments for selfless, skilled activity. To the extent that intensive imitative activity does not occur, Steiner said, the body will develop into a seedbed of thriving ani-

---

25. See *How to Know Higher Worlds: A Modern Path of Initiation,* "Some Effects of Initiation."

malistic desires which will become an impediment to the exercise of freedom in adulthood (Aug. 9, 1919).

At age four or five the child's own individual creative capacities begin to "come into play." Steiner points out that when we observe how a child plays at this age, we can catch a glimpse of the particular way it will take hold of life in its mid-twenties. A child of four or five, for example, who loves to arrange and rearrange all manner of available materials into intricate, harmonious patterns may well show unusual organizational talent at the age of twenty-four. In another context, Steiner spoke of how one could guide the child's creative play in such a way that it would lead to the capacity in adulthood to take hold of life in a skillful and effective manner (unpublished lecture of Feb. 24, 1921).

Thus, through participatory spiritual science we come to see human life as an interdependent whole. Such insight clearly indicates the nature of the practical pedagogical measures called for in this first phase of the child's development. Its environment should be one the child can enter with the full devotion of indwelling. Everything that the adult thinks, feels, and does should be worthy of imitation. This does not mean withdrawal into a disembodied state of saintliness. On the contrary, meaningful, practical activities that lead the child joyfully into life are what it needs at this age.

As I mentioned, the emergence of the adult teeth at around the age of seven is a sign that the intensive sculptural process described above has been brought to a certain stage of completion. The sculpting of the brain, though by no means complete, has achieved the intricacy of a work of art. At this point some of the formative forces that were engaged in this process are freed from their organic activity and become available for conscious, cognitive learning. This discovery of Steiner's throws a new light on the central insight upon which Polanyi based his philosophy. We can now conceive of the organic formative forces as the *same* integrative forces that Polanyi observed in both skillful physical activity and in cognitive activity: the focally directed forces that have the power to organize subsidiary particulars into coherent, meaningful wholes.

Steiner speaks of the freeing of these formative forces from their work on the physical body as a second birth in the development of the child. Academic instruction of any kind before this birth has taken place prematurely draws upon the forces the child still needs to fully remodel and penetrate its inherited physical body. It can be compared to forcing a plant to blossom before it has sufficiently developed its roots and leaves.

In the second phase of its development the child's focus shifts from imitation of its environment to engagement in the new realm of imaginative mental pictures it is now able to create within its own soul with the liberated formative forces that are at its disposal. The child loves these images and is inwardly nourished by them, particularly when they are saturated with inner life and meaning. What lived in the small child as will forces are now beginning to metamorphose into powers of feeling. In the elementary school years, Steiner said, powers of *Inspiration* are working unconsciously in the soul of the child. From the soul they work into the finer constituting of the body, fine-tuning particularly the rhythmical organization of the respiratory and circulatory systems. Thus, the child develops a lively feeling-relationship to what is taught. In order to speak to the child's feelings, an elementary school teacher needs to develop an inwardly lively physiognomic approach to the subject matter. When a subject is experienced in such a deeply animated way, it is not only remembered but also has a nourishing, health-giving effect on the soul, and through the soul right down into the bodily nature of the child.

Another essential aspect of the child's development and education in this second major phase of childhood is the acquisition of skills and habits. Like the powers of pictorial thinking and of memory, these capacities are developed in the child's "body" of formative forces (Steiner sometimes called it the "habit body"). Through rhythmical, rigorous yet lively and varied repetition, habits and skills gradually become part of the child's "second nature."

Whereas the child was united with its surroundings in the first phase of its development, it now begins to live more strongly in its own soul. By the age of nine or ten, children experience a separation from their surroundings. But they are not yet ready to make their own independent judgments. During these middle years of childhood, children are therefore deeply satisfied when they can look up to their teacher as a natural authority — as a mediator between the greater world and their own soul life. They want to look up to the adult as one who can represent the world (which for them still includes its deeper moral dimension) as one who *"knows"* and is *"fair."*

Meanwhile, as mentioned, Inspirational powers are orchestrating a phase of physiological development that comes to a certain completion at puberty. Just as sculptural forces predominated in the first phase of physiological development, dynamic soul forces of an inward, musical nature become more active in this second phase. Liberated at puberty from their engagement in the formation of the organism, these powerful soul forces, which are intimately connected with the young person's individuality, are now "born" into the consciousness of the adolescent. The impact of this momentous event rivals that of physical birth. But whereas at birth the physical body entered the outer world, this is the breakthrough of the awakening soul, with all the dynamics of its infinite inwardness, into the outer world and into its life and times.

Just as in the first phase of childhood the *physical body* was transformed into an instrument of the individuality and gained its orientation in space and its capacity to express itself through speech, in this third phase of development the *soul* needs to be transformed and structured into an instrument of the individuality, to gain its own inner orientation in life and a new capacity to express its relationship to the world.

With all of its intelligence and turbulent powers, the "newborn" soul of the adolescent is in some ways as uncontrolled and helpless as is the body of the baby. Humor, born of deeper human understanding, is therefore essential for anyone dealing with adolescents. Teenage boys, especially, have to learn to coordinate and raise themselves up inwardly just as infants have to learn to do so bodily. But whereas in the case of the infant the outcome of the struggle is assured, it is by no means certain in the case of the young person. If seventeen- or eighteen-year-olds have not learned to stand tall in an inner sense, if they have not begun to find an inner sense of direction and an inner sense of identity, then they may not be able to rise from what has sometimes been called "the fall of adolescence."

Steiner pointed out that, in the hierarchy of principles that comprise our being, each level is formed by the one directly above it. Thus the physical body is sculpted by the formative forces, and these, in turn, are stimulated and orchestrated by the sentient, musical forces of the soul. When these awaken in adolescence, they can only be ordered, nourished, and directed by yet higher principles: the spiritual principles that constitute the autonomous core, or I, of the human being and come into play when, through our thinking, we are able to penetrate to the hidden lawfulness of the world. It is with these forces that we need to work when educating adolescents.

To understand and direct the inner drama of adolescence, it is essential to know that the higher individuality of the young person is at work behind the scenes. In early childhood it worked through the power of Intuition; in the middle of childhood it worked through Inspiration. During this third phase of development these higher capacities undergo a further metamorphosis and begin to work as unconscious powers of *Imagination* (Sept. 24, 1919, and Aug. 16, 1922). These Imaginative powers work subtly on the physiology of adolescents, where they are engaged in the final molding of the limbs and metabolic system. They also work strongly into the soul life where they manifest as forces of love that seek a deeper understanding of the world and of human life. Though adolescents live strongly in their emotions, what they unconsciously seek at this age is nevertheless a deeper understanding of the world. Already at the age of eleven or twelve the child's powers of pictorial thinking begin to evolve into the capacity to grasp principles that have an inner logic and lawfulness transcending the pictorial. Later, the "newborn" soul of the adolescent connects with the world in a most vital new way through the living experience of ideas. This can be attained by formulating significant lawful principles as they manifest in the world and in human life. Such principles can also be experienced through creative artistic activity and through practical work. It is the discovery of the lawfulness working in the world that gives the adolescent soul the groundedness, strength, and inner orientation it needs. Insight into the working of such generative lawfulness becomes love for the world. Thus experienced, living ideas become ideals — the positive driving force in the life of the adolescent. Just as small children need human examples to imitate, adolescents need heroes whose lives demonstrate the indomitable power of ideals.

Steiner exhorted the teachers to whom he spoke to awaken in high-school students the deepest *interest* in the world. For if young people were unable to connect the powers of their own inner subjectivity with the creative principles at work in the outer world, then their inner life would fall back upon itself. The generative Imaginative powers working within them would then become active on a lower, instinctual level as eroticism and thrill-seeking through exerting power over others (June 21, 1922).

This brief discussion may serve to indicate how a participatory science arrives at profoundly important insights that can orient us in our daily practice of education. Deepened and intensified inner participation in the development of the child reveals how very particular organizational principles, or forces, work together in very specific ways in each of the major phases of childhood. Thus, some essential features of a dynamic picture of child development begin to emerge:

In the first phase, Intuition, the most powerful human capacity, works through imitation, guiding the sculptural formation of the physical body. With the emergence of the adult teeth this sculptural process reaches a certain completion, freeing organic formative forces that become available for *thinking*. In the second phase, Inspirational forces work harmoniously on the physiological development of the rhythmical system, stimulating the musical powers of the soul. The child now relates to the world primarily through feeling and an artistic sense and seeks natural authority and an inwardly alive physiognomic and rhythmical approach to learning. A strong educational focus should be on exercising the imaginative capacities of the child, on the development of basic skills, and on the formation of the "habit body." The powerful soul forces that work organically in this central phase of childhood are liberated during adolescence. Their release can be characterized as the birth of *feeling*.

In this next, youthful, phase, Imaginative forces, working into the physiological development and the soul of the adolescent, create an unconscious yearning to experience the dynamic lawfulness at work in nature and human life. Active participation in this lawfulness through thinking, creative artistic activities, and practical work provide an educational focus. The *will* forces engaged in the final molding of the limbs and metabolic system are liberated at around the age of twenty-one (Aug. 8 and 9, 1923).

The emancipation of the will, combined with the capacity to lovingly experience the inner lawfulness of the world, are the preconditions for inner freedom.

Around the age of twenty-one the autonomous inner center of the human being, the I, takes over where creative spiritual powers and human educators have left off. The creative powers that have accompanied the incarnating individuality — the powers of Intuition, Inspiration, and Imagination — now cease their upbuilding activity and become dormant. The spiritual umbilical cord that has connected us with these generative forces is now cut. From now on, all development is self-development.

The creative forces that have worked in the growth and maturation of the child are not, however, necessarily lost forever. Rudolf Steiner described how, by making one's way on a path of disciplined self-development, these powers can be reawakened — but now as fully conscious capacities of insight.

By awakening these capacities within himself, Rudolf Steiner was able to participate in the underlying dynamics of child development. It would far exceed the scope of this essay to go more deeply into the wealth of pedagogical insight or to describe the extraordinary palette of practical methods that Steiner derived from his spiritual-scientific research.

I will only stress that learning in a Waldorf school is entirely a participatory process and never an assimilation of abstracted facts. The main subjects are taught through immersion in blocks of three to six weeks and are conveyed as living experience and knowledge by the teacher — not through textbooks. Instead of being presented with finished "objective knowledge," the students learn to actively create their own "personal knowledge," which they then carefully formulate and illustrate in their own "book" for each block. In this way, also, they are prepared for inner independence and freedom in adulthood.

Steiner often stressed that true education can only be practiced as an art. Neither detached, outer observation nor a grasp of general principles can give one the direct insight and inspiration that one needs as a teacher.

> But it is, rather, between these two poles that insight into the human being lies. When we only grasp the outer appearances through our senses, we fall short of the human being.... When we only grasp the spiritual... we have to direct our attention toward such soul and spiritual heights, so to speak, that we lose sight of the immediate presence of the human being as he or she stands before us in the world. We need something that leads us still more intimately into the concrete reality of human nature.... There must be a sense organ — just as for colors the eye — for the immediate perception of the concrete human being.... Now this sense is none other than what is given us for the grasping of art: the artistic sense.... This artistic sense is at

the same time the sense that enables us to grasp the immediate presence of the human being so that this insight can also become immediate practice. (lecture of Mar. 25, 1923)

Thus, the art of teaching arises on the intermediary, sensory-supersensory level where the sense perceptible is seen as the manifestation of the generative forces that work within it. For the teacher it is essential to develop an artistic sense for the being, character, and temperament of the child. This can be achieved through exact participatory observation and by creating a living inner picture of the child, which takes on a physiognomic quality. Through this practice one can come to understand, love, and help even very "difficult" children.

Steiner insisted that Waldorf schools be fully independent and administered by the teachers themselves. Implementing an educational program through a bureaucracy thwarts the creativity of the teachers, who can no longer take significant initiatives out of their own insight. Steiner always hoped for the establishment of a worldwide association of independent schools, all working freely out of deeper insight into the nature and development of the child, all working in the interests of the children, of humanity, and not bound by the abstract programs of political or economic powers.

This now leads us to a consideration of the fundamental insights of participatory, spiritual science into social life. Steiner was challenged during World War I to understand more deeply the social forces working in contemporary civilization. His research revealed three fundamentally different aspects of social life, which arise out of the relationship of the individual to society as a whole. Steiner saw the first sphere of social life arising wherever the creative capacities of the individual unfold. This occurs in education, science, religion, art, literature, journalism, and all other expressions of human creativity. He characterized this sphere as that of the cultural or spiritual life.

As a second sphere of social life, Rudolf Steiner recognized the economy involving the production, distribution, and consumption of the goods we need for our physical existence. By 1917 it was clear to Steiner that a state-run, centrally planned economy could not work. But he also recognized the socially, humanly, and environmentally destructive tendencies inherent in an unregulated free-market economy. Steiner realized that economic life, like cultural life, needed to be placed under the control of those directly involved in it. This, he proposed, could be achieved through associations of producers, merchants, and consumers who would regulate the economy in a spirit of mutual understanding, cooperation, and service through meaningful and flexible planning. This would mean human emancipation in the economic realm: the blind, exploitative, and wasteful market mechanism would be replaced by sensible human agreements. Economic life would thus be humanized. The involvement of consumers in economic decisions would reorient production toward real needs. Cyclical overproduction and recession could be avoided. Profits accrued through economic activity would go — as free gifts — to support cultural life.

The third aspect of social life as Steiner described it is the sphere of human rights and of the necessary legal regulation of relationships between people and organizations. This, he said, is the justified domain of democratic government. The disentanglement of government from cultural life on the one hand and from economic life on the other divests the monolithic national state of its illegitimate and destructive powers.

Steiner spoke of the threefold social order as it has been very briefly indicated here as "Goetheanism in the twentieth century" (Nov. 22, 1920). He repeatedly pointed out that the threefold social organism is not an abstract program, but a perception of deeper-lying forces — a perception that can only be achieved by the participatory capacities first employed by Goethe in his natural science. Steiner often stressed that very well thought out social programs remained ultimately ineffective because they were conceived by an abstract intellect incapable of penetrating to a direct perception of the actual forces at work in social life.

Steiner further demonstrated the profound practicality of spiritual science by developing comprehensive new approaches to medicine and agriculture. Anthroposophical medicine and biodynamic agriculture, like Waldorf education and the threefold social impulse, are effective practical applications of a participatory spiritual science that comes to see the external phenomena as manifestations of hidden generative forces.

Goetheanism and its further development through spiritual science may not be useful in the conventional sense. In fact, their practical applications are neither labor saving nor convenient in the short term. They offer no quick fixes or shortcuts. They require original insight and a great deal of work and commitment. But concrete insight into the deeper, generative dimensions of reality is an ever renewable source of enthusiasm and inner strength. And working out of such insight leads to real progress. Steiner spoke of Goethe's thinking as being "attuned to reality" (Sept. 29, 1918). He therefore saw Goetheanism as "the very most practical thing in our present time," as a "method" that leads to a "healing of the contemporary human being" (Nov. 1, 1918).

Bibliography and Further Reading

I. Works by Rudolf Steiner

Anthroposophical Leading Thoughts. London: Rudolf Steiner Press, 1973.

Anthroposophy (A Fragment): A New Foundation for the Study of Human Nature. Hudson, NY: Anthroposophic Press, 1996.

The Boundaries of Natural Science, Hudson, NY: Anthroposophic Press, 1983.

Autobiography: Chapters in the Course of My Life, 1861–1907. Hudson, NY: Anthroposophic Press, 1999.

Goethe the Scientist (O. Wannamaker, trans.). New York: Anthroposophic Press, 1950; also: *Goethean Science* (W. Lindeman, trans.). Spring Valley, NY: Mercury Press, 1988; (**other translations of the present volume**). These introductions to Goethe's scientific works were originally published in Kürschner's "Deutsche National-Litteratur," Stuttgart, 1884–97.

Goethe's World View. Spring Valley, NY: Mercury Press, 1985.

How to Know Higher Worlds: A Modern Path of Initiation. Hudson, NY: Anthroposophic Press, 1994.

Introducing Anthroposophical Medicine. Hudson, NY: Anthroposophic Press, 1999.

Intuitive Thinking As a Spiritual Path: A Philosophy of Freedom (Catherine Creeger, trans.). Hudson, NY: Anthroposophic Press, 1995; also: *The Philosophy of Freedom: The Basis for a Modern World Conception* (Michael Wilson, trans.). London: Rudolf Steiner Press, 1999; and: *The Philosophy of Spiritual Activity: A Philosophy of Freedom* (R. Stebbing, trans.). London: Rudolf Steiner Press, 1992.

Light: First Scientific Lecture-Course. East Sussex, UK: Steiner Schools Fellowship, 1987.

Origins of Natural Science. Hudson, NY: Anthroposophic Press, 1985.

Riddles of the Soul. Spring Valley, NY: Mercury Press, 1996.

The Science of Knowing. Spring Valley, NY: Mercury Press, 1988.

A Theory of Knowledge Implicit in Goethe's World Conception. Hudson, NY: Anthroposophic Press, 1988.

Theosophy: An Introduction to the Spiritual Processes in Human Life and in the Cosmos. Hudson, NY: Anthroposophic Press, 1994.

Truth and Knowledge. Blauvelt, NY: Rudolf Steiner Publications, 1981; also *Truth and Science.* Spring Valley, NY: Mercury Press, 1993.

Warmth Course. Spring Valley, NY: Mercury Press, 1988.

II. Other Works and Collections

Amrine, Zucker, and Wheeler, eds. *Goethe and the Sciences: A Reappraisal.* Dordrecht, Holland: D. Reider Publishing Co., 1987.

Barnes, Henry. *A Life for the Spirit: Rudolf Steiner in the Crosscurrents of Our Time.* Hudson, NY: Anthroposophic Press, 1997.

Barnes, John. *Goethe and the Power of Rhythm: A Biographical Essay.* Ghent, NY: Adonis Press, 1999.

Bockemühl, J. *In Partnership with Nature.* Kimberton, PA: Bio-Dynamic Literature, 1981.

———, Ed. *Toward a Phenomenology of the Etheric World.* Spring Valley, NY: Anthroposophic Press, 1985.

———. *Awakening to Landscape.* Dornach, Switzerland: Natural Science Section, Goetheanum, 1992.

———. *Metamorphosis of Plants: Essays.* South Africa: Novalis Press, 1997.

Bohm, David, and F. David Peat. *Science, Order, and Creativity.* New York: Bantam Books, 1987.

Bortoft, Henri. *The Wholeness of Nature: Goethe's Way toward a Science of Conscious Participation in Nature.* Hudson, NY: Lindisfarne Books, 1996.

Capra, Fritjof. *The Turning Point.* New York: Simon & Schuster, 1988.

Colquhoun, Margaret & Axel Ewald. *New Eyes for Plants: A Workbook for Plant Observation & Drawing.* Stroud, UK: Hawthorn Press, 1996.

Davy, John. *Hope, Evolution and Change, Selected Essays.* Stroud, UK: Hawthorn Press, 1985.

Edelglass, Stephen; Georg Maier; Hans Gebert; John Davy. *The Marriage of Sense and Thought: Imaginative Participation in Science.* Hudson, NY: Lindisfarne Books, 1996.

Goethe, Johann Wolfgang von. *Faust* (Walter Kaufmann, trans., with the original German). Garden City, NY: Doubleday & Co., 1963.

———. *The Metamorphosis of Plants.* Kimberton, PA: Bio-Dynamic Farming and Gardening Association, 1993.

———. *Scientific Studies,* Goethe's Collected Works, vol. 12 (Douglas Miller, ed.). Princeton, NJ: Princeton University Press, 1995; formerly Suhrkamp Publishers, NY, 1988. This is the most comprehensive collection of Goethe's scientific writings available in English today. It is referred to in this book as the **Suhrkamp** edition.

———. *Goethe on Science: An Anthology of Goethe's Scientific Writings* (J. Naydler, ed.). Edinburgh: Floris Books, 1997.

Grohmann, Gerbert, *The Plant,* vols. 1 and 2. Kimberton, PA: Bio-dynamic Farming and Gardening Association, 1989.

Hartmann, Eduard von. *Philosophy of the Unconscious.* Westport, CT: Greenwood Press, 1972.

Herder, Johann Gottfried von. *Reflections on the Philosophy of the History of Humanity.* Abridged, and with an introd., by Frank E. Manuel. Chicago : University of Chicago Press [1968].

Holdrege, Craig. *Genetics & the Manipulation of Life: The Forgotten Factor of Context.* Hudson, NY: Lindisfarne Books, 1996.

Kranich, Ernst-Michael. *Pflanzen als Bilder der Seelenwelt.* Stuttgart: Verlag Freies Geistesleben, 1993.

―――. *Thinking Beyond Darwin: The Idea of the Type as a Key to Vertebrate Evolution.* Hudson, NY: Lindisfarne Books, 1999.

―――. *Planetary Influences upon Plants.* Kimberton, PA: Bio-Dynamic Literature, 1984.

Lehrs, Ernst. *Man or Matter: Introduction to a Spiritual Understanding of Nature on the Basis of Goethe's Method of Training Observation and Thought,* 3rd edition. London: Rudolf Steiner Press, 1985.

Pelikan, Wilhelm. *The Secrets of Metals.* Spring Valley, NY: Anthroposophic Press, 1973.

―――. *Healing Plants.* Spring Valley, NY: Mercury Press, 1997.

Polanyi, Michael. *The Study of Man — The Lindsay Memorial Lectures.* Chicago: University of Chicago Press, 1960.

―――. *Personal Knowledge: Towards a Post-Critical Philosophy.* Chicago: University of Chicago Press, 1962.

―――. *Knowing and Being.* Chicago: University of Chicago Press, 1969.

―――. With Harry Prosch. *Meaning.* Chicago: University of Chicago Press, 1975.

―――. *The Tacit Dimension.* Gloucester, MA: Peter Smith, 1983.

Prigogine, Ilya. *From Being to Becoming: The New Science of Connectedness.* San Francisco: W. H. Freeman, 1980.

―――. *Order out of Chaos.* New York: Bantam Books, 1984.

Proskauer, Heinrich O. *The Rediscovery of Color: Goethe Versus Newton Today.* Hudson, NY: Anthroposophic Press, 1986.

Schad, Wolfgang. *Man and Mammals: Toward a Biology of Form.* Garden City, NY: Waldorf Press, 1977.

―――. "The Historical Basis for Anthroposophy in the Modern Era" (Die geschichtliche Voraussetzung der Anthroposophie in der Neuzeit), in *Zivilisation der Zukunft.* Stuttgart: Urachhaus, 1981.

Schelling, Friedrich von. *Ideas for a Philosophy of Nature As Introduction to the Study of This Science.* New York: Cambridge University Press, 1988.

Seamon, David, and Arthur Zajonc, eds. *Goethe's Way of Science: A Phenomenology of Nature.* Albany, NY: State University of New York Press, 1998.

Snow, Sir Charles P. *The Two Cultures: and a Second Look.* New York: Cambridge University Press, 1963.

Thomas, Nick. *Science between Space and Counterspace: Exploring the Significance of Negative Space.* London: Temple Lodge Publishing, 1999.

Unger, Georg. *Forming Concepts in Physics.* Chestnut Ridge, NY: Parker Courtney Press, 1995.

Wilson, Edward O. *Consilience-The Unity of Knowledge.* New York: Alfred A. Knopf, 1998.

Zajonc, Arthur. *Catching the Light: The Entwined History of Light and Mind.* New York: Bantam Books, 1993.

CLASSICS IN ANTHROPOSOPHY